MA IN ALL CAPS

Jay Kuo

Dedication

To Ma, of course, forever and always.

Acknowledgments

A book like this requires many perspectives from people in the know to get right, so without the valuable feedback from my brothers, John and Kaiser, and especially my sister, Mimi, this would not have been possible.

My best friend from high school, Kinnari Shah, bravely volunteered to proof and edit my first drafts, which I put out on Patreon in sections for my early readers, whose input I also found most helpful.

Special thanks to Jim Levine and Shane and Sylvia Snow for guidance and encouragement, and Rob Pivarnik for a critical, amazing, and thankfully, final full review and proof.

Finally, thanks to all my friends and followers who have begged me to commit my Ma stories and conversations to print. I wouldn't have had the courage to do this without you.

About the Author

Jay Kuo is a Broadway playwright, composer, and two-time Tony-winning producer. He used to be an appellate litigator, but even after he left the law, his friends and relatives still ask him for free legal advice.

Jay is the founder and CEO of a digital publishing and social media company that rather unexpectedly grew the internet empire of actor and activist George Takei to tens of millions of followers. Jay serves on the board of directors of the Human Rights Campaign, the nation's largest civil rights organization serving the LGBTQ+ community, which Ma once described as the "trendy" people.

Jay lives with a roommate and a tabby in Harlem, New York. He writes a daily Substack on law and politics called *The Status Kuo*.

Foreword

The curious and amazing story of how I first met Jay Kuo, the author of "ma-moir" and the composer and lyricist of my legacy project, the Broadway musical *Allegiance,* is recounted in the pages of this book. But what he doesn't tell his readers is what I and others have often said to him: He changes lives, for the better, everywhere he goes, and in everything he does.

I'm currently sitting in a dressing room in London writing this Foreword because I'm performing eight times a week on stage in *Allegiance*, telling to British audiences the vital story of the Japanese American community's incarceration during World War II. I'm here because Jay, along with his creative and producing partner, Lorenzo Thione, willed the show into being, achieving the seemingly impossible through sheer grit, vision, and determination. "I'm going to write a musical, and it's going to get to Broadway" sounds like the stuff of fantasy, but in Jay's world every dream is not only possible, but to be pursued with vigor and determination until it becomes real.

It was the same passion with which Jay helped lift my presence on social media as my primary guiding light. He showed me the potential of reaching new and younger fans on places like Twitter, and on creating community on Facebook. With Jay, whom Brad and I love dearly like family, the sky was always the limit as he helped shape and craft my online presence.

Reading the pages of MA IN ALL CAPS, I now see where Jay gets much of his drive, creativity and pluck. I first met Mary Kuo, whom the world knows simply as "Ma," during the years we were workshopping our show in New York, and then again during our

World Premiere in 2012 at San Diego's Old Globe Theater before we, at last, opened on Broadway. I remember her as a vivacious charmer, beautiful and radiant even well into her 70s. A lot like me! We were, after all, contemporaries.

The thing that struck me most immediately about Ma was how proud she was of her four children, each as unique and different as the other, all accomplished offspring of Chinese immigrant parents who seemed perpetually surprised and delighted at their successes. You'll get to meet the entire Kuo clan in this book, so I won't spoil it for you here. But their life stories, through the generations and across continents, intertwined with rich history and even our current upheavals in America, will often stop you cold, make you catch your breath and sigh in wonder.

In this sense, MA IN ALL CAPS is not just a touching and often hilarious tribute to the indefatigable Ma, but a rare glimpse into the world as seen from the eyes of an unforgettable family. I was last gathered with all of them at the passing of Jay's father, Jenkai, who shared Ma's pride and love for his children. At Ba's memorial service, it struck me that a stronger family, with deeper bonds of love, could hardly be imagined.

I've always encouraged Jay to apply his creative talents to the writing of more music, more lyrics, more stories. To raise up our hearts and make them sing, whether with joy or sorrow, pride or passion. When he told me he'd taken the last two years to write a book, it didn't surprise me at all. And when he asked that I write a foreword to it, I was proud to oblige. I'm so very glad the world will have a chance to hear more from him and that Ma and the entire Kuo family will forever be honored in these pages.

— George Takei

A note on names:

While all of these stories are true, some of the names of people outside of our immediate family have been changed to protect their privacy.

A note on Chinese family titles:

Chinese family titles for grandparents, aunts, and uncles all change depending on the reference point.

For example, my mother's mother is my *laolao,* but my father's mother is my *nainai.* So I would call my two grandmothers Laolao and Nainai.

My mother's father is my *waigong,* but my father's father is my *yeye.* So I'd call my two grandfathers Waigong and Yeye.

I only have one *gugu,* or father's older sister, and there are lots of people called *shushu* or father's younger brother.

This book is told from my perspective, so thankfully those are the only Chinese family titles you'll need to know to not get hopelessly lost.

A note on when Ma speaks

Ma speaks in ALL CAPS in my head only when she speaks English, her second language. When she's speaking Mandarin, where her gift of oration shines, I have her in normal font.

Table of Contents

Dedication.. i

Acknowledgments ii

About The Author.. iii

Foreword... iv

A Note On Names vi

Preface viii

Chapter One..1

Chapter Two 38

Chapter Three 68

Chapter Four... 102

Chapter Five 139

Chapter Six 169

Chapter Seven... 227

Chapter Eight.. 265

Chapter Nine... 302

Chapter Ten 339

Chapter Eleven 368

Chapter Twelve 396

Preface

February 2022
Rossmoor, California

"I THINK MAN WHO LIVE HERE IS DEAD," Ma said.

"Who, your neighbor?"

Ma and I were on one of our daily walks, with me pushing her carefully around her block in the "WHALECHAIR," as she called it. Ma was certain that if I went any faster I'd somehow dump her off onto the hard pavement. So I stayed well below the unspoken, old-Chinese-lady speed limit.

Ma always took the time to appreciate her surroundings. Her disability and slow disfigurement lay in stark contrast to the manicured cul-de-sacs and tree-lined golf course of her San Francisco East Bay neighborhood.

"HE WAS FIRST PERSON SAID HI TO ME HERE. VERY NICE MAN. BUT OVER LAST MONTH, I DO NOT SEE HIM. AND THE BLIND HAVE BEEN DOWN, WINDOW ALL CLOSE IT OFF. I THINK HE MUST DEAD."

"Maybe he's just away for the winter," I offered. Ma always went straight to the morbid.

"SO MANY PEOPLE DIE LATELY."

We got to a bench, and with some effort she lifted herself up then over to sit on it. She sighed and stared at me with exasperation.

"I BECOMING SO STUPID. I DON'T KNOW WHEN LEG GETTING SO SOFT."

"You're not stupid, Ma. It's all just part of getting older."

"GETTING OLD NO FUN."

Through the years, and especially as Ma went deeper into her eighties, I had begun to capture my funny conversations with her, posting them verbatim to the delight of my friends on Facebook, a platform she thankfully had never learned to use. She didn't know it, but she was far more popular there than I ever was.

During the pandemic, and with not much else to do, I had also finally begun to pull Ma's stories together. She had dozens of her favorites. They were fantastical and sweeping tales, looming up like spirits from a village well. The stories were all, incredibly, true. Lately, I had been rushing to record them before they were lost along with her.

As I began to compile them, her narratives bunched into vaguely connected patterns: maternal, mitochondrial DNA interwoven with our family history, six generations and three continents connected by her telling and retelling. I secretly hoped her stories held the key to some vital but missing context for my own life, that they might finally explain why I felt so adrift. That they might even drive me to some deeper meaning or purpose. Was it all simply waiting to be discovered, excavated like so many terracotta warriors, or perhaps shrouded somewhere in our family tapestry, the grand picture revealed if only I could master how to gaze upon it properly? Stuck in months of pandemic isolation, could I somehow contact trace this all back? Lockdown proved a perfect time to find out.

"You have such great stories, Ma. I should put them all together someday," I said, not revealing I'd already assembled enough for a whole book of them.

"OH!" she remarked, laughing. "WHO WOULD READING IT?" I knew this was Ma's way of being modest. I would tell her many times over the course of the next year how my book was progressing, sometimes asking for clarification on stories, people, and facts. She would always downplay the idea of a book, even while clearly tickled by the idea of her life captured in print.

"OHHH, YOU GOING TOO FAST!" Ma complained as I set a brisker whalechair pace.

I slowed our roll. A pair of neighbors passed us in their golf cart, smiling pleasantly but with what I took as pity in their eyes. They had been witness to Ma's decline during the pandemic years, the lack of more regular human interaction having taken an obvious toll. Ma's once graceful back was now badly hunched, as if the sky itself were pressing her down, and she could only manage a pained shuffle when she was even strong enough to use her walker. I often caught her "very nice" neighbors passing looks at one another, plainly thankful that they weren't like *that* yet, a poor Asian woman who could barely get around. I wanted to shout at them.

You see a diminutive, old Chinese lady. But you have no idea who she is: a giant! Her family survived firing squads, locusts, and a world war. Battled starvation and communists and Japanese. She once gave a speech so powerful she had to flee all the way to America. She's published hundreds of stories, enough to fill whole novels. She's hosted the wives of presidents, married for love, and raised four children in a strange new country. Do you think you know her? How dare you look upon her with pity?

But Ma just smiled and waved, best she could, oblivious to their judgments or perhaps simply unfazed by them.

"MAYBE I DIE THIS YEAR, FINAL YEAR FOR ME."

"Or *maybe* you will outlive all of us, Ma," I said per usual, not wanting to drink tea at that pity party.

"YEAH. LUCKY YOU."

Chapter One

ORIGINS

or

"WUHAN SO SAD NOW"

March 2020
FaceTime Call

"Hi, Ma," I said after hitting accept. "How's California?"

Ma's face appeared off-center on the screen. "YOU STILL ASLEEP?"

Ma wrote her emails in ALL CAPS, so that was how I heard everything she said, too. She wasn't shouting. She was just extra.

I had made a point to FaceTime with Ma more often now that we had uprooted her from Beijing and plopped her down in Rossmoor, a retirement community in Northern California. Hundreds of her fellow elderly immigrants had decided, through some secret Mandarin chemical signal, that Rossmoor would make a suitable final neighborhood. To any polite "Where's your mom these days?" we could simply answer "Rossmoor," and our Chinese friends would nod and say, "Ah." *Good job getting her in there*, the unspoken part.

Ma had, at last, learned how to make video calls but never quite how to position her camera. I stared upwards at her chin now as she spoke, imagining the same view when she'd held me as an infant. She still had the face and black hair of a woman a dozen years younger, but that still meant she looked in her early seventies, which I wasn't ready to accept.

"I'm not asleep, no. I've been up for seven hours already, Ma. It's past noon here."

"WELL, HERE CHANGE TIME."

"The whole country changed. It's Daylight Savings. Or is it Standard? I can never keep that straight. Anyway, the whole country changed, except for Arizona."

That felt symbolic. My family had lived for two improbable decades in the scorching Arizona desert after Ba moved us from upstate New York to Tucson, a new-feeling city with its state-of-the-art IBM facility. Here in Tucson, Ma discovered real estate, Mexican people, and what it was like to be one of only two important Chinese families in a city.

The politically connected Kuos and the cotton-farming Zhangs had enjoyed a long and friendly rivalry. Influence versus money. New immigrants versus established generations. The matriarch of that other family was named Millie Zhang, which to my mind suited her Chinese-Western farmer heritage. Her daughter-in-law was the locally famous Rebecca Zhang, a perky reporter on Tucson's Channel 2 News with brilliant, long hair whom Ma regularly criticized for any number of unfair reasons. Rebecca, through her marriage to Millie's son, had a huge estate, a private helicopter, and an unquestionably gay son named Charles, which balanced out the fact that I slept with men, too. Ma called us both "trendy."

"WHAT TIME IS THERE? HERE IS MORNING, NINE FORTY."

"We're still three hours ahead. It's not suddenly, magically earlier here."

"WHA?"

"It's Twelve. Forty. Here. Three hours ahead still."

"ANYWAY, I CALLING TO MAKE SURE YOU NOT GO OUT. I HEARING ON NEWS, NEW YORK GETTING BAD."

In March of Year One of the Pandemic, a full lockdown hadn't been called yet in New York City, but it was probably just days away. Out where Ma lived, the six counties around San Francisco already had ordered everyone to self-isolate. At her age, Ma was a statistical risk if she caught the virus, and I nervously pictured every well-meaning assistant, acupuncturist, or nosy neighbor passing it to her. The thought of having moved her out of China only to have her die of Covid in America fulfilled my genetic urge to catastrophize.

As Ma warned that New York would go up in flames and riots, I stared out my window overlooking a "trendy" part of Harlem where, indeed, more gay men had been relocating, my close friends and I included. The normally bustling and rowdy streets blinked up at me, surprised by their own emptiness. Gone were the loud thumping and exuberant whoops that normally rose up a full twelve stories from the Angel of Harlem club below. Sirens now wailed *wooo-ahhhh* non-stop, the soundtrack to our escalating calamity.

There were certainly worse places to be stuck for weeks, perhaps months, as death counts and the cost of Lysol rose. In the background, Rachel Maddow pointedly described a proposed stimulus package. Two trillion dollars—twelve zeros, I thought. *Million, billion, trillion, quadrillion, quintillion…* I heard them in my mind as I once recited them dutifully to Ba as a child. Could the government really just hand out money until this was over?

An off-kilter bottle of cologne demanded I move it squarely to one corner, imposing order where I could.

I could not get my head around how our lives had upended in just a matter of days, how the world could simply overturn itself so quickly. Unbeknownst to us, we were about to face months of quarantine, and

I might have done some things differently had I known, but I can't say now what those would have been. I did, however, call Ma nearly every day, and that was new, though taxing. My sister Mimi called it "testing our strength." She was an expert at the positive glossing of everything.

Having nothing much else to talk about on our daily calls, Ma began to tell stories again. She kept many of them rattling around her head. Her favorites were now on repeat as her hippocampus went to war with itself. She deployed them as mental barricades, weights and measures on the value of her own life and time, the urgency of her mortality more apparent with the death of yet another of her many friends.

"IS TRUE? NEW YORK GETTING BAD? I SEE ON TELEVISION."

"It will be bad everywhere soon," I said, using my *I know things* voice, first developed and expertly refined by my brother John. "I wear a mask out and carry hand sanitizer, and wash my hands all the time. We even use disposable gloves to head out to the store, but they say it just gives everyone a false sense of safety and doesn't actually do anything. In fact, they might make things worse. I heard the virus is still on your gloves when you open your phone, so you get germs on there. Then you touch your face—anyway, I saw a YouTube all about it. Totally nuts. They are only letting people in twenty-five at a time now to the food market. It's still too many, though. You can't stand six feet apart in a New York City grocery store. I don't know who they're kidding."

Ma was silent, and I realized I was scaring her. These were the days before we knew very much about how the virus spread.

"Anyway, your helpers should wash their hands, too."

"I KNOW IT."

4

"Are you getting them to wash their hands?"

"OTHER DAY, SHE DOING DISHES WITHOUT GLOVE."

"It's not about the dishes, Ma. It's about contagion from outside the house. Do we need to have a discussion with them? John said he talked to them."

John, my eldest brother, lived in Oakland, a mere twenty-minute drive from Ma. At the urging of Mimi, he had secured the help of two young ladies from the Philippines who tag-teamed as Ma's nurse assistants. She didn't really need them for medical reasons. It was more to ensure she wasn't always alone and could sound-off to someone else besides poor, beleaguered John. It was also to make her feel as spoiled as she had been in Beijing, where pay scales were still low enough that an upper-middle-class Chinese American widow could enjoy a maid, a driver, and a cook. In her suburban Rossmoor property, Ma had insisted on "Philippine helpers" because, she claimed, they were honest Catholics who wouldn't steal from her.

"THEY AFRAID GOING TO HELL," Ma explained once in her *low* voice, layering her words with an extra helping of judgment. I also suspected she had made a choice in assistants because her friend Suzie also kept a "Philippine helper." Ma brought up Auntie Suzie, who also had an excellent *I know things* voice, whenever she wanted to provide credible third-party support for any of her decisions. Suzie had a keen nose for what the community was up to. She had been the one to convince Ma that Rossmoor was the hopping place for retired Chinese matriarchs. But since Ma moved in, Suzie had only come to visit her once, and Ma seemed disappointed by the reception. She made excuses, often saying she had heard Suzie wasn't doing well.

"No gloves for the dishes is fine. Just tell them to wash their hands for twenty seconds before they do anything in the house. And don't shake hands or hug them."

5

"WHY I HUG THEM?"

"I'm saying, don't. If you can help it."

The Chinese news channel Ma was glued to each day was starting to unnerve her. Lately, she had begun sending daily howlers to her four children, long forward- forward- forwards of email threads from her many politically active friends, mostly in Chinese nationalist groups, who were convinced, it turns out correctly, that the U.S. would blame China for the virus. My second brother, known for his long, rockstar mane and his improbable yet memorable name, "Kaiser Kuo," hosted a popular podcast about Sino-U.S. relations, and he would fire back exasperated replies, warning Ma not to spread fake news and conspiracies. But none of his missives changed her habits. With the world's attention now on Covid-19, Ma took any criticism of China personally and was working overtime to defend it both from the western media and the microbetrayals of her children.

It had become popular online to bash "wet markets" of exotic animal meat, particularly the one in Wuhan, China, where a bat likely had passed the coronavirus to a human. That image had burned itself into round western eyes everywhere. I had been to hundreds of wet markets in China and Chinatowns around the world, including one right in New York City. To me, they were just open-air butcher shops, like a farmers' market of fruits and vegetables. The goods were far more sanitary there than the factory-farmed cuts in our commercial supermarkets—meat which, as my very 'trendy' and stridently anti-animal protein roommate Blair loved to point out, might *look* pristinely packaged but was actually crawling with salmonella. To the world now, though, wet markets were dirty and unsafe, a place of contagion, and my memories of them were invalidated.

Wuhan as a city also had been invalidated, its proud history forever overshadowed by the virus. "REALLY, WUHAN SO SAD NOW," Ma had remarked. "GETTING BLAMING EVERYWHERE." Ma had been born in Wuhan in 1938 and still had extended family there—two half-sisters and their families. My father had even dragged the whole family to Wuhan during a family trip in 1981. Ba had been so eager and happy to show us China, though back then, places like Wuhan were still distressingly undeveloped and poor. I now wish I had paid closer attention on that trip instead of complaining nonstop about the heat and the crowds.

"DID I TELL YOU HOW IT WAS I BORN IN WUHAN?" Ma asked.

"Yeah, you did. Unlucky place. Well, at least everyone knows about Wuhan now," I said.

"WUHAN IS FINE NOW. IT IS AMERICA WHO IS SICK."

I imagined the virus spreading outward from Wuhan. History tugged at my brain, twin yarns of cause and effect, insisting I untangle its knots. A bat had flapped its wings in Wuhan and had brought the world to its knees.

"ANYWAY, DON'T WORRY. I DON'T HUGGING," Ma insisted. "NO ONE ELSE AROUND HERE."

"John's nearby. And you have your helpers if you need anything."

"NOT LIKE BEIJING, KIND OF QUIET."

"There are lots of your friends there. That's why we chose it, remember? But you have to make an effort to see them."

"I DON'T EVEN TELL MANY PEOPLE I AM LIVING HERE NOW. TOO MANY PEOPLE WOULD WANT SEE ME, FOR SURE! ANYWAY, FOR NOW WE CANNOT EVEN SEE EACH OTHER."

"We can show you how to do video calls with more than one person."

"YOU KNOW, TO BE HONEST, NOTHING TO DO HERE. YOU PEOPLE MAKE ME MOVE BACK FROM CHINA, I DON'T KNOW WHY I AGREE."

A familiar frustration welled up, her expert shaming an unswallowed capsule in my throat. Five years after Ba had passed on, Ma had continued to live in their giant house in Beijing, a twelve-hour flight away from any of her children. Living there by herself anymore was a non-starter, especially after she'd taken a fall in her bathroom. To get her to agree to move, I had deployed guilt trips worthy of a Chinese mother: "I can't sleep, knowing that you might fall going up and down those marble stairs," "You don't want me to sleep badly, do you?" and "Just tell your friends you have to move because your son is too worried, and his blood pressure is high because you live so far away from us."

"I UNDERSTAND, MOVING HERE, BE CLOSE TO YOU PEOPLE. BUT STILL, KIND OF BORING."

The cologne bottle inquired if I'd like to throw it at the wall.

"CALIFORNIA NOT LIKE BEIJING AT ALL. NOT EVEN ANY OLDIE WALKING GOLF COURSE."

"That's good! The fewer people, the better right now," I said tersely.

"NOTHING TO DO, REALLY. TAKING WALK BY MYSELF. NO VISITOR LIKE IN BEIJING. NO FRIEND EVEN KNOW YET THAT I MOVE HERE. BUT IT'S OKAY."

"We're all going to have to adjust to more isolation. And wash our hands!" I quipped too brightly.

"ANYWAY, I SEE ON NEWS THAT NEW YORK IS BAD."

"I'll be fine."

"ARE YOU SURE?"

"Why do you worry?"

Ma adjusted the camera finally to stare straight at me. She cocked her head and narrowed her eyes, her smile vaguely triumphant.

"YOU HUGGING TOO MUCH."

September 2020
FaceTime Call

A hotel room in San Jose Del Cabo, Mexico.

JAY takes his temperature again. The thermometer beeps, and he reads it. He puts his hand to his head, then resets the thermometer. Same result, no fever. Yet.

A text from his roommate, BLAIR, back in New York, chimes.

"It definitely would have been Thursday that I was exposed."

JAY does the math in his head and winces. Six days for actual symptoms to show. JAY texts back.

"What is the plan? I'm not quite sure what to do here since it could take days to incubate if I got it."

JAY waits. The ellipses at last resolve into a response from BLAIR.

"I mean, I tested positive on Wed. I didn't interact that much with you before you left, but I would just keep a mask on as much as you can if you're concerned."

JAY takes a deep breath, trying not to feel scared or frustrated. Or angry. He texts back.

"More importantly, how are you feeling?"

Another wait, then:

"Better today than yesterday."

JAY clicks a "heart" icon and then puts down his phone. He opens his iPad and stares at the screen. He begins to type, stops, picks up the thermometer instead, then curses, putting it down.

He calls MA. She answers, the camera trained as usual on her chin.

MA: HI, JAY. WHERE ARE YOU?

JAY: Calling from Mexico.

MA: SOMETHING WRONG?

JAY: Um, no. Why? Do I look bad? Can you even see me?

MA: SORRY, JUST HAVE FEELING.

JAY: No, everything's fine. Healthy. I mean, don't worry. Really. I'm fine. Anyway I really was just calling to say hi. I'm here in Cabo.

MA: IS IT CROWD?

JAY: No, it's pretty empty here. That's why I chose to come here. No crowds. No one much around the hotel.

MA: GOOD TO HEARING.

> JAY stares down at the chapter he is writing in the book MA doesn't yet know about.

JAY: Hey, do you remember when we went to Wuhan the first time? And I asked how it was that you and Ma Zhen's mom were half-sisters. I mean, with different moms, but how is it you were so close in age to each other?

MA: WHY YOU WANTING ASK ME THIS?

JAY: Just thinking about it. About our trip there. How awkward it got when I asked that question.

MA: I DON'T REMEMBERING THAT TRIP.

JAY: Of course you do. Ba got all your family bicycles? I'll always remember what you said.

MA: WHAT I SAY? ON TRIP TO WUHAN?

JAY: Come on, Ma. I know it was like 40 years ago, but—

July 1981
Wuhan, China

Not many American families, even Chinese ones, could have found their way around Wuhan in the early '80s. It was summer; I was a whiny 13-year-old and Wuhan was, as the locals liked to remind us, one of "China's furnaces." The streets seemed to cook the air itself, and there was a sharp scent of too many people in too small an area, a sourness layered with faint mildew from clothes washed without strong detergent or bleach. Ma had a frequent scowl that managed to both condemn our surroundings and warn us not to complain about them.

Wuhan felt like a city that had developed with zero plan, then been forced haphazardly into different ones. The main streets, paved first by the Nationalists and then by the Communists, as Ba explained it, were wide and straight but with no character or purpose other than to flatten and divide. The side streets, however, were winding and crowded, bustling with activity as the populace awoke to new commercial possibilities. With economic reforms, the barest traces of capitalism had taken root. Ba said that in the *new* China, farmers now sold their produce for a profit, which meant a lot of chaos and jostling for the best spots and customers. *To Get Rich Is Glorious!* proclaimed a wall, sloganed in bold, red characters.

Once upon a time, on October 10, 1911, a revolution to topple the Qing Dynasty and depose the hated Manchu rulers began near Wuhan,

12

in a region then known as Wuchang. As Yeye (my grandfather on my father's side) would say, because of Wuhan, thousands of years of imperial rule ended on that day. Yeye had been a professor of—and one of the definitive voices for—modern Chinese history. It was probably why Ba often told us about a place's history before we arrived.

Wuhan had always been a major transportation hub, so it was unsurprising that the 1911 incident began over the seized railways. The story went like this: China's Manchu rulers had been shamefully cooperating with the European powers who had already carved up the country. This was a frequent fallback of Ma's whenever China did anything questionable: "YOU HAVE TO REMEMBER, CHINA HAVE TO FACING SO MANY ENEMY AT ONCE. ALL GANG IT UP."

When the railway shareholders were handed mere government bonds for their shares, they revolted. And the good and loyal Chinese people joined them in a brave display of anti-Western, anti-imperial sentiment. The Qing court promptly sent in troops to squash the rebellion, but this only led to more unrest and escalation—triggering a nationwide uprising and the toppling of the empire. The match may have been lit in Wuhan, but the conflagration grew because of far larger failures in leadership.

Somewhere, a novel coronavirus was taking notes.

Something else that also would wind up mattering nearly forty years after our family trip: The City of Wuhan lay along the mighty Yangtze River, where it met its largest tributary, the Han River, making it a key access point for nine of China's provinces. It was an easy city for merchants, soldiers, workers, farmers, and a virus to get in and out of by boat or rail, or, later, plane.

13

Back in 1937, five years after my father was born, Wuhan briefly became the wartime capital of China during the Japanese occupation. Ma was born in Wuhan a year later, her very pregnant mother, my *laolao*, having fled ahead of the Japanese, who had razed the capital city of Nanjing and murdered its inhabitants wholesale. Wuhan was now a natural stop along the Kuo grand tour of the Middle Kingdom, which my parents had planned meticulously, wanting their four children to experience China firsthand. It was *important*.

Besides, Ma's extended relations still lived in Wuhan, and though she hadn't seen them in four decades, they were still family. As the impossibly wealthy *American* relations, people who owned cars and houses of their own, we Kuos were part of the first wave of returning Chinese after the country had cracked open its doors. So our hosts pulled out all the stops. A feast was prepared, with duck and pork and even local fresh river fish. The Americans had brought Coca-Cola as an offering, which the Chinese relations warily agreed to try. It was flat and warm and, as the Wuhanese collectively decided, rather medicinal.

"You have to drink it cold," I said, in odd defense of America's national beverage and apparently chief export to China at the time. But with no refrigerator in sight, this was useless advice. The cousins, aunties, and uncles politely sipped the dark liquid, then quickly returned the chipped teacups to the rickety table. I could see Ma's eyes expertly appraising everything around them, her judgments of our poorer relatives silently validating many of her own life choices.

"Americans love cold drinks," Ba explained, making it clear he also considered the practice an abomination. "In restaurants, they fill the glasses up with ice before pouring in the soda."

The Wuhanese imagined tall glasses full of ice in air-conditioned American restaurants. This was what the relations had all come to hear from the Kuos, whose children, as Ma theorized, were big-boned from

14

years of drinking milk and eating steaks. The Chinese relations looked at our feet a lot because we mysteriously insisted on wearing heavy American sneakers even in this heat. Our hosts often wore thin black socks with sandals, which looked ridiculous to our eyes.

The ice in glasses remained a point of discussion. "It is so they make more money," a cousin offered, well-versed in American greed. "They give you mostly ice so they can cheat you."

"Not true," said another cousin. "I hear they give you as many drinks as you like."

"Free bread, too," said Ma, an unlikely source of this information. Ma firmly believed the family should never go out to eat if we could help it.

We had dined in a Western restaurant only a handful of times. So limited was my own restaurant experiences that, as a child, I had once gone around to all the tables inside the DoubleTree Inn, where my uncle Stanley was hosting a dinner, and had gathered up the bills and coins other patrons had left behind. It was the first I'd learned of the strange practice of tipping. My mortified parents returned the money to the waitstaff.

The even stranger practice of giving out free bread seemed to impress our Wuhanese relations, but some looked upset by the unfairness. More American extravagance.

"Coke actually does taste much better cold," I offered again, seeking some common ground.

My cousin Ma Zhen laughed. "Cold? How could that possibly make it taste any better?"

"So you don't like it."

"It really is terrible," Ma Zhen said, her voice flat as the Coke.

I laughed aloud, and once they realized we weren't offended by her bluntness, everyone laughed along with us.

A few years later, Ma Zhen spent the summer of 1985 with me in Beijing, where Ba had sent me to teach English and "form roots," and where Ma Zhen was studying physics at the prestigious Tsinghua University. She invited me on an outing with her classmates to a local lake, where I felt the eyes of a tall and dashing sophomore boring into me. He finally worked up his courage, leaned over and whispered something to Ma Zhen. She giggled into her hands explaining to the stupefied classmate that, despite my longer hair and delicate features, I was a boy and not a "lovely girl" at all. The classmate, his face now red as dried chilis, as an old Chinese song went, managed to steal more looks over at me as if pondering the unthinkable. I stared back, smiling and enjoying the unintended gender bend.

Ma Zhen and I bonded that summer. My favorite pastime was sharing one of my Walkman headphones with her as I dutifully but clumsily translated lyrics of songs by American divas, her favorite being Tina Turner's "Private Dancer," which both scandalized and moved her. Ma Zhen would go on to help develop the national ballistic nuclear missile arsenal at China's space agency.

Our second day in Wuhan was for sightseeing. We were in an open-bed truck that bounced along Wuhan's uneven streets with no shock absorbers to cushion our behinds. My brothers looked miserable, especially John. One of the younger male cousins insisted on holding his hand, as boys in China did then without a second thought. John was too polite to attempt a disengage, and he looked to Kaiser for sympathy. Sweat soaked through John's shirt and down his neck, his face a study in exasperation. Kaiser grinned at his misfortune.

Ba had said it was good for us boys to put up with some discomfort, to learn how to *chi ku*—"eat bitterness"—as he had for the first part of his own life. Ba's childhood had been war and deprivation and, as he often described it, a house with just wooden planks over a dirt floor. And to eat? Only rice with—if they were lucky—a bit of lard and red pepper paste to mix in. There were few cars and even fewer trucks like the one we were riding in. If someone had offered *him* a ride back then, he would have been thrilled, not petulant.

Mimi, the youngest Kuo and Ba's greatest joy, was as usual attentive and excited, taking everything in without judgment. She never complained, always checked in on others, and was frugal to a fault. Ba had once taken Mimi shopping for a new pair of shoes at Tucson's Park Mall using her saved-up allowance. She had crisscrossed the property four times, stopping in every shoe store to investigate prices and style selections, finally settling on a modest pair nearly two hours later. Ba had been proud of her, as he was of all his children, but in keeping with his Chinese stoicism, he wouldn't tell us that until much nearer to his death 33 years later.

Mimi studied the local sites and faces with curiosity and concern, withholding judgment until we passed an open sewage cart. Her face collapsed as she nearly retched from the stench.

"What the hell?!" Kaiser cursed. He was the only one of the Kuo children to swear regularly. I was pretty sure he'd started it to set himself apart from his more obedient siblings, but then it had become a habit he couldn't shake.

Mimi wrinkled her nose and shot a distressed look over to me, and I wrinkled back in sympathy. She giggled, and I made my *I'm dying* face, tongue lolling out to the side. This had become a habit between us, mirroring each other's reactions to an absurd world, whether funny or disastrous or, in this case, smelly. We didn't know it then, but our instinct to seek each other out would carry us through the family's most soul-crushing moments.

Ma's family in Wuhan was anchored by her two weathered half-sisters, each a more successful Communist party member than the other. Despite their positions, they lived modestly and had to save carefully to afford anything beyond basic food and clothing. Earlier in the day, Ba insisted everyone go shopping for new bicycles, which was still how people principally got around the city. He purchased one for each adult in each family, paying with special Foreign Exchange Currency that looked like Monopoly money to us kids. Ma's half-sisters protested vehemently, wringing their hands in appropriate consternation. It was too much! They could not possibly! But Ba ignored their refusals, knowing how much a bicycle could change their lives.

So the bicycles had come off the display walls where they hung, like grand birds to be roasted. The sisters wept and shook their clasped hands in thanks, tears running down their faces.

"Are they crying because they're happy?" Mimi asked Ba.

"A bicycle to them is like a car to us," he explained. "They probably cannot believe their good fortune."

Ma clucked. "They are also crying tears of shame," she said in Chinese quietly to me, within earshot of Ba. "Their pride tells them to refuse, but the gift is too great to pass up. So they are happy but still ashamed. Do you see?" It was as much a rebuke to Ba as it was a lesson for me.

I remember a profound sense of recognition, gauzy layer upon layer of meaning, which I could now somehow peer through. I recall seeing, for the first time, how complicated the world could be.

"CAN I HELP WITH ANY DISH?"

There it was, that familiar impatience starting in my gut and working its way up. Ma had come to visit me in New York for a full week—something that sounded doable and noble when I'd offered but felt like a terrible mistake four days in. A month later, when the city shut down, I would be grateful that she had come before everyone was stuck inside their homes. But at that moment, I was near my limit.

"Let me do them. You shouldn't stand up for so long," I said.

"FEELING USELESS, JUST SITTING HERE WATCHING YOU DO ALL WORK."

"You should relax," I said, forcing a smile.

"ALL I DO IS RELAX! NOTHING TO DO. SUCH A GREAT LIFE." Ma picked dog hair off her pants and showed it to me accusingly. My roommates and I kept two dogs and a cat in our Harlem apartment, something Ma could never understand, both the pet part and the Harlem part. While she was staying with us, I forced myself to wake up half an hour early to sweep the floors and brush the couches free of fur, but by the end of the day, it was back everywhere. *Meiyou banfa.* Nothing to be done.

"You should try to enjoy your old age," I sighed.

"YOU MISSED PIECE OF RICE."

I shut my eyes and counted to five, something a parent once told me they did when dealing with difficult children. I put the pot back into the sink to scrub it free of errant grains.

19

"Ma. You're not relaxing if you're watching me do the dishes and commenting on my every move."

"I JUST TRYING TO HELP." Ma's "hurt" face was something I knew well, but it had long since lost its intended effect.

"You can help best by not watching me, waiting for me to do something wrong."

"WATER STILL RUNNING."

"Ma! Stop telling me how to do the dishes! I know how to do dishes!"

"I JUST WANT YOU TO NOT WORK SO HARD!"

"I am working harder with you hovering and criticizing," I said with an increasing edge. *Respond, don't react. Respond, don't react.* I tried coaching myself.

"I NOT CRITICIZE! ANYWAY, MY FRIEND ALL SAY YOU SHOULD NOT VISIT YOUR CHILDREN, WILL JUST GETTING IN THE WAY OF THEIR LIFE."

"Well, we can work on that not happening, right?" I said, gritting my teeth.

"MAYBE I STOP VISITING SO YOU DON'T FEEL I CRITICIZE. ANYWAY, TOO OLD TO BE TRAVEL."

"You're fine, Ma. Just stop hovering."

"YOU NEED A SPONGE FOR WATER. GETTING ON COUNTER."

Thankfully, Ma flipped on the TV and put on the Golden Phoenix News broadcast from Hong Kong, which she watched for hours every day. The segments were on repeat—coverage of the Covid crisis long before it became a big news story outside of China. How the Chinese government was urging all Chinese to defeat the hidden viral enemy. How they were all "One Nation" against this scourge. They even had catchy patriotic jingles sung by school children paired with cute animations about how to properly wash your hands. I had wondered at the time how something like that would go over in the United States. One nation? Ha.

I opened my laptop and scanned my inbox. There was a note from our attorney about an upcoming arbitration. Another deadbeat client had stiffed us. Still fuming from my back-and-forth with Ma, I was in the perfect state of mind to fire off a response. *Response, not reaction,* I reminded myself. I hadn't practiced actual law for years, so it felt good to stretch the old litigation muscles.

"DID I EVER TELL YOU STORY OF HOW I WAS ACTUALLY BORN IN WUHAN?"

I had, in fact, heard this before and recently, along with fifty other of Ma's favorite stories. The pop-psychology internet articles I'd read, the ones about caring for elderly parents, had advised empathy and engagement. Let her tell her remembered life, even if on repeat. Repetition could help with recall and cognitive function. Familiar stories were like a lifeline for the older brain.

Today, however, I ignored that advice in favor of expediency and peace. I was in the middle of something *actually important,* said my brain, something that would help bring in *actual money.* But Ma had a knack for wanting to chat at precisely the wrong moment. She was rather like a cat in that sense, knowing the precise point of greatest disruption. She was born in the Year of the Tiger, after all.

"Ma," I said, working to contain my annoyance. "You actually told me this story like fourteen times. I don't need to hear it again. Actually, I really just need to send out this—"

"MY MOTHER AND FATHER AND WHOLE FAMILY HAVING TO ESCAPE NANJING. RUN FROM THE JAPANESE."

I kept typing while she spoke, barely listening. "Yes, right. Your mother was already carrying you."

"NO, YOU REMEMBER WRONG! NOT CARRYING. I WAS NOT BORN YET. STILL INSIDE."

"I meant she was carrying—well, never mind. Go on."

"ANYWAY, THEY ESCAPING TO WUHAN ON THEIR WAY TO HENAN, WHERE MY FATHER FAMILY LIVE. SO ON THE WAY, I WAS BORN IN WUHAN. THEY STAY THERE FOR SOME TIME."

"Right. So Laolao could recuperate." Laolao was my grandmother on my mother's side. It literally means "old old" in Chinese.

"WELL, THAT WHAT SHE SAY. BUT EVEN AFTER MY MOTHER GET BETTER, SHE DOES NOT WANT TO GOING TO HENAN. YOU KNOW WHY?"

Because it's in the middle of bum-fuck nowhere, I thought. And who could have blamed Laolao? A beautiful, sophisticated, educated young woman, born into wealth and power, living on the coast, riding prize horses, and starring in movies. Why would she want to go to Henan, which might as well be rural Nebraska or Kansas in my mind?

"No. I don't know why," I said wearily. "You should tell me."

"BECAUSE YOUR WAIGONG ALREADY HAVING A WIFE THERE."

I looked up from my email. "Wait, what? Waigong already had a wife?" Waigong is what you call your grandfather on your mother's side of the family. The email could wait.

Sometimes, Ma would nonchalantly drop a bombshell in the middle of one of her old stories. Like the time she'd revealed that I had a "twin" in the womb with me, who had never been born:

"YOU KNOW YOU HAD A TWIN."

"Um… what?"

"YEAH, HAD TEETH AND HAIR AND FACE. THEY HAD TO REMOVE YOUR TWIN LATER. IT WAS MONTH LATER."

"How… Why are you only telling me this now?!"

"I THINK IT TIME I TELL YOU. BEFORE, IT MIGHT UPSET YOU."

"Before. Right. Thanks, Ma."

For some time after that, I pictured my evil twin developing out of my own head, a crazy half-formed Voldemort hidden inside a turban, slowly sucking the life out of me. Finally, I googled the phenomenon and discovered that the "twin" was likely nothing more than a cyst with some disgusting keratin growths, which had to be suctioned out of the womb if it didn't slough off on its own. Ma still periodically brought up my "twin" for shock and awe missions.

"DID I TELL YOU STORY OF WHAT HAPPEN AFTER YOU BORN?"

"Yes. You went to have a cyst removed."

"MORE THAN JUST CYST. IT HAVE A HAIR. AND A NOSE."

"Ma, I hate this story. You sprang this whole evil twin thing on me four and a half decades into my life and freaked me out for a year."

"NOT YOUR TWIN. MAYBE COULD HAVE BEEN THOUGH."

"Can we talk about something else?"

"DOCTOR SAY I JUST HAVE TO HAVE IT SUCK IT OUT."

"Ma…"

"YOU KNOW I WANTED SIX CHILDREN ONLY GET A FOUR."

"Four plus this. It's creepy."

"DOESN'T LOOK LIKE MUCH."

"Like a ball with hair, yes."

"AND NOSE."

"Ma!"

Back in my apartment at this moment, Ma was again revealing something I'd never heard before, this time about my grandfather's "other" marriage. It was time to get the real story.

"Wait. Hold up. How could Waigong's wife still be there? I thought Waigong ditched her."

"NO, YOU THINKING OF HIS FIRST WIFE. THE DUMMY."

I winced at her word choice. The story of "the Dummy" went like this: Waigong had originally been matched to the daughter of another family by a long-standing agreement between their fathers. But he had actually never met his bride, and as the day of their wedding drew near, Waigong's curiosity drove him to cross the county and take a peek for himself. His bride-to-be had Down's syndrome, which was obvious even from a distance. He fled his home and joined the army rather than marry the girl, but a deal was a deal: She went to live at the Liu family compound and was thereafter part of, and more importantly, an expense of, the Liu household, even if the "groom" was nowhere to be found. Later, according to Ma, many would say that the "Dummy's" condition resulted from something missing in her mind but not her soul. In fact, everyone saw that she was the gentlest and happiest of all the people in their extensive compound, at least until my great-grandfather refunded her dowry and then some, sending the girl in tears back to her first family.

"Ma, please. We don't say 'dummy' anymore."

"WHY NOT? THEY NOT DUMB?" I wasn't sure if she was intentionally goading me.

"We just try not to add stigma. Just like we don't say 'retarded' anymore."

"WHAT WE SAY?"

"Mentally handicapped. Or special."

"SPECIAL? WHY?"

"Because special sounds better. I guess?" I was currently writing the libretto for a new musical about an autistic girl—or was it a girl on the autism spectrum? I still fumbled when it came to the right way to refer to people. "I think the idea is, they want a positive, not a negative, connotation."

"ANYWAY, I NOT TALKING ABOUT THE SPECIAL DUMMY. I TALKING ABOUT HIS SECOND WIFE. YOU KNOW THE STORY?"

I closed my computer.

"Actually, I don't. But that's why you have half-sisters in Wuhan, right?"

"OKAY, YES, BUT I HAVE TO TELL FROM BEGINNING. WHEN I WAS JUST BORN IN WUHAN."

February 1938
Wuhan, China

"Scoundrel!" Laolao cried. "Lying scoundrel!" Laolao hoisted her sword and slashed it at Waigong.

As a child, I used to spy on Laolao while she practiced *taiji*, two long-drawn swords whirling and slicing dramatically while she balanced, sometimes on just one foot, out on the swimming pool deck of our house in Tucson. It was an incongruous sight—and also the most bad-ass thing I'd ever seen an old woman do. Laolao looked straight out of a kung fu movie, which made sense once I knew she actually used to star in them during the silent-film era. The beautiful and deadly sword maiden. It's how I've pictured her ever since. And now, in some weird genetic pass-down, my sister has taken up *taiji* with a Chinese master and films herself for her social media followers wielding traditional Chinese curved hand blades.

As Ma related the curious circumstances of her own birth and the humiliating matter of her father's second family, I pictured my formidable Laolao confronting Waigong, as if in an epic movie scene. The war against Japan had just intensified. Ma had just been born. I

26

gave Laolao a sword to fit the scene in my head and the argument Ma said had taken place based on Laolao's own vivid accounts.

Waigong dodged and raised his hands in surrender and supplication. "I meant to tell you about her. Forgive me for being a coward. Please put the blade down! You still need to rest!"

Three servants cowered behind her, one holding Ma, who had the given name Tanlee, just a newborn girl of a few weeks.

"THE 'TAN' WAS BECAUSE I SUPPOSED TO BE BORN ON CHRISTMAS, BE A CHRISTMAS BABY. BUT GOOD THING I COMING LATE, BECAUSE JAPANESE ATTACKING NANJING AND LAOLAO HAVING TO RUNNING TO WUHAN," Ma explained.

Infant Ma wailed after another clay pot crashed against the wall behind Waigong's head, just missing him. Laolao was a sword maiden, true, but she had pretty good aim, too. She had trained in martial arts with her father who, Ma explained once, was part of the *Hong Bang*, a secretive offshoot of the Heaven and Earth Society that aimed to end the Qing dynasty and restore the Ming to power. Pretty intense stuff. Laolao reserved most of her considerable fighting prowess for her movie roles, but they served her well in presently threatening her husband.

"Get her out of here!" Laolao screamed. "Take her away, I don't want to see her!"

Of course, it's a girl, Laolao had lamented upon Ma's birth. Now Laolao understood: All the lies her husband had told had angered the gods, and her family was now cursed. It wasn't very Christian to blame the lesser gods for her misfortune, but she had never fully shaken the superstitions she absorbed as a child before the missionaries had come and opened the doors of Heaven to her family.

Laolao flashed her blade in a full arc and rounded furiously on her lying husband. Her hair, once so nicely curled and bouncy, now swept across her face like a crazy woman's. She wailed loudly and incoherently, a skill Ma would inherit, her eyes wide like a lunatic. *Let that haunt his dreams!* Then she charged her sword in a blur, Waigong retreating behind the poster bed. She pursued him around it while he begged her to calm down.

"I would never have married you had I known about her!" Laolao spat. "And you! How can you call yourself a Christian? How could you take up arms and fight for our country in His name, then marry me knowing you are already a husband and a father?"

"I do not love her!" Waigong exclaimed. "She was forced upon me! It was my mother's doing. You know how controlling she is. She said I had to marry her because you would not wed me! For two years, I begged you to marry me, but you refused."

"WAIGONG CHASING LAOLAO FOR *THREE* YEARS," Ma corrected. "NEVER GIVING UP. OF COURSE, SHE GET TIRED AND SAY OKAY IN THE END. BUT SHE WAS STUBBORN."

"But wait, he was seeing someone else, too, while courting Laolao?"

"NOT JUST SEEING. MARRY TOO. HAVING GIRL ALREADY."

"Oh, shit!" I said.

"So now I am to blame?" Laolao continued. "How dare you turn this upon me! I refused you for *three* years because you were not enough of a man when I met you. You were a boy begging for a job from my uncle."

Or at least that's how Ma told it. Unfortunately for him, Waigong is long dead and can't exactly provide a more flattering version of his early job prospects.

Laolao snarled with contempt at the man now pleading for his life. "I was right to refuse you. I should have listened to my doubts. Look where it has gotten me! I am humiliated!"

"The family needed an heir! But God still gave me a girl with her," said grandfather, self-pity washing over him. "After that, I said I would divorce my mother's..." (he searched for the right word here) "*selection*, to marry you! I told her it is *you* who will bear my heirs!"

"God laughs at your plans," Laolao sneered. "'What a great man is Liu Jingjian, who has two wives but only two girl children to show for it.' I hope to hear the world mock you."

Waigong sighed. He might as well rip off the bandage now, he thought.

"Actually, three."

Laolao blinked. "What do you mean?"

"The woman gave birth again a few weeks ago. It was another girl."

It took Laolao just seconds to run the math backward in her mind. "So, when you went home to Henan last year... you put another child in her while you were pledging your love for me?!"

Her aim was better this time. The jade carving she'd thrown was heavy, and it clipped him in the ear before thudding to the ground.

"Forgive me!" he pled. "How was I to know that we would be forced out of Nanjing and sent home to live with them?"

"So now you blame the Japanese?" she screamed. They had fled to Wuhan from the old capital just a few weeks earlier, with Laolao well into her eighth month of pregnancy, spending a bitter Christmas on the road just ahead of Japan's imperial troops. It was a miracle they had escaped at all. The Japanese were maiming, raping, or murdering every person in sight. Babies were being pulled from pregnant women and bayoneted before their mothers' horrified eyes by soldiers trained in cruelty and instructed to terrorize.

Laolao in wartime China had been like us, more than eighty years later, deep in pandemic lockdown, or rather more like the Ukrainian people, who never thought Russia would go through with a land war in Europe. Like many today, she could not have conceived how their lives could upend in just a matter of days, how the world could simply overturn itself so quickly.

But there they were, in 1938, nameless among tens of thousands of other refugees from a war. Waigong and Laolao, with Ma in her belly, had fled the war and stopped in Wuhan on their way to Henan Province, where Waigong's extended family was ensconced in their ancestral compound, apparently with his *other* wife and daughter. Make that, daughters.

"Everyone there will look upon me as a common whore," Laolao said, wiping tears with one wrist while still brandishing her sword with the other. "I am just the concubine of a petty *kuomintang* officer. My children will never be heirs."

"No, no!" Waigong cried, seeing an opening. "You misunderstand. Because I am divorced from her, those girls are no one. In fact, they are being sent to live with my brother and his wife, who will raise them as their own because they have no children. They are now my 'nieces,' not my daughters. Tanlee will be their little cousin!"

"Their little cousin?" Laolao said, trying to sort it all out. "So when I bear you sons—"

"They will be my heirs. And the heirs to my grandfather's vast property. They will be rich men, and you will be a wealthy matriarch one day."

"This changes nothing," she lied, shifting into how to leverage this. "You kept all this from me to trick me into this marriage, and now I cannot ever trust you again. How do I know you do not have more children lying about the countryside? Can you swear to me now there are no other surprises? No more hidden wives and families?"

He sighed. One more bandage to rip off: the matter of the Special Dummy. "I need you to be calm first," he says.

He had barely begun to explain about his *first* wife when a jewelry box flew straight at him and shattered into a thousand pieces.

July 1981
Wuhan, China

We were nearing the end of our miserably hot but character-building few days in Wuhan. More of our extended relatives eagerly awaited us in the city of Changsha, at the end of a riverboat cruise up the Yangtze, where Ba no doubt would buy more bicycles to impress them.

But there was a problem. My brother Kaiser was missing his beloved knife.

For a few days now, Kaiser had harbored suspicions about our cousin. Or second cousin or something, which still meant he was technically family, but there was something just *off* about him. We had been steaming in the moist heat of Wuhan for almost three days, and our obsequious hanger-on was really starting to grate on us. His fawning reminded me of Gollum from *The Hobbit*. Someone with an agenda, not to be trusted.

It wasn't just how he showered affection on poor John, who was too polite to tell the dude to please stop holding his hand. No, it was the way his eyes took in our belongings. Everything from our clothes, to our disposable plastic bags (Americans threw them away after just one use!), to our boombox, to—and especially—Kaiser's Craftsman lock-back knife.

The knife had an ebony handle inlay, a honed steel blade with a thumb notch for easy opening, and a soft leather sheath that slipped perfectly onto his belt. Well-balanced and a pleasure to hold, it was the perfect tool for slicing the soggy, warm watermelon our aunties in Wuhan insisted on serving. And whenever Kaiser pulled the knife out, there was Gollum, coveting it with glinting eyes.

Kaiser had always had a love for weaponry. His fascination with heroes in full armor began early when our parents had taken us to see *Camelot* in a local community film house in upstate New York. By the time the credits rolled, Kaiser had decided two things.

First, he was clearly destined to become a Knight of the Round Table and therefore had to protect his queen, our mother. Indeed, his very name suggested kingly aspirations: In *What To Name the Baby*, our parents noted that "Kaiser" was the German word for "king" (as well as forming part of my father Jenkai's name). If not yet quite a king, Kaiser was certainly on his way toward knighthood, having taken to standing guard outside of our parents' bedroom until he was too sleepy to remain upright. Ba often opened the door to find him curled just outside, toy sword clutched with both hands.

Second, because knights only spoke (and sang, apparently) in English, Kaiser decided he would no longer address the family in Chinese. This second edict was something of a blow for Ma, whose English was primarily used for "baby talk" with us kids. She forever marked that moment as the point when the Kuos started to become less Chinese and more "ABC"—American-born Chinese.

At two years older and therefore far cooler, my brother John was already a voracious consumer of fantasy and science fiction. He encouraged Kaiser's love of chivalry, knights, and rather dangerous weaponry. In one memorable encounter, armed with a fully operational bow-and-arrow set, John had been practicing archery when Kaiser had begun to taunt him.

"You can't shoot me! You can't shoot me!" shrieked my ever-confident, once-and-future-king second brother.

Then John, deadly serious, had quietly taken aim, judged the distance between hunter and hunted, and deftly shot Kaiser in the face with an arrow, striking him between the eyes and leaving quite the gash. A half-inch, either way, would have blinded him, so the story goes. Ba, in a rare show of anger, had broken the bow and each arrow in half.

Our collective love for the medieval and fantasy genre carried over into an obsession with *Dungeons and Dragons*, which preoccupied us for whole weekends of campaigning, interrupted periodically by Ma poking her head in and scolding, "YOU STILL PLAYING? TIME TO WRAPPING IT UP. SO UNHEALTHY!" It also, somewhat embarrassingly in hindsight, involved some serious cosplay before it had ever become cool. Kaiser, John, and their misfit friends battled with wooden swords and shields for glory and valor, and to impress not a few female participants who had attached themselves to their merry band of losers. I got up the courage to tag along with them just once, but the terror of hand-to-hand combat deterred me from future participation.

As Kaiser grew older, his arsenal expanded. Ba indulged his passion by allowing all manner of what had become a growing stockpile: BB guns, a 22-caliber rifle, a pistol, swords, daggers, and his favorite buck knife. Once, during his frequent target practices, a stray BB ricocheted disastrously and struck a neighborhood girl named Rosie Fiore in the thigh. This was concerning in the extreme, not only because Rosie

33

herself was of imposing girth and strength and could kick our asses herself, but because her father, Mr. Fiore, had charged across the street to demand justice.

"Did you *shoot* my Rosie?!" Mr. Fiore bellowed in his scratchy *Godfather* voice that I still can hear if I summon his broad visage. "Did you shoot *my girl*?!"

The neighborhood of Apalachin, New York, wasn't known for much outside of a famous local incident involving the arrest of several high-profile mobsters who had picked the town as a point to gather for, well, a meeting of mobsters. Armed with this backdrop, the Kuo children were convinced that Mr. Fiore was a capo and could have people killed for any reason. Even kids.

"It—it—it—was an accident…" Kaiser stammered, his hands raised.

"Hmmm," Mr. Fiore said, sizing up the BB gun. "You better be more careful with that. You're lucky, *for your sake,* she wasn't hurt. Do you understand me? *Lucky.*"

Lucky, indeed. I already had imagined the violence, the kidnapping, the concrete shoes pulling Kaiser to the bottom of the Susquehanna River, and the grim reports of one of only three ABC boys from the whole neighborhood gone missing.

At the moment, though, in the summer of 1981, the thing missing was Kaiser's prized buck knife. As the family prepared to leave Wuhan on a riverboat-that-could-not-be-missed, Kaiser began turning the apartment upside down, searching for his favorite blade. His suspicions that Gollum had taken it were strong. He dropped his voice to raise the question.

"Ba, I believe we have a thief," he said.

"I believe you are correct," Ba said, somewhat amused by the whole situation.

"I THINK HE LOOKING SO GUILTY," agreed Ma in English, so that Gollum wouldn't understand. "AND HE LOOKING IN PLACES MAKE NO SENSE. LIKE HE TRYING TO SEEM HELPFUL."

"Maybe it just fell somewhere when we were out," Mimi offered, ever willing to see the best in people.

"Are you kidding?" I scoffed. "That knife is like a part of Kaiser's hand. No way he'd just lose it."

"Why don't we just forget about the knife," Ba said, concerned about the time. "We can't prove he took it. We will get you a new one when we get home."

For Kaiser, though, I knew it had become a question of honor. A common thief was among us, and he needed to be flushed out and humiliated. Kaiser went full TV cop.

"Why don't you just admit that you took it?" growled Kaiser in Chinese, suddenly turning on the cousin known as Gollum.

"What are you talking about?" Gollum squeaked. "I am helping you look for it!"

"You've been eyeing our stuff this whole time. I've seen you look at my knife while I use it. I know you're lying. I know you took it. What else did you take, I wonder?"

Gollum looked like a trapped animal. "How can you accuse me of such a thing?" he wailed. "I have been nothing but kind to you, and this is how I'm repaid?"

Gollum shot me a look for support, but I just narrowed my eyes. So transparent.

But Kaiser hesitated. I could tell he was worried Gollum was telling the truth. But to my ear, he was guilty. In fact, he had very carefully not actually denied taking it.

At nearly six feet tall, Kaiser was an imposing figure compared to his cousin-or-second-cousin, who was five foot five even in his shoe risers. Kaiser took after Ma's younger brothers, the three Liu uncles, all of whom towered over six feet. That whole side of the family were giants, even Laolao, who stood at an impressive five-nine. Kaiser used this now to his advantage. Grabbing Gollum by the shirt collar, he hauled him up to get in his face with mere inches between them.

"Stop lying and give me back my knife!" Kaiser roared.

Gollum was clearly unused to physical threats. If he had peed himself right there, I would not have been surprised.

"If you took the knife and can return it to us now," Ba said quietly, somewhat startled by Kaiser's sudden escalation, "we won't mention this to your family."

That seemed to work. Gollum nodded, and Kaiser put him down. He went to his room and emerged, head down, holding out the missing item.

"I have never had anything nice in my whole life," Gollum said through what were almost tears. "Nothing at all. Then you came here, and you gave us bicycles, brought Coca-Cola, and played your American music. You may think you were being kind, but we feel ashamed. We are so poor. You have everything. We have nothing. You judge us from your place of wealth. We have struggled even to have what we have. It isn't fair."

Kaiser seemed unready for this speech. Like Ba, he had only seen our gestures and gifts as generous.

"If you had asked for the knife, I probably would have just let you have it," Kaiser muttered. I sought out Mimi and rolled my eyes at her. *Not a chance.* She suppressed a giggle.

Stolen goods recovered, the family headed to the ferry station. This time, Ma's half-sisters wept true tears, a rare and likely unrepeatable family reunion coming to a close. As our car pulled away, Ba sat back and considered.

"You got de knife back," he remarked. "But I don't tink, Kaiser, dat you handled it as well as you could have."

Kaiser grunted. "But I got it back, and that's what matters."

"Kaiser handled it like he always handles things," Ma said in Chinese. "He is very much a Liu, not a Kuo. Act first, clean up the mess later."

Ba chuckled. "But he needs to learn not to lose his temper like dat," Ba said, as Kaiser pretended not to hear him.

Ma put her hand out to pat her husband. "YOU KNOW, SOMETIME IT IS JUST GOOD THING HAVING KNIGHT TO PROTECT FAMILY."

Chapter Two

PARENTING

or

"I BLAMING YOUR FATHER"

October 2019
New York City, New York

"THEY SAY SON ALWAYS FOLLOW MOTHER GENE. NOT FATHER. IS IT TRUE?"

"What?" I said, somewhat startled by Ma's sudden science inquiry. "No, it's not true. Where do you get these ideas?"

"I READING ABOUT IT," Ma said with great confidence.

"Technically, the children get half from each parent. There are special genes from the mother's side called mitocho—well, forget that, for the regular genes, we get exactly half from each parent."

"OKAY. WELL, I SURE HOPE YOU GETTING MY HALF."

Ma had always been obsessed about whether her children's fundamental personalities sprang from her or Ba. Her genes or his, as if one always predominated. The two families of their union—the Lius and the Kuos—were so different in temperament that it was tempting to sort the resulting children into sides. Anything sounding in emotion, passion, artistry, or charisma was Liu, while anything based on logic, science, fact, or reason was Kuo. The sorting was, of course, selective; in the great battle of nature versus nurture, whenever anything negative went down, ancestry was usually to blame, while anything positive suggested good parenting.

Ma often remarked that while Ba was not a great husband, he made up for it by being a good father. She said this to his face sometimes, but he never took the bait. Ba was designed to be a great dad: patient, dedicated, even-tempered, and wise. Ma admittedly never really was any of these things (though she was spontaneous, energetic, theatrical, and clever), so she often looked to her four children for clues and assurance. Whenever we succeeded, she claimed at least half the credit, usually more. After all, Ma was the one who spent the most time with us, read to us at night, dressed us, fed us, set the rules at home, insisted on music lessons and drove us to them each week, and settled disputes when Ba was at work. If we turned out to be smart, industrious, wealthy, or famous, or preferably all four, her time as "just a housewife" would be affirmed as well spent.

Once my brothers were toddlers and she could put them in a playpen, Ma began sitting down next to it, writing essays and stories for overseas Chinese periodicals and papers. The subject was sometimes our family, but more often they were fictional stories of strong women—a mother with cancer, an avid gardener, even a biracial love story. Often they told of women caught between family obligations and wanting to strike out on their own. As her pieces were accepted and published, and as her reputation as an author grew, she began to dive into politics, a rare thing for a woman of her generation. Ba saw no harm in this since Ma wrote under a pseudonym, and many of her readers assumed that the author Xiao Xiangpo ("Little Country Maid") was a man anyway. Her writings were her second source of pride and further evidence of fulfilled potential. When she reached her 70s and '80s, however, Ma wrote a lot less, complaining that whenever she sat down to do so, the details about her experiences had already escaped her.

"WHERE WE TRAVEL AFTER SPAIN? PORTUGUEE?" she asked me once, suddenly.

"Right. We went to Lisbon. Remember, we had those cream pastries? *Pastèis de nata.* And you said the food was so good and so cheap?"

"CANNOT REMEMBERING. NO DETAIL AT ALL."

"The hills around Lisbon were too hard for you to walk, so we took trams up and down them."

"I SIT DOWN TO WRITE ABOUT MY TRAVEL BUT CANNOT REMEMBER ANYTHING AT ALL."

"Well, if you like, I can help you with the details."

"NO, I HAVE NO INTEREST IN WRITE FOR SOME REASON."

"Yeah, I totally get that," I said, not sure how to help.

We sat quietly for a while. I understood her reticence to pick up a pen. It had been four years since my first musical ever to get to Broadway had closed, and I hadn't written a single song in all that time. It wasn't that I felt sad or resentful about the lukewarm to bad reviews of my score (nearly all of which I had refused to read: "Why do I care what someone who isn't a composer or even a musician thinks about my music?!" I would assure myself) but the urge to write new music simply hadn't arisen since. Without that gravitational pull, I didn't even bother to try. Ma was clairvoyant about my emotional needs, so she began tiger-momming about it.

"WHEN YOUR NEW MUSICAL GOING TO PLAY?"

"*Indigo*? It's still in development. But everything in the theater biz is dark now. Shuttered by the virus. Anyway, it's not really my music. I'm just writing the libretto."

"WHA?"

"The words between the songs. I'm writing the story, basically."

"NOT YOUR MUSIC?"

"I'm advising on the music."

"I THOUGHT WAS YOUR MUSIC."

"Well, I picked this composer because I like the way he writes songs. He writes the music a lot like I would."

"SOUND LIKE EXCUSE."

She was trolling me, but she was also right, which made the moment even more difficult.

"YOU ALWAYS SO GOOD AT MUSIC, EVER SINCE YOU WERE LITTLE, PLAYING FUR ELISE, DEE-DA DEE-DA DEE-DA DEE-DA-DA! YOU NEVER WANT TO GET AWAY FROM PIANO, HAVE TO PULL YOU AWAY."

Fifty-plus years of being Ma's son still hadn't inoculated me from her *I know what's best for yous*. While I had come to accept that being a mother gave her the right to press on my pain points, I hadn't learned to relax and give in to her therapy. In her own way, she was urging me to be better. And she wasn't doing it simply to bask in reflected pride. I was willfully ignoring something that used to make me happy and was willing to go to war over it. Being stubborn like Ma, I dug my foxhole deeper.

"I think I'm happier just writing the story for now."

"YOU MUST BE GETTING WRITER GENE FROM ME. DO YOU THINK?"

"Well, it's not from Ba," I said, knowing what she wanted to hear.

41

"YOUR DADDY NEVER COULD UNDERSTAND WHY EDITOR-IN-CHIEF OF BIG PUBLISHER LIKE 1970 COULD TAKE INTEREST IN ME." *The '70s* was a biweekly magazine that had been popular among the Hong Kong and overseas Chinese community back when Ma's career as a writer really took off.

"You mean Li Shushu in Hong Kong?" I asked. The title *shushu*, meaning uncle, was conferred upon family friends as well.

"YEAH," Ma said, looking away as she recalled a conversation. "I SAID TO YOUR FATHER, SOMETIMES PEOPLE CAN JUST LOOK AT YOUR WRITING AND SEE SOMETHING THERE. HE REALLY LIKE MY PIECE: 'CHINA, I'M VERY CONCERNED ABOUT YOU.'" She was getting her timeline mixed up. That piece was published many years later when she started writing more politically, but I played along.

"That one was a big hit, right."

"I TOLD YOUR BABA, 'HE SEE MY WRITING AND HE KNOW RIGHT AWAY.' ALSO CAN TELL JUST LOOKING AT ME."

"Just by looking at you, he could tell you were a writer?"

"WELL, HE CAN SEE I HAVE SOMETHING TO SAY. IT NOT LIKE WHEN YOU LOOK AT A SCIENTIST OR ENGINEER. WHEN YOU DO, YOU NEVER THINK THEY ARE THINKING DEEP THOUGHT."

September 1976
Apalachin, New York

We had never had our own rooms. The three Kuo brothers, who rebranded as "The Three Musketeers" after Ba let us watch the film, would learn how to share our possessions, keep our common area tidy, and look out for one another. At least that was Ba's plan. Ba and his own little brothers had lived in a cramped space, even sleeping together on the same dingy, bedbug-ridden mattress. Ba insisted that experience had made him a less selfish person. I can't remember a time as a child when I wasn't sharing something generally with my brothers: sleeping quarters, meals, television time (strictly controlled with a special screen lock Ba installed), or even clothes, which passed from John to Kaiser to me. Ma explained that her own clothes growing up were hand-me-downs from a girl named Lorraine Fu, who was her mother's friend's daughter, and that we shouldn't take anything for granted.

What we never managed to share in equal measure was attention from our parents. Ma often muttered that she and Ba had been too strict with John because he was the oldest, that they had fussed over and constrained him more than needed. This was beyond dispute. As Ma liked to tell the story, a ball had once escaped the confines of the Kuo yard and bounced across the street to our "bad" neighbor Joey Slate's lawn. John stopped at the curb's edge, the ball in plain sight but technically beyond bounds. As he ran to ask Ma for permission to cross, Kaiser laughed and traipsed across the pavement to retrieve it. John began shouting after him that they hadn't been given permission to leave the yard.

Ma watched all this from the living room window and thought with horror, *what have I done?* Well, at least that's the version she always told everyone, even John's friends, to his annoyance and chagrin. "FIRST BOY ALWAYS GOING A LITTLE TOO STRICT, SECOND ONE TOO EASY," she said, Goldilocks-ing them into neat buckets.

Kaiser was never happy to share anything, especially our parents' approval. John had once drawn a picture, and Ma hung it up on the wall with honor. Then Kaiser attempted his own drawing, eager to match John's talent and see his masterpiece displayed, too. He failed to create a *chef d'ouevre*, but after all, he was much younger, as John said to try and comfort him. Then, when no one was watching, like the tragic Biblical story of the first brothers of all humankind, Kaiser ripped down John's drawing, crumpling it, and hanging his own in its place. John thought for certain Kaiser would get in trouble, but Ma only laughed while Ba frowned in thought.

The need for attention had rubbed off on me, too. I had witnessed the love and care Kaiser received from scraping his shin in a bike crash. Ma had swabbed hydrogen peroxide over the raw skin while Kaiser, pale, turned his head aside, unable to look down upon the small wound. Ma dabbed it with mercurochrome before smoothing on a bandage. But John had not even put away the first aid kit when I ran into the room with my own injury. I had purposely stapled through the tip of my finger and held it up to show Ma, the blood still dripping down my hand. Ma angrily removed the staple.

Maybe these increasing rivalries drove Ba to begin his new nightly lessons with us. One evening, instead of turning off the light and closing the door, Ba paused to ask how our day had gone. When we murmured "good" and "okay," he wasn't satisfied. He wanted real details. What we had learned, with whom we had argued, and what thoughts were still in our heads right before bed.

These weren't the questions a teacher might ask at school. Ba's questions were odd, taking on big, squishy subjects: love, respect, honor, and trust. Not "Where's Botswana?" or "What's the cube root of 125?" His were questions that didn't have real answers.

"What did you do today, Jay Jay?" Ba asked.

"I played with my friends!" I gushed, eager to be *first*. "We played tetherball. And I won the math game in class. It was too easy! Just multiplication."

44

"I bet you showed off," muttered Kaiser.

"Did not!"

"I bet they all hate you for it, too," Kaiser added. "No one likes a show-off."

"So you played with your friend, huh?" Ba said. I nodded. "So. Do you like your friends?" I nodded a bit more slowly, and I saw John's mouth moving with an answer, rolling the question around in his own head like a marble as if he wasn't very sure of the answer.

"What do you tink friendship is?" Ba asked me gently.

"Um…" I said, struggling to come up with the answer I thought Ba wanted. "Friendship is—when you have someone you can do fun things with?"

"Dat's true. Friends do fun tings together," Ba said. "But what makes a good friend?"

"When they're nice to you?" I tried again.

"Dat's also true, and friends are good to each other. Dey try to be helpful and kind to each other. But is dat all?"

"Yes?" I said, unsure.

"You have to trust each other," John offered, saving me. "Friendship is about trust."

"Dat's a good answer," Ba said. "So, what creates trust?"

"Being good to someone over a period of time. Being honest and making good on your promises," John said.

"And not betraying them by ratting them out," Kaiser added, needling me. "No one trusts a tattler."

"Trust means not breaking the rules!" I said, my fur up.

"Okay, okay," Ba said. "Trust is important for friends to have. Do you agree?"

"Also, brothers," John said. "Trust means you put each other first. It means you don't have to ask someone if they'll be there for you. You just know that they will be."

Kaiser looked sullen. It hadn't been meant for him, but he took it that way anyway.

"What if they're not?" I asked.

"Then they've broken trust," John said with a shrug. "That means they're not really your friend. Not really your brother."

The thought of not really being brothers made me tear up. Kaiser said I cried a lot for a boy. "We can lose our brothers?" I whispered aghast.

Ba sighed and looked sad. Maybe he was thinking about his own little brother, the one we called Xiao Shushu, little uncle, who had been really cruel towards our grandmother, whom we called Nainai. After Yeye had passed away, Nainai went to live with Xiao Shushu and his wife Lisa, who loved her yappy dog more than anything in the world. Lisa had been so nasty that Nainai finally had called Ba in tears, begging to be taken in. Ba had driven out that night to get her, and he hadn't spoken to Xiao Shushu since.

"We can lose trust, yes, but dat doesn't end brothers," Ba said. "Same goes for old friends. Sometimes dey will let you down. But we can forgive dem over time. Have your friends let you down before?"

46

"Yes," I said. "I used to play with Mikey, but now he teases me by pulling at his eyes every time he sees me. 'Chinese, Japanese, Dirty Knees! Look at these!'" I yanked at my shirt like there were tiny boobs there. "I hate him."

"Mikey may one day feel bad dat he lost your trust, acting dis way," Ba said.

"The guy is a dick," Kaiser said. "Just ignore him."

"So, how do you know if your friends actually like you?" John asked, still troubled by the question. "If you're always doing things to get them to trust you, how do you know they actually want you around, you know, just because they like you and not because you're useful?"

John had always been the one to step up and help, to offer to do the things no one else wanted to do, as a way of showing he was a good friend, a good brother, and a good son. Years later, when he knew bigger words to throw around, Kaiser called it John's "martyr complex," which stung because it hit close to the truth. John had, in fact, already begun to worry that people, including his best friends, took his help for granted. Maybe their friendship was just them taking advantage of him. Maybe if he stopped being helpful to them, they would have no more use for him.

"Knowing dat about a friend is something only experience can build," Ba said. "Experience and time."

"I like you," I said to John. "I think you're a good brother."

"Naw, he sucks," said Kaiser, laughing but uncomfortable.

If John sometimes went too far out of his way to help others, Kaiser was the opposite, avoiding chores and tasks whenever he could. Kaiser never worried whether his friends liked him just for being him because Kaiser didn't offer them much beyond Kaiser. He would never offer to help finish a project or take care of a pet turtle as John would. He'd do it if asked, but he usually wouldn't think to offer, at least not on his own. Kaiser's way of living seemed so easy, but John probably already knew he didn't want that for himself. John understood that his life was mostly about promises kept and hard work done for others. That was the Kuo family side, for sure. Kaiser was more a Liu, clever and charming but, like their mother, drawn into the orbits of people like John and Ba.

"Yeah, I suck," said John, laughing a bit too casually.

September 2019
Rossmoor, California

> JAY has been visiting MA in California for a week and is ready to head back to the safety of New York. He has packed his bag and has begun to strip the sheets off the bed in her spare bedroom.

JAY: Should I put the sheets in the washer?

MA: WHY?

JAY: Because I slept in them for three days.

MA: YOU SHOULD LETTING THE GIRLS DO IT.

JAY: They're being paid to take care of you, not me.

MA: NO, ALL THEY DO IS SITTING AROUND. THEY SHOULD BE WASHING THE SHEET.

JAY: I'm just doing it better than them, so they can't say anything. Just like you said you did.

MA: WHEN I SAY?

JAY: Just now! That story you told me about you and Laolao and the dishes!

A beat.

MA: THAT DIFFERENT TIME.

February 1946
Nanjing, China

"What are you having my daughter do?"

I pictured Laolao sizing up her fool of a husband.

"You have her working like a scullery maid!"

"She is my daughter as well," Waigong sighed. "And she is learning how to run a household, something no one ever bothered to teach you, it seems."

"You have her washing windows and scrubbing pots like a peasant," Laolao hissed. "Think what her hands will look like, soaking in those chemicals!"

"Her hands will be fine! If anything, the lye will make them softer!" he said.

They were both speaking as if Ma, then just a girl of nine, wasn't there. But she was used to that. She didn't want to be caught in this fight, which she already understood was more about who was in charge of the house than whether her own hands would be ruined from dishwashing. She slinked back to the pile of pots and pans, where the hot water still smelled strongly of soda powder. It was the New Year, and my *waigong* had said she must set an example. She must make the house sparkle!

The task, ambitious as it was, didn't bother her. In fact, she rather liked the feeling of making dirty things clean, of bringing order to chaos. No one else, not even the kitchen girls whose actual job this was, could make the pots gleam as she could. And she wasn't afraid of the rats, bugs, or spiders that lurked in the unswept corners of their compound and made the servant girls shriek and cower. One of the pans beckoned, "I'm still covered in grease!" and she seized it. Who had washed this before her? They had done a lousy job. As she scrubbed, her hands did look a bit red, but they would fade. Ma always sang when she was most happy, so she began a tune for her work:

The chili pepper girl is thin and sallow

Her eyes are black and shining

One day she would teach her own children how to sing folk tunes while washing up and to not be afraid of critters. She would have three boys and three girls, she decided. And she wouldn't fuss about whether their hands were smooth or knew about proper decorum. And she wouldn't make them go to church! Such a waste of time.

In the background, she could still hear her parents arguing.

"Manxi," Waigong said, calling her by her given name. "You are my wife, and that means you, not I, are supposed to supervise the houseworkers. But you don't know how to do any of these things yourself. The windows are filthy. And there is baked rice on the bottoms of the pans. If Tanlee learns how to do it, she will be able to instruct the servants properly."

50

"YOU WAIGONG ALWAYS ACTING LIKE GERMAN AFTER HE SPEND YEARS THERE. ALWAYS SO NEAT AND CLEAN. A LITTLE STRANGE," Ma explained.

Waigong had fled to Germany, along with many of his fellow officers, when their leader, the "Christian Warlord" Feng Yuxiang, suffered a humiliating loss to Generalissimo Jiang's forces in the Northern Expedition before switching sides. Germany had offered aspiring military officers "rigorous education and training" and a place far away from the treacherous politics of China.

Laolao often made fun of Waigong's admiration of the European imperialists. The Germans had set up a colony of sorts in Laolao's home province of Shandong in the city of Qingdao, which most Americans now know for its beer, after seizing the fortified city from the Qing emperor. There the Germans built European-style chateaus and taught the art of brewing hops.

One day, early in the 1980s, the local Qingdao government offered my father an exclusive U.S. distributorship for Tsingtao Beer (using the old-fashioned spelling), which he foolishly declined, thinking "Who in the world would ever buy Chinese beer?" Only every Chinese restaurant in the damn country, it turned out. Oh well. *Meiyou banfa*. Nothing can be done.

"LAOLAO VERY WESTERN BACK THEN. STRICT CATHOLIC, EXCEPTING LIKE TO WEARING DRESS AND HIGH BOOT FROM EUROPEAN," Ma said, bringing me back to the moment.

Laolao had even changed her name, from the hated "Xiuwen," which implied dainty and softness, to the unusual "Manxi"—a name roughly implying "westward."

"*Slowly* westward," she had explained to Ma, who had wondered why her mother had had two names, three if you counted her stage name, which few knew. "I chose to add '*man*' to suggest a more deliberate pace."

But there was nothing ever deliberate or slow about fiery Laolao. Ma knew the stories told to her over breakfasts of duck eggs and pickled mustard greens. When Laolao was a little girl, they had tried to bind her feet, as they did to nearly all girls of her mother's generation. "It was how they controlled us," she explained. "Hard to run away when your feet are tiny and can only shuffle." The bindings had lasted one day, with Laolao slicing them off and jabbing her dagger at anyone who came near. Her father finally acquiesced, and no one dared approach Laolao again with the stinky, painful foot cloths. From that point, her father taught her how to properly use that dagger. And a sword! And a bow and arrow! She rode sidesaddle on her mare alongside the train delivering coal for the family factory. Her long hair, loose and unbound, flowed behind her just like in her movies, while the peasants and workers on the train gaped at her beauty.

"A woman must be her own self," Laolao had taught Ma as she balanced on one of those strong, unbound feet, a long sword in each hand, practicing ancient *taiji* maneuvers. Those rare martial skills, as well as her ample bosom, had landed her silent film roles before she had married, but no one brought up her early fame anymore, as it made her grow irritable and distant.

Ma watched her mother with fearful respect but had never possessed the slightest desire to pick up a sword or bow. She'd much rather dream up tall tales and practice writing her characters. But even at calligraphy, Ma was always getting it wrong. "You need to stay within the box," her tutor had lamented so many times. "Your strokes are unbalanced, and look! They run outside the lines. See? There are nine squares within the box, and each must be considered." Ma never understood why it was so important to make the characters fit within strict confines. Perhaps she was also Western in her thinking.

"SO MANY YEAR LATER, IN UNITED STATE, I HEAR PEOPLE SAY, 'NEED TO THINK OUTSIDE OF BOX' AND I REALIZE IT APPLY TO ME! I ALWAYS WRITING OUTSIDE OF BOX."

"Okay. These are clean enough," Laolao declared back in the old Liu Family courtyard, yanking Ma upright from the pile of pots. "I won't let the water ruin your skin."

"I can get them cleaner," Ma protested, still not able to see her own reflection on them. "They will be shiny and perfect for the new year."

"The ideas your father puts in your head!" Laolao cried, scowling. "You are the daughter of Liu Jingjian. What would the Fu family think if they saw you like this? I would never hear the end of it."

"Who cares what they think? They are bad neighbors. I hate them, especially that girl." The Fus' eldest daughter, whose Christian name was Lorraine, never wasted any opportunity to make Ma feel small and useless.

"I HAVING TO WEAR LORRAINE SECOND-HAND CLOTHES HER MOTHER CAME TO GIVING AS GIFT. SHE KNOW WE HAVE TO ACCEPT, HAVE TO WEAR. IT A KIND OF HUMILIATION, YOU KNOW. DID ON PURPOSE."

"Like the Fus," Laolao continued, "you are a part of a dignified class. What divides us from the servants is this kind of tedious work. Let the scullery wenches do their jobs!"

"But they can't do it as well as I can!" Ma insisted. "Look how dirty this one still is, even after they cleaned it."

"You are making them feel bad by doing it better," Laolao said, appealing to her daughter's sense of compassion. "You will scare them, make them think they won't have a job here if you are in charge."

"But what of the lesson you put in my head?" Ma chirped. "Always do things better than the others, and they will have nothing to say!"

Laolao looked like she was going to offer a retort, but instead, she pursed her lips. "Well, you might look like a scullery girl, but you are no fool. Now go! Get dressed and cleaned, and you look a sight."

September 2020
FaceTime Call

JAY: Are you there?

MA: YOU FINALLY PICK UP.

JAY: Actually, I called you.

MA: OH. WELL I CALLING YOU TWICE TODAY ALREADY, DIDN'T GETTING THROUGH FOR SOME REASON.

JAY: Oh, sorry. I don't always have my phone nearby.

MA: YOU OKAY? WHY YOU MAKING FACE?

JAY: Yeah, everything's fine. You shouldn't worry about me.

MA: WELL MY FRIEND SEND ME STORY OF CHINESE WOMAN KILL IN NEW YORK. YOU SHOULD TAKE CAREFUL.

JAY: They aren't killing Chinese people in the streets here, Ma. At least, no more than anyone else. And the city isn't burning down. That's just the media making it seem worse than it is.

MA: I READING EVERYDAY NEW YORK TIME PAPER YOU GET FOR ME. NOT ONE GOOD STORY ABOUT CHINA. ALL NEGATIVE.

JAY: That's not surprising. China has been doing some bad things lately.

MA: WHAT BAD THING?!

JAY takes a deep breath.

JAY: Hong Kong? Camps in Xinjiang? Ma, I don't want to get into it. How's your dizziness?

MA: NOT SO BAD TODAY. BUT BAD THIS MORNING, AFTER I CALL YOU AND YOU DON'T PICK UP. I THINK SOMETHING MUST BE WRONG, MAYBE YOU ARE SICK? I WORRY, SO THEN FEELING A LITTLE DIZZIER.

JAY: Ma, I told you, you don't need to worry about me. Really. Please don't worry yourself about me.

MA: OF COURSE I WORRY!

JAY: But why?

MA adjusts the camera and looks straight at JAY.

MA: I AM YOUR MOTHER.

It was important to plan ahead. That was what kept families, companies, and countries secure, according to Ba. You made a plan, and you executed it with discipline. You took into account big and small factors, and you thought about contingencies. That was how you succeeded, even in a family, a company, or a country where things were stacked against you.

The importance of planning ahead was why Ba had taught me chess when I was just four years old. Chess wasn't even Ba's favored game of strategy. That was *weiqi*, or "go," as it was known in the West. But my four-year-old eyes preferred the beautifully carved pieces on the board, and so chess became our game. Every day, during his lunch break, Ba would drive home from the IBM plant in nearby Owego to join Ma and me for a home-cooked meal while John and Kaiser were at school. Ma's cooking was far better than the American cafeteria food, and besides, this daily ritual gave him undisturbed time with me. His own father had ignored him as a child—most Chinese fathers did—until he had passed his university entrance exam. Ba didn't want that kind of relationship with his own sons.

He would pull up the driveway in his prized orange-red Datsun 240z, the ultimate symbol of his success in America. I waited by the screen door, defrosting the glass pane with my breath, ready to leap into Ba's arms and be spun around and around. Ma typically remained upstairs, scooping rice out of the cooker and taking plastic wrap off the plates of steaming chopped vegetables with black fungus, twice-cooked pork, and dried tofu, a dish Ba loved but I refused to eat properly, stuffing it instead into my cheeks like a hamster and leaching the juices out slowly over time, not ever daring to spit it out.

After lunch, I would set up the chess board, and Ba and I played while Ma gave us time alone. As each game progressed, he queried about any significant moves, prodding me to articulate what I thought he was planning. That was the secret to winning, Ba said. Put yourself in your opponent's mindset and discover his schemes. Was it to gain the center? To force an exchange of bishops and knights? To apply pressure to the flank?

Chess was like war or politics, as Ba would often say when I was a bit older. Each side had its leaders, armies, and powerful warlords. China's history in the 20th century had been a giant chess match, the struggle for dominance between the Communists and the Nationalists, interrupted by another larger game being played by Japan and the other great powers on a worldwide board.

A good chess player saw all possible outcomes and moved to respond and seize an advantage, even long before battles played out in real-time on the board. A player, a politician, or a general who did not plan ahead and account for every possibility was doomed. Ba's own father, my *yeye* Tingyi, who was the preeminent Chinese historian of his era, wrote treatises full of the failures of important men whose fortunes had collapsed due to unanticipated circumstances.

Ba spoke to me like I was an adult but, it turns out, he wasn't really treating me like one. When I won a game against him, I felt elated, until one day early that spring, I realized that Ba had been letting me win. "Don't do that! I want to win on my own! Don't treat me like a baby!" I cried. Of all things at that point in my life, and really for most of it since, I hated not being taken seriously. I would scream and throw a tantrum whenever it happened.

I didn't know it then, but Ba didn't have that same luxury. Ma once put it this way: "YOU KNOW, YOU FATHER WORK TWENTY-ONE YEAR IBM, AND THEY PASSING HIM OVER, GIVING JOB TO PEOPLE HE TRAIN. HE NEVER COMPLAIN."

"Maybe he should have," I said.

"COMPLAINING TO WHO?" Ma asked, and I fell silent.

Ba kept his head down but taught his children how to recognize inequity and how to plan our response. He liked to point out that other immigrant groups—the Irish, the Italians, and the Jews—had all once suffered the same exclusions and prejudices. But he was confident that his children would succeed in America even where he had been thwarted. But to get there, we had to plan ahead.

At my insistence, Ba began to play against me as if I were an adult, and he stopped asking me any questions about his moves. I lost, and lost, and lost. My frustration (and self-loathing as a perpetual loser) had probably started to show, but I wouldn't let Ba go easy on me. Instead, I lay awake at night going over all the wrong moves from the day before, and I tried to recognize when I was about to make the same mistakes again.

Then one day, I upped the stakes. I realized it wasn't enough to try to anticipate what Ba was going to do. That left me on the defensive the whole game. My assaults had been too obvious, and though I could apply considerable pressure, a good player like Ba knew how to push back with equal force. No, what I needed was subterfuge. I needed to unbalance the scales enough so that he was thrown off by my moves.

I had been studying magic tricks out of a used book Ba had picked up for me, and it had shown me a bit about how to deflect and distract in order to fool the human mind, which was easier to do than seemed possible. So that's what I would do. I would play a trick. During one of our games, when I was losing, I made what I hoped looked like an incredibly foolish move, placing my rook directly in the path of Ba's queen, then waited for him to take the bait.

"Do not try to lose on purpose," Ba said quietly. "It is not a good sport who does dat."

I shook my head stubbornly. Ba sighed, taking the rook with his queen. "You cannot win by lessening an opponent's victory," Ba said, repeating a lesson his own father had taught him. He called it "playing smart." I later learned it was sometimes called "scorched earth." It was, quite simply, not an honorable way to play, losing on purpose and out of spite to render the win worthless to the other side. I would learn to recognize that kind of spite. It was sometimes as subtle as refusing to let someone ahead of you in line or as devastating as missiles raining down on population centers when your own armies had failed.

But Ba was mistaken. This wasn't spite. It was a trap I had planned. I moved a knight from out where it had been hidden, threatening both Ba's queen and king at once. He hadn't seen it coming.

"Check," I said slowly, not ready to believe this had worked. I later learned in a chess book that this was a classic move called a "fork," and Ba had walked right into it.

"Oh!" Ba exclaimed, standing up. "Good! Very, very good!"

From that moment, I realized I had a secret power. It was to deceive others, even my own father, by getting inside their heads. It was as if the gates to Illusionland had been flung open. Lying, tricking, and manipulating were all a matter of being clever and bold enough and knowing what people feared and avoided instinctively.

"LIU FAMILY, ALWAYS KNOW HOW TO TRICKY," Ma observed.

It turned out to be a fine way to make extra money. I used it against my brother Kaiser in gin rummy, picking up cards I didn't need just to throw him off the trail. He lost more than a thousand dollars to me over the course of one summer, even at just a dime a point. It was something I took to law school and later used in contract negotiations, low-balling offers to tip the other side off-balance, then acting like any concession from me was hard won. I played Texas Hold 'Em when I needed rent money as a jobless composer in New York, going all-in on dead cards like a 10-6 unsuited to shake loose any cowards. And I used it for years to keep my most intimate thoughts and acts secret, even from those I loved most, leading to years of detachment and loneliness.

Decades later, I finally figured out there was actually a flip side to the lesson Ba had tried to teach me. It never occurred to me that my tricks might serve anything more than my own advancement. They were, after all, simply a skillset. But I didn't necessarily have to see weakness as an opportunity. Instead of getting inside people's heads for my own gain, I could use it to help them, to help others get inside their own. I could use it to better understand them and maybe one day feel genuine connections. Ba knew better than to try and teach this to a preschooler bent on dominating a board game. So he simply sharpened the tools and left me to figure out how to use them.

Against Ba, I now won in chess more than half of the time. But something had changed. I was playing not for the fun of it or even the intellectual stimulation, but to win at all costs. Ba stopped coming home every day, and after I began kindergarten, we barely played at all. I joined a chess club at school, where I got to spin more traps and try out more tricks. Seven years later, I found myself in a sudden death round at the state championships, where we were all assigned chess clocks that forced more concise thinking and more rapid play. My opponent in the finals was clever but meek, so with each move, I slammed my hand down on the timer just a bit harder than I needed to, increasingly rattling him. He wound up making one very small mistake, going down one pawn, but that was something from which we both knew he could never recover. I returned home with a trophy taller than myself. Ba looked at it and nodded.

"Good," was all Ba said.

He didn't ask anything else about the tournament, and I realized that I didn't want to play chess anymore.

December 1984
Tucson, Arizona

Mimi just wanted her ears pierced. She was almost twelve and had already launched minor suburban rebellions, shutting herself in her room to yak with friends for hours while sporting a new look that would have made Madonna proud: asymmetrical hair in a teased-out nest up top, eyes dark with heavy liner. Her look made a *statement*, though of what no one was quite sure. The look was missing earrings, however, and clip-ons were unthinkable.

Earlier, Mimi's unique hair had even triggered an all-hands family meeting. It had become clear our current foreign exchange student, Anna, had also caught some kind of New Wave bug. Ma and Ba were speaking in hushed tones to the assembled Kuo children when Anna burst into the family conference in tears, her voice trembling as she asked, "Are you 'talkeeng aboot' my 'air?"

Unlike Mimi, Anna remained overwhelmed by the magnitude of her decision, which had been boldly arrived at while seated in a chair in a downtown salon, to allow her "trendy" stylist to take her from Swiss Miss braids to a buzz cut up one side.

"Actually, it's about *my* hair," Mimi said as Anna wiped away tears. Mimi practiced her distracted look as Ba laid out his case for normalcy. Mimi's eyebrows conveyed a bored shrug, so I stepped up to defend her, reminding Ma and Ba and the rest of the jury that, when I was her age, I once returned from a party with my hair peroxided to near orange. Ba had merely shaken his head and told me I looked foolish. So there was certainly both precedent and a double standard at work. Mimi caught my eye with a half-hearted thanks.

61

Ma's unvoiced fear was that Mimi's hair presented a harbinger of a dire adolescence full of parties, drugs, and sex, none of which Mimi had yet tried by age twelve, but one couldn't be too careful. As for her hair, "It will grow back," said Ba, and that concluded the discussion.

Mimi dressed the part of a popular girl in the mid-'80s, all black layers, lace, and jeans with the requisite Sony Walkman. Only her untouched earlobes still said "little girl" to the world. Ma would never give her permission to pierce them, of course. Good Chinese girls didn't have piercings or tattoos. So Mimi did as any teenager faced with such antiquated restrictions would: She waited until Ma was out of town.

The business trip must have been difficult because Ma was in a particularly foul mood upon her return, the worst time to surprise her with an act of insubordination, let alone auricle disfigurement. Ma immediately spotted the studs on Mimi's once pristine lobes. She grabbed hold of Mimi's shoulder and pulled her in for a closer inspection, and began screeching.

"YOU GETTING THEM PIERCE?!"

I rushed in from the kitchen at the sound of Ma's distress.

"It's no big deal, Ma…" Mimi began, her explanation rehearsed in advance, but Ma gave no room to finish.

"NO DAUGHTER OF MINE LOOKING LIKE PROSTITUTE!"

"Ma, don't say that! Mimi's not like that," I offered, managing only to poke the tiger.

"DON'T TELLING ME WHAT I SAY, DON'T SAY. I SAY SHE LOOK CHEAP. LIKE FOR SALE! GIRL WHO PUTTING ON EARRING SAY THEY ARE FOR SALE!"

"That's not what it says," Mimi protested. "I just like how they look."

"YOUR LAOLAO STRICTLY FORBID ME FROM GETTING PIERCE UNTIL I AM OLD ENOUGH. YOU ARE ONLY TWELVE! YOU WANT TO GET SUCH BAD REPUTATION ALREADY? SHAMING ON YOU! SHAMING ON YOU!"

Ma's voice had managed to jump a full octave as she masterfully summoned the pain of years chafing under Laolao's very Catholic rules. Inexplicably, she now held a glass from the cabinet in her hand, something she had bought as part of a set while visiting Switzerland.

Ba had taken Ma to Europe in the year after Mimi was born to help her get out of what was likely undiagnosed postpartum depression. She had brought back a set of crystal from Zurich. The main decanter and a few of the glasses had shattered earlier that year when vibrations from Kaiser and my rock band's practice had sent the prized set over the edge. The pile of broken glass hadn't been discovered until the rehearsal was over. To everyone's surprise and relief, Ma merely laughed when she saw the remains. She later demanded to know how we could play so loud as not to even hear the glass falling. "YOU GOING TO GO DEAF," she warned. (This held some prophetic power, in that Kaiser did go deaf in one ear decades later due to Ménière's disease, a rare disorder that affected his balance and gave him bad bouts of vertigo, and ironically not due to the loud rock music he had played for more than three decades).

As for the remaining, unbroken glasses, Ma now one held in her hand, shouting "SHAMING ON YOU!" to Mimi, whose eyes were wide with real terror. They grew wider still after Ma hurled the glass to the ground, sending shards flying and achieving the desired escalation of drama. Ma grabbed another glass, and now Mimi began shouting, too.

"Ma! Stop it! What are you doing?!"

"YOU WANT TO LOOK LIKE YOU A GIRL FOR SALE, YOU CAN BE A GIRL FOR SALE!" Ma shrieked as she chucked the glass at Mimi's feet, the murderous fury of it all forcing her into retreat. "YOU WANT TO BE SEXY, GO BE SEXY!"

"Stop it! Stop!" Mimi cried, real tears now flowing. She had rarely experienced our mother in this state and certainly never with glassware projectiles. A vision of a certain feral cat, which we called Fuzzy, sprang to my mind. Fuzzy used to come around our backyard in Tucson as a sort of domestic terrorist. Kaiser had shot the poor creature once with his BB gun, but he only blinded it in one eye, an act of teenage cruelty that haunted Kaiser for years. Sometimes Fuzzy got caught between the wire screen and the thick, plastic sheeting of the patio, his fur bristling and his one-eyed face a mask of pain, hissing and spitting, claws flailing wildly about for anything on which to find purchase.

That cat had nothing on Ma.

Ma grabbed a third glass, the last of her Swiss crystal.

"YOU WAITING UNTIL I AM GONE TO DO THIS? YOU TRY TO TRICKING ME? YOU SHOULD BE SHAME! SHAME!" This time, Ma threw the glass at the wall, not aiming at Mimi but intending for maximal effect upon shattering. Mimi howled and ran back to her room, slamming her door shut and yanking at the studs of her new piercing, the blood still pooling on her lobes as she pulled them free from the offending metal.

"DID YOU TAKING HER TO GET THIS DONE?" Ma demanded, rounding on me now. "ARE YOU BETRAY ME, TOO?"

"Ma, why don't you sit down? Are you okay?"

"I BLAMING YOUR FATHER, LET MIMI GET SO WILD."

"She's not wild, Ma. She just got her ears pierced. She should have asked you first."

"IF SHE ASK I SAY NO WAY!"

"Which is probably why she didn't ask."

"I FEELING SO DIZZY."

"You need to not work yourself up anymore."

"CANNOT STANDING UP."

"Just... don't break anything more, okay?"

"LOOKING FOR MY MEDICINE."

"Okay, I'll go get it. Is it in your purse?"

In her room, Mimi stared into her wardrobe's three angled mirrors, the center one reflecting how much she hated Ma at that moment, the two sides reflecting her bloody ears. Mimi would spend a lot of time fighting back against self-contempt, already piled high from years of living with three older brothers who had learned from our father all the ways to calmly belittle and talk down to women and girls. Through her childhood, she rarely stood up for herself with any of us. We excluded her from our political banter at the dinner table, where we argued as if we could solve the world's problems before dessert. In general, we never listened to anyone else, meaning Mimi knew all about us and our beliefs, but we knew almost nothing about hers.

The worst part was, we didn't think there was anything to learn from her. And Mimi blamed herself for remaining quiet for so long, a situation she resolved one day to change.

Mimi wouldn't attempt another ear piercing until she had moved to China, far from home and Ma's glass-shattering judgment. When she finally did it, the earrings went over without a word of protest or even a glance of disapproval from Ma, though Mimi had prepared herself for more histrionics.

Three Chinese zodiac cycles later, I understand that the piercings meant more than just rebellion to Ma. They meant Mimi was now in control of her body and would soon become a young woman on her own terms. Ma's role as child rearer and primary nurturer to her last child was nearing an end. The breaking of glass was, in that way, symbolic: marking a new era in Ma's life, like stemware broken underfoot at a Jewish wedding.

Ma's dizziness and bouts of crippling vertigo would return after Ba died in 2014. The many doctors and specialists consulted had not been able to offer any good explanation for her head-spinning spells. Mimi wondered whether it was simply general anxiety. Even where Ma lived now in Rossmoor, without the pressures of a business to run or a husband to criticize, Ma could always find a way to conjure stress and lie awake at night, fretting and rehashing. It was the kind of anxiety that wore at the edges of the spirit, casting long shadows of doubt and demanding answers about one's own purpose and value, the kind of uncertainty that pulled the very ground out from under when the answers came up short or caused destruction of beloved things, even a favorite crystal set.

By then, Mimi was a grown woman who taught courses and wrote books on self-cultivation and mind-body awareness, someone very much in touch with her inner inherited demons, but she was curiously unable to recall anything about the afternoon when Ma hurled glassware at her over pierced ears. "I must have blocked it all out," she said simply to me as I tried to get all of the details of that day right.

Unlike Ma or Laolao, Mimi would learn to recognize anger without hitching a ride with it. While Ma and Laolao could count many shattered dishes and glasses between them, the physical detritus of their destructive emotions, Mimi preferred to seek the counsel of living things. In particular, she sought out trees, which she loved to lean against and sometimes even rubbed up against, hoping they might impart some of their old wisdom. If this seemed odd to her students in England, where she and her husband now lived, that didn't bother her. Chinese people have been rubbing themselves on trees for millennia, after all, evidenced by the smooth and polished spots on their bark across China's thousands of public parks.

Ma's neuroses and pain sat within each of us children in equal measure, but only Mimi would ever gain full mastery over it. She had learned to welcome the storm when it arrived, like an old guest rolling up with a bag. Over time, she had also learned not to feed that guest from her mental cupboards, and soon enough, the visitor would grow restless, packing up and departing as quickly as it had arrived. She wished she could instill some of that serenity in our mother, but Ma's spiritual bark was thick and impenetrable, no matter how long or patiently anyone rubbed at it.

Chapter Three

MONEY

or

"HOW I KNOW HOW MUCH TO TIP?"

October 2015
New York City, New York

"I NEVER UNDERSTAND WHY WOMEN CARRYING BRAND PURSE. MAYBE THEY JUST WANTING TO FEEL RICH."

Ma and I ambled through Union Square Park. It was a crisp but fleeting afternoon, the kind for courageously announcing "I love the fall!" even as the threat of a New York City winter was already squeezing the air tight around us. Busy women with brand-name purses were indeed about, lifelined to their phones, unready for Ma's barbed critiques. Her eyes didn't miss much, and though she didn't carry a brand-name bag of her own, she had a quiver of opinions about the fancy ones displayed by other women.

"TWENTY YEARS I HAVING THE SAME PURSE, A FRIEND GIVE TO ME. I NEVER NEEDING TO FEEL RICH, CARRY EXPENSIVE PURSE," Ma said.

Wait, was this actually her way of saying she needed a new purse but didn't want to buy it for herself? I wondered. Passive aggression was not just her emotional go-to, it was her religion. Gazing at her small and rather beat-up handbag, I knew I would need to probe deeper but also delicately. The challenge of procuring for Ma a purse to carry her through her next twenty years felt daunting.

At the time, Ma could still get around without her walker, which wouldn't become part of her daily life until two years later when her vertebrae went on strike. My ex, Zhang Yan, had discovered the walker in China. It was really a small wheelchair that she pushed around and could also sit upon when humiliatingly necessary. She frequently remarked how fortunate she was that Zhang Yan had found it, especially for that price. "EVERYBODY HERE ASK WHERE I GET, AND I SAY CHINA! FOR LESS THAN EIGHTY DOLLAR! THEY CANNOT BELIEVING."

That day in the park, though, nearly a year into her '80s, Ma still stood more or less upright and looked twenty years younger, and in that, she took pride. She managed to work her actual age into nearly every conversation with complete strangers, if only for the reassurance of hearing them exclaim, "I never would have guessed!" Lately, she had started roping me in on her schtick, asking drivers, cashiers, and doormen to guess *my* age, after which she would reveal hers as if an afterthought and not the true point of the exercise. Still, though her visage may have masked her true age, it did nothing to dull the aches in her body, so she preferred to stop frequently and take a seat. Every time she did, I remembered she was, in fact, an old woman, a great-grandmother, someone with possibly only a few years left.

I snapped a selfie of the two of us on the park bench. This was how I wanted to remember her, still sharp and unwittingly hilarious. Unlike many of my friends, whose Instagrams felt curated for the Frick, Ma didn't demand to approve pictures before they got posted. She knew she looked fantastic and didn't care about the photographic record.

"You know, I don't wear name brands either. Seems like a waste of money," I said, trying still to tease out whether Ma wanted a new bag and, if so, with how many zeroes in its price. "I hear some of those purses are thousands of dollars."

"I KNOW."

"Some, even tens of thousands of dollars," I cautioned.

"SICKENING." Ma's face, when deploying her favorite pejorative, could strip away pride like detergent on grease. Centuries, perhaps millennia, of judgment and disdain had passed down and evolved from Chinese mother to Chinese daughter, finally reaching an apex with Ma whenever she furrowed her brow, narrowed her eyes, and let fly a single word.

When I took Ma a year later to see the movie *Crazy Rich Asians*, a film I was proud to have seen made and succeed despite a formulaic storyline, I thought Ma would enjoy all the shade and judginess of it. But on the way there, she seemed nervous to be seeing the movie with me. It was, after all, the first blockbuster Hollywood rom-com about Chinese, written and directed by Chinese. The cab ride there confirmed her anxiety:

"WHAT WE SEE? CRAZY CHINESE?"

"HOW LONG IS? I DON'T WANT FALL ASLEEP."

"IS IT YOUR FRIEND, SOMEONE YOU KNOW WHO MAKE MOVIE?"

"WHY WE SEE CRAZY ASIAN MOVIE?"

"I REALLY DON'T EVEN LIKE MOVIE. LAST COUPLE I SEE NO GOOD."

"WHY YOU SEE MOVIE AGAIN? DON'T SEE IT JUST TO SIT WITH ME."

Her reaction as we were leaving the theater shouldn't have surprised me. You could put good money on Ma disliking anything Chinese that didn't come from the resurgent mainland.

"IT KIND OF A SILLY MOVIE. SO MUCH LIKE A TV SHOW ALREADY PLAY IN CHINA. I THINK PEOPLE JUST WANT TO MAKE PEOPLE BELIEVING SINGAPORE IS NOT SO POOR. REALLY JUST A SMALL ISLAND. NOTHING TO SEE. AND THE WAY THE YOUNG PEOPLE SPENDING MONEY. CRAZY RICH ASIAN? SICKENING!"

Ma and I continued to watch and judge the crazy ordinary people in Union Square. One of Ma's favorite pastimes was to compare herself to others, something I assumed she picked up while in Taiwan, which was known for disquieting societal insecurities. Ladies would pass us, and Ma would barely glance at them, but I could register the rapid firing of Chinese Mother neurons, a complex algorithm that emerged from some secret, old-lady hive mind and then pulled equally from selective memory, maternal instinct, and prefrontal Asian skepticism.

"ONE TIME KAISER BUYING ME AN EXPENSIVE PURSE," Ma noted. "VERY FAMOUS BRAND. THEN IT TURNING OUT, HE BOUGHT IN HONG KONG. WAS A FAKEY FAKEY. COST VERY LITTLE."

Ma's eyes followed a young woman wearing very short shorts, barely more than underwear, despite the coolness of the late afternoon. Ma's inner judgment was already lobbing pointed questions about the hussy's lineage, imagining a life full of poor choices and complications from venereal diseases. Women who flaunted their sexuality were particularly bothersome to Ma, something she had absorbed from her own mother's priggish Catholicism. Even Mimi's early efforts at young ladyship had often crashed uselessly against a Great Wall of conservatism and disdain.

I tried to imagine Ma carrying Kaiser's fake gift purse. I pictured her meeting up with any of her socialite friends who were sure to discover the fraud. Leave it to Kaiser to get Ma a purse she could use against him his whole life as a parable. (Kaiser later insisted it was never something he had gotten for her and that it must have been one of our uncles, who were known for such deceptions).

The insult of the gift was up there with one near-fatal Christmas when Ba saw fit to purchase a clothes steaming machine for Ma. To Ba, it was a marvel of engineering and an obviously useful addition to a properly functioning household. To Ma, it was a raw slap in the face. "ALL THESE YEARS AND YOU DON'T UNDERSTANDING WHO I AM!" she cried. The machine remained in its box in the laundry room for weeks until Ba quietly returned it.

Years later, Ba wisened up and took Mimi along with him to buy Ma an anniversary gift. "Buy her something useless but pretty," Mimi suggested. They settled on a Tiffany's crystal heart with two little bears inside it. Ma kept that heart on her dresser for decades.

"EVEN FAKEY PURSE, IN A WAY IT MAKING OTHER PEOPLE THINK I AM RICH," Ma said, as we sat there in the park together.

I chuckled. "You are rich, Ma. At least compared to most people, you're very well off."

"HAHA. WITH PURSE KAISER GIVE ME, THEY ALL DO THINK THAT I AM RICH! SOMETIME ALL IT TAKES IS ONE THING." Her mother-in-law—my *nainai*—understood this well. Nainai had been the eldest daughter of a wealthy family that grew destitute during the war against Japan after she and my grandfather fled inland, surviving only on his academic wages. Nainai's "one thing" was her high-heeled shoes, which she continued to wear, even on dirt floors, in defiance of their poverty.

Ma paused to observe an older Chinese woman with a horrific dye job, artificially jet black, with gray roots already ruining the illusion, her Louis Vuitton bag clutched to her like a life preserver. Ma reserved her most cutting assessments for her fellow Chinese, as if they ought to know better than these white and brown people who, in her mind, lacked significant cultural grounding.

"OF COURSE," Ma said, considering the fake hair walking past her, "THEY THINK I AM RICH, UNLESS THEY CAN TELL PURSE IS A KNOCKING OFF."

"Hmm. So if they can tell it's a fake, then what?" I asked.

"THEN?" Ma frowned. "THEN, NOT SO RICH."

March 1944
Chongqing, China

"Tell him what we always tell him," Nainai said to my father, who was then just a boy of 12 years. "Thank you for thinking of us. Your generosity is appreciated. But we cannot accept any money. But you still stand there like a monkey caught stealing." Sometimes Nainai called her eldest son, my *ba*, a monkey. It was not only because he was clever but rather because, like her, that was his birth year. It would be my birth year as well, two full zodiac cycles later. Three monkeys, all known for and limited by their own cleverness. Nainai would tell me this story a few times, filling in additional details as she recalled them. Ba told a slightly different version of it to us, but the gist was the same.

Ba, who was named Kai but later added a syllable to make it a more dignified Jinkai (or Jenkai in the American spelling), was Nainai's most promising child, the one who would one day move to America, marry a beautiful wife, and raise a family of four children.

"ALSO HE TAKE GOOD CARE NAINAI AFTER YEYE DIE," Ma reminded me, with approval.

73

Here before Nainai today, however, was just a petulant and headstrong boy. Ba twisted in place where he stood, clearly struggling to articulate his frustration. Nainai sat in the nearly dark room on a rickety chair that creaked unsteadily on the thin plywood they had laid over the dirt floor. Theirs was a house with four plain brick walls, no separate rooms, covered by a mildewed thatched roof. A single light bulb flickered, and Ba gazed at it rather than meet his mother's eyes.

Nainai knew their home was far too small and that the roof leaked during hard rains. With not even any room separators besides thin sheets hung from the ceiling, it was hardly suitable for a family with five children.

"SHE ALWAYS THINKING SHE STILL HAVE FIVE CHILDREN, WHEN ONLY HAVING FOUR LEFT," Ma said. "SO SAD, REALLY."

Nainai's youngest had perished from dysentery after eating a red bean cake during the Moon Festival. It was an extravagance to have bought the cakes to start with, and Nainai took the toddler's death very hard. From that day, she would never allow mooncakes into their house again, festival be damned.

Ba glowered at her from the doorway where he stood, and instinctively she folded her hands away. Once lovely, they were now calloused and worn from unending menial tasks while the war dragged on. Her hands might be gnarled like a peasant woman's, but on her feet, she didn't wear peasant slippers.

"SHE HAVE ONE REALLY FANCY PAIR OF SHOE, WITH ACTUAL HEEL, BECAUSE SHE WAS ONCE FROM WEALTHY FAMILY, AND THIS HOW SHE REMINDING EVERYONE WITHOUT SHOWING OFF TOO MUCH. BUT HARD TO WEARING HIGH HEEL ON DIRT FLOOR, HAHA!" Ma recounted.

Paired with her silk blouse, they were her lone protestations about her former elevated status as an educated *da xiaojie*—the eldest daughter of a wealthy family, one that frankly would be shocked at how she chose to live now.

Their poverty was indeed a choice, as Ba's accusatory look reminded her. Every night any of them went hungry, Nainai considered this fact. And so it was not easy to turn down money once again. But worn hands and decrepit house notwithstanding, she still held an honored status, and that was wealth enough for her. Her husband, my *yeye* Guo Tingyi, was a respected professor of history at Nankai University. Students came to him with their lengthy theses and treatises, and he would be helpful but tough, sending some away rejected as many as four times. They all said of her husband, *"Laohu miankong."* The face of a tiger. His counsel was sought at the highest levels of government because wise presidents and generals alike saw history as the best guide for predicting outcomes. Yeye even had as one of his students the son of Generalissimo Jiang (though Yeye confessed, despite his best efforts to instill a love of learning, Jiang Jingguo was no great scholar).

The elder Jiang would repeatedly come by their house in person to offer Yeye a position in the government, but Nainai would put him off, bar him from entering, and claim the children were sick or that the house was in no condition for guests. Nainai knew that her husband could not say "no" to Jiang, and this would be their undoing unless she prevented it. Politicians wound up dead or in prison these days, even if they bet correctly. Yeye protested, but Nainai argued forcefully and convincingly: Men like Jiang admired him because he was not a party member and stayed above the fray. The moment Yeye descended into politics, he would lose their respect and possibly his life. So Yeye remained a scholar, not a partisan, despite constant entreaties from the Nationalist leadership.

This, unfortunately, also meant not much more than a subsistence wage for their only breadwinner. In these times, a college education seemed a quaint luxury, a reminder of how things once had been, and no one would increase college funding when there were soldiers to arm and feed. Over one hundred higher institutes of learning had relocated inland to Chongqing, and there was simply no paying for all of the scholars. Nainai also suspected that the poverty-level salary was the Generalissimo's way of reminding her husband of the consequences of his neutrality. So she began to see their poverty as a badge of honor, her family's good name preserved.

It was this sense that Nainai held in her breast now as she addressed my *ba*.

"You have something to say to me?" she asked him sternly. "I have asked you to go and tell the Accountant, 'No, thank you.'"

"We could use the money," Ba murmured.

"What is that you say? Speak up. If you have an opinion, at least say it with conviction."

Nainai was a rarity among women of her generation, a woman who typically spoke her mind. Her husband had insisted he would never wed a woman with bound feet, a barbaric practice of a decaying Qing empire, and Nainai's had remained untouched. Women should be lifted up, the father of the Republic, Dr. Sun Yat-sen, had proclaimed. They should be permitted an education and a place of honor in the new China. Perhaps those seemed like empty words at the time, as there were precisely no places of honor held by women in the government. But Nainai had availed herself of the spirit of the promise and gone to college, even studying abroad in Germany for a time. She had a sharp and practiced mind, which suited her husband's thirst for modernity. Of course, that didn't stop him from relegating her to performing all the household chores once the war forced them inland to Chongqing, now the third provisional wartime capital of China.

"I said," Ba muttered, now working up more courage, "We could use the money. It is a lot. Even one of these gold ingots would be enough to feed us for months. And there is a whole box. At least two kilos. The Accountant brings a box each time. We wouldn't have to live on rice and lard. We could have meat, a house with a floor, and more electricity."

Nainai eyed her son, head cocked. "Did you earn this money?" she asked.

"No," Ba admitted. "But it belongs to us. That's what the Accountant is saying. It is ours by right."

"Is that so?" she responded sharply. "So you must know how it comes to us, so regularly every month?"

The gold came up the river from their compound in Henan Province, sent by Yeye's uncle, one of the patriarchs of the big Kuo clan. Their vast land holdings, farms, serfs, and even a sesame oil factory and cigarette-rolling machine provided a bounty for all their relations. Their family manager, simply known as the *Kuaiji* or Accountant, kept a meticulous ledger of who was to receive how much, and his instructions were to deliver it, no matter the circumstances. It was dangerous work in wartime China, even after the collaborationist officials were paid off, and the trip required armed guards. There was a commercial blockade of the capital, but resourceful parties could find a way through it. Yeye's share of the payment was considerable, but he barely thought about it, so busy was he in his writings and teaching and his ignoring of household chores. Nainai managed the family finances and income within his professor's salary. They wouldn't starve if she was careful with expenses.

Nainai's own family had been wealthy once. But her father, who everyone said must not have been pure Han Chinese because of his heavy beard, had sunk into a deep opium habit. He had sold off the family's gold, brick by brick, to pay for it. Though he was a wastrel, Nainai was grateful that he had taught her to read and write, and he had encouraged her to go to a women's college in Beijing before his addiction took him to his predictable end. The rest of her family fared no better. Her brothers were now *liaodao*, poor fellows from once-rich families who had squandered their fortunes and become bandits, preying on innocents out of the chaos of the war. That was another reason not to take the gold, Nainai thought. The money would invite unwelcome relatives.

"What does it matter how it comes to us? It is money!" Ba said, his face growing flushed.

"With quick money comes lasting sorrow," Nainai warned. "And with this kind of money, even greater sorrow."

Already, money had begun to drive wedges within her family. While her son blamed her for standing in the way of a better life for them, her daughter Qian, my aunt whom we called Gugu, accused her of belonging to the corrupt landholding classes, the people who had ruined China and made it weak. She held that accusation against Nainai like a hot iron. Ironic indeed, Nainai thought, for a girl who couldn't be bothered to help around the house and dirty her own hands. In that, her daughter was much like her father, face always in a book, grand ideas forever floating in that hard head, ready to write them all down for whoever would bother to read them in any of the dozens of revolutionary periodicals that had sprung up since the warring political factions had agreed to a Second Unity Government.

Despite their political differences, there was no question why Gugu was Yeye's favorite, so alike were they in temperament and poor habits.

78

"GUGU ALWAYS LOOKING DOWN ON NAINAI FOR TRYING TO LOOK NICE IN HER HIGH HEEL," Ma explained.

Gugu also held Nainai in disdain for having obtained an education but done nothing with it except being a wife and mother to a more educated man. In this, perhaps Gugu was partially justified, Nainai thought. But ought she not wear her best shoes and blouse, given the dignitaries that her husband might thoughtlessly bring by unannounced, including the president himself? And what good was an education if not to have the right to choose the life you wished to live? And as for their "classist" roots, Gugu was also not entirely wrong, but surely they lived like poor but pure, scholarly intellectuals now! Yet, for all Nainai's credible arguments, Gugu only seemed to detest her more.

Her two oldest children could be haughty and self-righteous, but Jenkai was correct in one thing: That gold, even a bit of it, would have been life-changing for them. It could afford them a decent home, new clothes, shoes, and meat more than once a week. But the fact remained, the money was not truly theirs. As far as Nainai could gather, it was also dirty. One prized cigarette-rolling machine operated by the family could not alone generate that much gold, she figured. Nor could even their landholdings and rents. A few years later, she would be proven right, and Ba would learn of this betrayal, too, and be wholly disgusted by it. That resulted in an angry, drag-down argument with his third uncle, one that would be told and retold for many years and across generations.

The matter of the money at the moment, though, concerned whether to accept it. My father stood before my grandmother, arguing that such sums could change their lives and that it was sitting in the dock just waiting to be claimed. And already it was putting another wall between them, thought Nainai, who appreciated the larger workings of the world more than her teenage son.

"We are poor. You are just too proud to admit that and to accept help from another!" Ba shouted at her. Once the words were out, there was no taking them back. My father had never in his life criticized his own mother.

Nainai regarded her son coolly. This was an important moment. Her son was standing up to her and, by extension, to authority. His *qi* was hot inside his body, the first pimples on his face a testament to the changes he was beginning to endure. His older sister had long since begun her rebellion and war of attrition against her parents, spewing catchphrases nonstop about the need for revolution and an overthrow of the existing order as "the only way to save China." At least her son seemed content to focus only on overthrowing the household.

Nainai stood up, and the young man who became my father instinctively took a step backward. Good. He is still unsure of himself, she thought. She banged a hand on their wooden table. "You will go to The Accountant, and you will tell him what we have always told him. 'Thank you for thinking of us. Your generosity is appreciated. But we cannot accept any money.' Are you clear on what is expected, or do I have to go myself?"

Ba bowed his head. "I will go," he said. Nainai had already traveled to the river earlier that morning to haul water some two kilometers back to the house after her regular water deliveries had failed to appear. Into that water, she had added aluminum sulfate as a purifier, patiently stirring for hours as the particulates settled out. Sending her out again to the river would be cruel.

Ba looked within his heart and felt genuinely ashamed. Nainai hoped he could hear her own unbidden wish: If his mother could eat bitterness every day and turn aside the money that would change her own life, then the least Ba could do was support her. As the eldest son, that was his obligation. And it was obligation, after all, that gave life purpose and meaning.

"Thank you," my grandmother said. "And if you see your father, tell him not to bring any guests home tonight. We do not even have enough rice and tea for ourselves, which he is too absent-minded to realize."

"NAINAI SAY YOUR YEYE HAVING GUEST WHO EATING UP ALL EGGS SHE SAVING FOR WEEK FOR THE CHILDREN," Ma once recalled. "CAN YOU BELIEVING?"

"Also, tell him I do not care to hear them gabbing late into the night while the rest of us try to sleep," Nainai added.

Ba nodded. He would fail to deliver this request, of course. First, it would do no good trying to get Yeye to change his ways, and second, Nainai knew her son loved to eavesdrop on those late-night conversations, where important people sought his father's advice, and where they planned a new China to emerge victorious from the rubble of the war.

"Of course," Ba said. "I will tell him."

"Thank you," Nainai said, sitting back down. My father turned to leave.

"Little monkey," she called. He stopped.

"Money can change things for the better, but also for the worse. All the riches in China could not stop the Japanese from coming."

He nodded.

She sighed. "In fact, those riches are probably why they are here."

> JAY and MA are in JAY's living room. JAY is checking social media while MA talks to him. He does not meet her gaze, and his tone is absent and distracted.

MA: IT TURNING OUT I HAVE A LOT OF OLD FRIEND IN ROSSMOOR. DID NOT KNOWING EVERYONE WINDING UP THERE.

JAY: That's why we picked it. Pretty much every Chinese of your generation lives there if they're near San Francisco.

MA: THEY HAVING OVER THREE HUNDRED PEOPLES AT THE LAST LUNCH. THEY CHARGING FORTY DOLLAR JUST FOR A MEAL, CANNOT BELIEVE!

JAY: That's expensive for old Chinese people, for sure.

MA: THEY ALSO HAVING ENTERTAINER. SINGING, DANCING.

JAY: Well, that costs money. Forty dollars is actually cheap for a whole package like that.

MA: SO MANY PEOPLE THERE.

> JAY is focused elsewhere as he doomscrolls on his phone, but still manages to keep the conversation going.

JAY: But… that's good, right?

MA: WHEN YOU ARE OLD YOU HAVE NOTHING ELSE TO DO, SO YOU GO TO THESE GATHERING.

JAY: And pay forty bucks.

A beat. MA sighs.

MA: IT RUN BY CHINESE PEOPLE. HAVE TO MAKING MONEY.

August 1979
Tucson, Arizona

"Why do we keep so many quarters in the safe?" I asked Ba. For many years now, Ba required us children to examine every coin we got back as change to see if the date preceded 1965.

"The government stopped making quarters out of silver de year John was born because de material cost was getting too high," Ba explained. "The silver in de coin has become more valuable than de coin itself. Dey will have de same problem with copper pennies one day."

As a child, Ba had taken Chinese government-minted copper coins and lined them up along the local railroad tracks. When the trains delivering munitions, coal, and grain rumbled by, the coins would heat to melting and could be retrieved and sold for more than their printed value. The trick to surviving in a world of limited resources, Ba learned and passed on to us, was to discover value in something others had overlooked.

"So what will dat will mean for de quarters dat were made before 1965?" Ba pressed.

I was nine years old at the time but used to Ba's line of questions. It was a matter of just working through the logic of it. The government had stopped minting coins out of silver. There must be many families, especially Chinese ones, that were hoarding them. When people hoard things, prices go up. Sometimes leading to ridiculous results, as we learned during a pandemic over forty years later.

"The quarters will become worth more," I said confidently. "And they will keep going up the older the quarters get."

Ba nodded, satisfied. Nainai had kept a portion of the family's money in gold rather than as paper money. Ma's family had done the same, stashing precious metals away in secret places. A deep mistrust of the government drove this behavior. When the Nationalists had decreed that they would print a new currency for all of China, good patriots turned in their gold in exchange for paper bills. Yeye (whose social circles included only good patriots) happily complied, under protest by Nainai. He ignored her, eager to play his part in a new China free from foreign influence and imperial rule. All their years of saving, measured in coins and ingots, became mere entries in a bank ledger. In short order, the people got used to buying and selling things with the new paper, and it had given Yeye joy to see Chinese characters and faces on modern bills.

But when tax receipts dwindled, and the government began taking rice directly for its soldiers, the value of the new Chinese currency plummeted. It was rumored that Nanjing couldn't make good on its debts and that the encroaching Japanese threat would cut off trade and what tax base remained for the shaky new government. So the government simply decided to print more bills, and the paper money's value fell in half. Then in half again. And again. A *mantou* bun that cost one yuan today would cost ten the next week and one hundred by the end of the month. They kept adding zeros to the cost of everything, yet were far slower to add zeros to government salaries. Soon, all those good patriots were destitute, their life savings insufficient to buy even a few days' worth of food. When Yeye ashamedly explained their predicament to Nainai, she showed him the gold she had stashed away. "*Hao! Hen hao!*" he had cried. Good! Very good!

"Should we count them, maybe put them into rolls?" eleven-year-old me asked Ba.

"No," Ba said. "We won't ever be taking dem to de bank. Maybe to an exchange one day, but dey will only care about how much it weighs if it comes to dat."

I opened another bag from the safe. Inside were ingots, chains, and medallions, all pure gold. Whenever our *laolao* had come to visit, she would first hand each of his children a firecracker-red satchel with a gold offering inside. "Thank your *laolao*," Ma would remind us, right in front of her, as if to prove she was a good mother who taught her children manners.

"Thank you, Laolao…" we would drone in response, eyes down. None of us cared that she brought gold each time. Dollar bills, maybe even a ten dollar bill, would have been more welcome and useful. Ma would collect up the satchels and put them in the safe, only to be taken out when there was an accounting someday.

Many years later, when Ba put me fully in charge of the family's nest egg—grandly named "The Jenkai and Mary Tanlee Kuo Revocable Trust"—I grew an interest in rare coin collecting and began purchasing pristine American Liberties, Indians, and other beauties for thousands of dollars each. They arrived in vacuum-sealed plastic casing, forever frozen in the present. Each came with a complicated grade from the American Numismatic Society, which I would explain carefully to Ba, who had to take off his glasses to inspect the coins more closely. Ba seemed satisfied with the investment, though he would never live to see it pay off.

"Keep this for another two generations," he said of them, "And my great-grandchildren will be rich.

July 2019
Walnut Creek, CA

A mediocre Chinese restaurant within driving distance of the retirement community of Rossmoor, California. MA and JAY have just finished lunch, and JAY is paying the bill. MA leans over, trying to get a glimpse of the receipt, but JAY is keeping it out of her line of sight.

MA: TIP IS INCLUDE?

JAY: No, the tip's not included.

MA: I THINK IT MUST BE. LAST TIME DEFINITELY INCLUDE.

JAY: Did you have more than six people? That's when they include it.

MA: HOW MUCH TIP WE PAY?

JAY: We don't technically have to pay any. It depends on the service.

MA: SERVICE TERRIBLE.

JAY: It's a Chinese restaurant. It's expected to be bad.

MA leans forward.

October 2017
Fort Lauderdale, Florida

Every year, Ma went on a cruise with a large group of overseas Chinese retirees. They were all alumni, or spouses of alumni, of *Tai Da*, shorthand for *Taiwan Daxue*—Taiwan University. Ba had attended *Tai Da* and had graduated second in his class, which surprised no one more than his own father, who had been the reluctant president of the college and who never figured his eldest son had the discipline to study hard and succeed.

Ma had earlier claimed the mantle of "most active spouse" in the alumni group, meaning she knew everyone in it and all their misfortunes, particularly whose children had been the most disappointing. At one point in time, the merry band of elderly schoolmates would travel to more interesting destinations, such as Egypt and Brazil, which left them feeling better about how China was advancing. But as the average age of the group rose over time, the average mobility steadily declined until, at last, someone suggested it was time to find turn-key solutions like cruise ships, where food and activities were more readily accessible, even if dispiriting.

Ba had passed away three years ago, and with each reunion, there were more widows in the group as the men succumbed to heart disease, cancer, or fatigue from being married so long to Chinese wives. Ma had stayed on as self-appointed cruise director. Each year, she re-upped for the annual gathering, and I discreetly upgraded her stateroom. No other travelers in the group had an upgraded suite, as she frequently yet deftly mentioned, with a table for tea service right in the room. Ma appreciated that extra bit of fanciness, though she would never admit it. Having acquired a taste for her fancier suite, Ma also had grown unsubtle about expecting upgrades. With her most recent cruise, I had neglected to put in immediately for a higher-class cabin, and the cruise line had sent Ma an email reminder that a higher-end option was still available.

"WHAT DOES THIS SAY, I CANNOT READ, TOO SMALL," Ma demanded as she forwarded the offer to me by email.

"Don't worry. I'll get you the upgrade. There's still plenty of time," I wrote back, knowing full well Ma had read through the entire offer.

"YOU DON'T NEED TO SPEND MONEY ON THIS OLD LADY," she replied the next day, giving me a whole night to let the guilt of my inaction seep in. "EVERYBODY WONDERING WHY I SPEND SO MUCH JUST TO HAVE A TEA TABLE IN MY ROOM. I TELL THEM MY SON INSIST ON WASTING MONEY ON HIS MOTHER. HAHA."

Her annual seven-days-at-sea with her friends was one of the few times my siblings and I ever went without hearing from Ma daily. Although I always pre-ordered internet service on board, she had never quite mastered how to connect to it. In the ports of call, her less technophobic friends would text me pictures, usually groups of older Chinese ladies in wide-brimmed hats, still conscious of keeping their faces out of the sun, their ever-fewer-in-number husbands hanging towards the back. The group of them looked happy and unselfconscious.

White people seeing the group would probably dismiss them all as random, annoying tourists from Asia and not realize they were the best and brightest of their generation—the scientists, engineers, writers, and activists who had helped China rise out of the ruins of two wars.

Usually, one auntie would include a note saying they were taking good care of my mother, meaning they weren't letting her be alone and missing Ba. I always thought Ma looked much younger than the rest of them, at least until her back started curving as the muscles atrophied.

She had just come off her latest cruise and was in great spirits when she called.

"HI JAY. I AM OFF SHIP AND AT AIRPORT GATE NOW!" Ma shouted through her speakerphone.

My phone inquired if I wanted to pretend to lose battery life suddenly.

"Okay, great. Please just email me when you land safely in China." After this trip, she was heading straight back from California to Beijing, having already made the obligatory tour to see her scattered sons in New York, North Carolina, and California before getting on board.

"YEAH MY EMAIL ALL IN CHINESE, DO NOT WORK IN THE STATE!"

"Ma, I can hear you fine. You don't have to shout into the speaker." This was several years before Ma needed a hearing aid, which we finally got for her after an ear doctor confirmed her hearing indeed had declined. When we put them on her, she immediately complained that now everything was too loud, and that she unfortunately could hear everyone talking again.

"MY EMAIL LOOK ALL GOOFY GOOFY. I PROBABLY HAVE FIVE HUNDRED NOTE WHEN I GET HOME!" Ma shouted, still just as loudly.

"You have a lot of friends, and you should be happy to get so many emails."

"MOST OF THEM JUST SENDING NEWS STORY. THEY HAVE NOTHING NEW TO SAY, UNLESS ONE OF THEM HAS DEAD."

"Well, have a nice flight back," I replied, uncertain how to respond to that. *Are you about to enter an elevator and can't talk right now?* my phone suggested. I ignored it again.

"IS BUSINESS CLASS AGAIN?"

"Yes, it's a lie flat, Ma."

"WHA?"

"It's business class, yes," I said.

"YOU KNOW I DON'T NEED."

"It's a long flight, and I want you to be able to sleep."

"I NEVER SLEEP ANYWAY, SO YOU WASTING THE MONEY. TOO EXPENSIVE! YOU SURE ARE SPOILING THIS POOR MA. THAT WHAT I HAVE TO TELLING ALL MY FRIEND. MY SON INSIST ON BEST FOR ME."

"Ma, you shouldn't tell your friends about your flight class. They might get jealous!" I played along with her game. It was one of the few times I felt good about what I'd been able to provide her since Ba died. If I couldn't make enough money to upgrade Ma for her final adventures in her golden years, what kind of son would I be?

A disappointment, I answered in my own head.

"Just be sure to ask for help when you land."

"DID YOU GET WHALE CHAIR?"

"Yes, Arthur has told them you need a chair to the gate."

Arthur knew the drill when it came to Ma's travel. Ma found frequent opportunities to mention to her friends that her son's "assistant" was arranging everything for her, and I was pretty sure they imagined Arthur to be some harried young professional, frantically working the phones at a chic Manhattan office, à la *The Devil Wears Prada*, which couldn't be further from the truth. In reality, Arthur was a gay boy who resembled James Van Der Beek from his *Dawson's Creek* days. He hailed from a small Texas town and had moved to New York to find something other than Texas. He liked video games, marijuana, and a life free of the pressures of ambition. He was also an excellent assistant. Ma adored Arthur once she had confirmed that we were not, in fact, lovers. She always asked me what gift she should bring him for all the help he provided. I reminded her that this was actually part of his job, but Ma insisted on gifts, usually another cashmere scarf or pair of nice gloves, which she had forgotten she'd already bought him before. He was good enough of an assistant to remember to sport them whenever she was in town.

Ma was actually perfectly capable of getting through airports without a wheelchair, but she had explained her preference for them to me once over the phone:

"THEY PUSH ME AROUND AIRPORT IN WHALE CHAIR BUT I DO NOT REALLY NEED."

"You're okay to walk to the gate?"

"YEAH. I WALK FORTY MINUTE EVERY DAY NOW. MY LEG OKAY."

"So why the wheelchair?"

"IN CHAIR I SKIPPING ALL THE LINE. GO RIGHT THROUGH SO FAST!"

Within two years, the wheelchair would become an actual necessity in airports, but for now, it was a great travel hack.

"I TRY TO TIP THE MAN PUSH MY CHAIR, AIRPORT SO BIG, BUT YOU ONLY GIVE ME SO MANY HUNDRED DOLLAR BILL. SO I DID NOT TIP." Only Ma could make an accusation out of having been given *too* much money. Plus, she'd forgotten that the stack of hundreds on her person was actually the cash she herself had withdrawn. When Ma arrived from China, she usually had precisely $9,900 on her, an amount just under the maximum allowed for international travel without needing to declare it.

It was a distinctively Chinese practice to press your legal rights as far as technically allowed, a trait best exemplified by the towers of salad created at Pizza Huts all over China. The fast food giant had imposed a rule that the presumably greedy and wasteful Chinese could only go *once* with *one small bowl* to the salad bar with any single salad order. To protest this affront to the Chinese character and stomach, enterprising patrons had created two-foot high towers of salad, supported on the sides with cucumbers and daikon radish sticks in interlocking structural beams, with walls of lettuce and tomato slices, proudly presented on social media as the ultimate sick burn on Pizza Hut. I often google "Pizza Hut China salad bowls" to show friends how Chinese the Chinese really are.

While I understood the impulse to funnel as much money out of China as possible at every opportunity, I could never understand why my parents had always insisted on carrying so much cash around in the States. This once nearly resulted in disaster when Ba had left a briefcase with five thousand dollars still in it, forgotten on a bench inside an In-and-Out Burger joint in California, which Ba had wanted to try because he'd heard the burgers were superior. (He determined, after a few bites, that he still preferred Burger King, which remained the unbeaten favorite fast food joint for all his days. Ba loved Burger King so much that when one opened in the Beijing International

Airport, he happily volunteered to drive forty-five minutes to pick up any visiting guests himself, just so he could order a Whopper). It was hours later before Ba realized that he'd forgotten his briefcase full of cash at the In-and-Out. When he returned to the restaurant, the manager was still there with it, all the money intact. Ba was impressed by how honest the staff had been. I explained that the company was owned by very religious people, pointing out the Bible verse at the bottom of every paper soda cup. Ba was grateful that In-and-Out apparently preferred to hire Mormons and devout Christians to work there, reinforcing Ma's theory that workers with deep religious beliefs were the most God-fearingly honest.

Whether and how much to tip service workers was a subject of intense debate with Ma, who was now seeking my input on her failure to tip the airport valet. "You don't actually have to tip them. They work for the airline," I explained. "But if you want to tip, you can tell them you only have large bills. They might actually have change."

"I DON'T WANT THEM SEEING MY MONEY, MAKING ME NERVOUS."

"Okay. I'll try to make sure Arthur gets you smaller change so you can tip them next time."

"I GIVE TWENTY DOLLAR TIP TO THE NICE FILIPINO HELPER ON CRUISE SHIP. HE SAID 'THANK YOU, MARY' AND BOW DOWN, WAAAA!"

Ma's habit of talking to every stranger in sight, particularly valets, cashiers, and doormen, was said to be part of her charm, but it regularly made me wince. I tried to tell myself that strangers probably found it cute and disarming, and probably more than a bit comical, that an elderly Chinese woman would engage them randomly on any number of topics and then tip them on the low side.

"EVERYONE ASK HOW HE KNOW MY NAME. 'BECAUSE I TALK TO HIM!' I SAY."

"Imagine that," I said to the universe generally, but Ma heard me instead agreeing with her.

"YEAH, IT TRUE. NONE OF MY FRIEND EVER ACTUALLY TALK TO THE HELPER."

"Ma, don't call them 'the helpers.' That's considered rude."

"WHY RUDE? THEY NOT HELP?"

"It just sounds dismissive, like '*The Help.*' It's like you think you are superior to them."

I suspected that Ma sometimes used her somewhat broken English to make points that other people weren't allowed to make, like when she referred to me and my gay friends as "YOU PEOPLE," as in "DO YOU PEOPLE ONLY HIRE OTHER GAY AT YOU COMPANY?" After I explained why she shouldn't use this phraseology, Ma leveled the field by starting to refer to all of her children as "YOU PEOPLE," and "YOU PEOPLE MUST TOO BUSY TO CALL THIS WEEK." We tried to get her to stop using that construction, but by highlighting it, we seem only to have reinforced it.

"I NOT THINK I AM SUPERIOR. BUT YOU KNOW HOW MUCH THE HELPER MAKE ON SHIP?"

"I actually have no idea," I said truthfully. I felt a bit ashamed to have never thought about that, considering how many gay cruises I'd been on.

"ONLY MAKE EIGHT HUNDRED DOLLAR A MONTH." Ma said triumphantly, happy to know something about the world that I didn't.

"And how do you know that?" I questioned. "Please tell me you didn't ask him."

"NO, I ASKING HIM! SO HE TELL ME."

"Ma, you shouldn't ask people how much money they make. That's not a question you're supposed to ask anyone."

"OF COURSE I ASKING. OTHERWISE, HOW I KNOW HOW MUCH TO TIP?"

April 2002
Beijing, China

Laolao was crying again downstairs. It was a soft, shaking sob and then a series of moans. She muttered some words, but they weren't intelligible. Ma roused herself once more from bed and pushed hard on the bedroom door, wood scraping across the marble. The door had warped not long after being installed. No matter how quietly you tried to push the door open, that scrape would announce you were up and about.

Ma flipped the light switch, producing a hesitant buzz of cheap fluorescent bulbs, so ubiquitous in China. She descended in slippers.

"Mama," she said. "*Xuyao shenme?*" Do you need something?

Laolao continued to sob. She was having another one of her bad spells, where she believed she was somewhere else, maybe even someone else, and nothing seemed familiar.

It had started after Laolao's surgery for an obstructed artery. It was supposed to be a routine procedure, but things had gone horribly awry. According to one of my uncles, Laolao's heart had stopped for a dangerous amount of time, and not enough oxygen reached her brain. She went into a coma, and when she finally came out of it, she was not herself. The doctors said some memory loss was to be expected, but it became clear that she had lost a good deal of it, as well as many basic cognitive functions. She didn't recognize people she'd known her whole life, including her own daughters sometimes.

Specialists were consulted, and they said that her memories might come back, but instead, Laolao began to retreat further. Sometimes she was eight years old and called out for her own parents. Sometimes she was a young woman, worried about the invading Japanese. Ma brought up the failed surgery every moment she could with her brothers, who had pushed for it, as a stern reminder that she should make all the important family decisions from now on.

Once, when John and his wife Rachael were visiting Beijing, Laolao fixated on him, glaring from across the table. None of the family knew what to expect, and Laolao didn't disappoint. "You are a very bad man!" she cried suddenly and with great intensity.

Startled, John flinched. "What do you mean, Laolao?"

"You are a very bad man because you beat your wife!"

There was stunned silence, and then they all began to laugh. Rachael laughed too, in her open, American way, once they translated what Laolao had blurted out. She continued to stare John down. We never learned who she thought he was and what the story was behind her accusation.

My ex-boyfriend, Zhang Yan, was admittedly very good with Laolao. Even after we'd broken up, Zhang Yan had stuck around, working as an assistant around the house and for the family company in Beijing. He instinctively knew how to interact with Laolao, especially when she began to repeat herself. "Who are you?" she once asked me, blinking but smiling and gracious. Zhang Yan jumped in to rescue me.

"This is your grandson," Zhang Yan said slowly and deliberately, and loud enough for it to penetrate her increasing deafness.

"I have a grandson?" Laolao said with true wonderment.

"You have many grandchildren," Zhang Yan said. "*Hao fuqi.*" Very fortunate.

"Why, that must be true. I must be fortunate," Laolao said, trying to piece it together. "But who are their parents?"

"That is your daughter over there, Tanlee," Zhang Yan said, taking Laolao's hand and indicating over to Ma, knowing that this news might come as a shock.

"Your firstborn," Ma emphasized from across the room, with considerably less patience and quite loudly. "You are Song Manxi. I am your firstborn, Tanlee. You have two daughters and three sons. I have three sons and a daughter." Ma went back to reading her paper. A version of this conversation played out several times a day, sometimes several times an hour. Only Zhang Yan never seemed to tire of walking Laolao through it.

"Are you my grandson?" Laolao asked Zhang Yan. "You are very small to be part of my family," she said skeptically.

Zhang Yan laughed. "No. I am—" Zhang Yan looked over at me with mischief. "I am a dentist," he lied. Even Ma had to smile at his improvisation. This was the part he enjoyed, making up whatever story he wanted to tell her about himself. All the lives he never actually got to lead. "I fix old people's teeth. I really like to make dentures for people, so they can have a full set, like mine!"

"You do have wonderful teeth," Laolao said as he permitted her to inspect them, tipping his head back and opening them wide. "Very straight and healthy." At least Laolao seemed satisfied and happy at the moment.

"I am a grandmother of a dentist, even if you are very small. Who would have thought that possible?"

After a moment, Laolao took a sip of tea and sat quietly, her brow furrowed. I wondered how her brain was dealing with the information she'd just heard, how it was constructing a new reality, even if for just a moment. I could tell when it slipped away from her again. Zhang Yan could as well because he took her hand and held it.

"Hello. Who are you?" Laolao asked him. "Do I know you?"

"I am—" Again, with an impish look. "I am your driver," Zhang Yan said reassuringly. "I'll take you around in a nice car."

Laolao did seem reassured. "Ah, I see," she said. Then she frowned deeply. "You seem young to be a driver. Are you sure you can drive?"

"I have been driving since I was twelve," Zhang Yan said, breezily spinning out his tale. "I learned from a famous race car driver. So I'm very good."

"Drivers are expensive," Laolao said. "Do I pay you?"

"You pay me well, yes. You pay a whole staff of helpers," Zhang Yan said.

"We pay everyone too much," said Ma pointedly in Mandarin, turning Zhang Yan's face red.

After their family had fled to Taiwan, when it was clear the Nationalists had lost the Civil War to Mao Zedong and his Red Army, Laolao had managed to keep a driver, maids, a butler, and a cook for the Liu household. As the family of an influential politician, they had

98

lived in a grand house and had not one but two cars. But their wealth would prove to be fleeting after a trusted friend of the family betrayed them and disappeared with most of their cash. Ma could still remember the argument when her father broke that news. Given this experience, it wasn't surprising that lack of money was often Laolao's go-to fear whenever she grew lost in her head.

"Don't worry, Mother," Ma said. "You are still a wealthy woman. Please don't work yourself up."

Laolao herself had often said that money could come and go in an instant, particularly in an unstable world. When the family flew on a private plane to Shanghai—a stopover to their new home in the restored capital in Nanjing—Ma personally had witnessed how financial ruin could destroy lives. A rumor had circulated that one of the banks was near insolvency, and throngs of worried depositors turned up to pull their money out. The bank, fearing a run, decided to shut its doors rather than let anyone in. Ma was just eight years old when she saw one frantic man try to scale the massive iron gate of the bank as it was closing, shouting that his life savings were inside. The heartless guards slammed the gate shut, severing the man's hand. The servant with her tried to shield her eyes from the sight and the blood, but it was too late. The people lost their money, the government lost their faith, and the man lost his hand.

Now Laolao wailed about being poor, about having nothing left, even about having once again to sell face creams and make *shao bing* just to make ends meet. For a time when the family had gone inland to serve in the national wartime legislature, they were left without any actual income and their money back in Henan. To generate cash, Laolao had begun to sell European-style face creams to other wealthy family matrons. With the creams, she was quite successful because there was no competition for such a novelty, and she could charge whatever she wished. All the same, touting beauty products was humiliating work for a former movie starlet, but Laolao faced down their poverty with determination and humility.

"Look!" said Ma to Laolao, hoping to calm her. "See this bank statement? Take a look at it. It's in your name. It has over a million *taibi* in it. You have nothing to worry about."

The bank statement had been my aunt Theresa's idea. She had asked her son Arvin to mock up a fake statement and print it out, showing a large sum of Taiwanese dollars in a personal savings account. They kept it by Laolao's bedside to show her whenever she worried about finances. Years ago, Laolao had been swindled in a real estate scam and had lost what was left of her life savings, a considerable loss of status and security that Ma also pinned on her brothers' failures as sons. The incident embarrassed and rankled Laolao, so no one spoke of it to her after it happened. Now her children took turns looking after her and making sure her fears didn't endanger her health or cause her to lose too much sleep.

Aunt Theresa was masterful at concocting credible lies that let Laolao form alternate realities. Once, on a drive down Chang An Avenue, the main thoroughfare that cut horizontally across Beijing, Laolao's eyes widened as they passed the Forbidden City, where Mao Zedong's larger-than-life portrait hung above the imposing gate.

"Mao!" Laolao shrieked as if she'd seen a ghost. "Mao! No, no, no! Mao is here? The Communists are here?"

"Oh, that!" Aunt Theresa said casually but thinking quickly. "Don't worry about that. The Communists were here a while back, but now the Nationalists are in charge again. Everything is okay. The *kuomintang* won. We won, don't worry. They just haven't gotten around to taking down his portrait."

Laolao stared with wonder at the colorful, perfectly manicured streets and the abundance all around her in the new China.

"I see," she said. "Well, what a wonderful job they have done! Chang An Avenue is so beautiful. China is so beautiful."

"Yes, it is," Ma. "Don't worry. China is rich now, Ma. Everything is okay."

Chapter Four

BUGS

or

"THEY TAKING EVERYTHING AWAY"

April 2020
FaceTime Call

"TRAMP IS CRAZY."

Ever since Trump's election, Ma had referred to the orange guy in the White House as "Tramp," the "Tr-" combo causing her to open her mouth wide, transforming -ump into -amp. This kept my friends cackling whenever she talked politics, so I never bothered to correct her. Ma would shake her head, eyes narrowing with practiced disdain, as she sang, "TRAMP, TRAMP, TRAMP!" We would all sing along. Even outside her presence, Trump became Tramp.

By the second month of lockdown, I began to prioritize calls with Ma, even if we had nothing new to talk about. Food and weather usually absorbed a welcome few minutes of our check-in chatter. She often complained that my brother Kaiser never called her because, after all, "HE SO BUSY WITH WORK." When he finally did, after Mimi and I guilted him mercilessly, Ma wasn't fooled. "YOU TOLD KAISER TO CALL ME, I KNOWING! WHY HE SUDDENLY CALL OUT OF BLUE?"

Apart from our calls, I fretted over what Ma actually did the rest of her day, whether she was bored and stir-crazy or if she had learned to tolerate silence and inactivity after 82 eventful years. The monotony of the pandemic was proving good practice for my own golden years to come.

Ma glued herself to one of the mainland-friendly broadcasts out of Hong Kong, which served up stories with a heavy pro-China/anti-America bent. The very serious hosts stood on a green-screened background that mimicked the bridge of the Starship Enterprise, delivering their alternate version of state-friendly facts while snugly fitted into what could only be described as Starfleet uniforms. The effect was clearly intended to convey "future forward."

"Tramp? Again? What now?" I asked as I absently scanned liberal outrage over the latest Trump tweet.

"TRAMP WANTING TO BLAME CHINA FOR ALL DEATH IN UNITED STATE!"

"A lot of people do," I said. Even some of my smarter friends were indignantly calling for a boycott of Chinese goods, and it made me wince. The near daily anti-Chinese garbage coming from the White House had spawned hundreds of brutal attacks upon people assumed to be Chinese, including Koreans, Thais, and Vietnamese. It reminded me of when Sikhs were targeted for assault and even murder after 9/11 just because they also wore turbans. Stories of attacks on the Chinese were on rotation from Ma's Starfleet newscasters, eager to portray Ugly Americans at their worst. It wasn't hard.

"Blaming China gives people somewhere else to direct their anger," I sighed, recalling some recent headlines.

Asian Grandmother In Queens Set On Fire, Suspects Still At Large.

"I DON'T WANT YOU GO OUTSIDE. PEOPLE ATTACKING ASIAN JUST FOR BEING OUTSIDE."

Bronx Woman Hit In Face With Caustic Liquid.

"I'm fine, Ma. I live across from a police station. They aren't going to attack me on the street."

"ANYWAY, TRAMP SAY CHINA START VIRUS, BUT ARTICLE I READ SAY IT WAS AMERICAN SOLDIER FIRST CARRY IT TO WUHAN."

"I'm sure China wants to deflect blame, too," I said, not up to the effort of debunking yet another conspiracy.

"IF YOU WANT I SEND IT TO YOU. OH BUT YOU CANNOT READING THE CHINESE. TOO BAD!" Ma used "Too bad!" the way Tramp used "Sad!"

"Ma, you should be careful," I said, declining to take her bait about my Chinese illiteracy. "There's a lot of propaganda flying around on both sides right now. Some of my friends are even saying it escaped from a lab in Wuhan because that's where the Chinese Centers for Disease Control are located." I'd earlier skimmed an article touting this particular fantasy, hoping to make some sense of the claim, but it was so flimsy that I didn't finish it. I refreshed an open tab, where I was morbidly tracking cases and deaths in the U.S. We were up to half a million cases, 18,000 deaths. *So many*, I thought at the time.

"HOW ARE YOUR BUSINESS DOING?"

"We're lucky," I said, trying to believe it. "We just got money from the government to cover payroll." We had built a digital publishing business catering to the social media fans of George Takei, who was best known for playing Sulu on *Star Trek* some 50 years earlier. Ma didn't really understand our business, and I never tried to explain it to her. But for some reason, she had signed up for George's twice-weekly, often irreverent newsletter. The last installment had teased, "Man's Attempt at Anal Sex Goes Hilariously Wrong." I hoped Ma would never ask what "anal sex" was. At least she still didn't know how to Google things.

"HOW MUCH YOU GETTING?"

"Almost $300K."

"THEY GIVING YOU THAT MUCH?"

"It's a loan. Well, it's forgivable. Anyway, it's so we don't have to lay anyone off."

"YOU KNOW IN BEIJING I SPENDING ALMOST NOTHING. MAYBE JUST ONE THOUSAND YUAN A MONTH."

"Wow," I said, humoring her. "Well, you are frugal. But things in the U.S. cost more."

"I NOT SPENDING ANYTHING EXCEPT ON FOOD HERE," Ma said. "ALSO SOME ACUPUNCTURE AND A MASSAGE. THAT ABOUT ALL."

And your homeowner's fees, your cruises, and your business class flights, I thought to myself, but instead said, "You're great at saving money, Ma."

"THEY REALLY LOAN YOU THREE HUNDRED THOUSAND? IN DOLLAR?"

"Well, it's not yuan, Ma. Of course, it's dollars."

"OH, I KNOW," she said, my humor flying past her. "BUT SEEM LIKE A LOT."

"That's just enough to survive on for another three months," I said, not wanting to get into how badly we'd actually been hit. We relied on ad revenue, but suddenly there were no sports, no movies, no travel, and no in-shop retailers who needed to advertise. The pandemic was a black swan event, said my company's co-founder and one of my besties, Lorenzo, who had been sick for days with a high fever, aches, and a cough, and had lost his sense of smell and taste. He had caught the bug early on, and he was already on the mend when his antibody tests came back positive. He seemed quite happy about the results. At another time, a positive antibody test was a death sentence for a gay man. Now it was an update to a Grindr profile. Negative for HIV antibodies, positive for Covid.

"THAT IS GOOD TO HEAR. CONGRATULATION! I KNOW ALL MY CHILDREN WILL WIND UP OKAY." Ma said this so often that I wondered if she was trying to ward off evil spirits with insistent optimism. "BUT IN ALL MY LIFE I NEVER SEEN ANYTHING LIKE THIS VIRUS. JUST KIND OF CRAZY."

I thought of several of Ma's stories that were easily on par with being shut inside during a global pandemic but didn't challenge her with them.

"Just be extra careful. No guests, okay?"

"YOU SHOULD BE CAREFUL, TOO. DON'T GOING OUTSIDE."

"I only go outside to walk the dogs, Ma."

"YOU KNOW, DOG CAN GETTING VIRUS, TOO," she warned. This rumor had been largely dispelled, but in Ma's eyes, pets were carriers of all kinds of germs and served no useful purpose.

"I'm not worried about catching this from our dogs."

"NO, I NOT WORRY FOR YOU. I WORRY FOR DOG!"

"Actually," I said, ignoring her dig, "I read that cats can get this, not dogs."

106

"I KNOW. I SEEING NEWS STORY THAT TIGER GET SICK IN NEW YORK ZOO. CANNOT BELIEVE!"

"This year is filled with tiger-related stuff," I said. I had binge-watched *The Tiger King* recently and had gotten through about five episodes before I felt my brain melting.

"I KNOW. AND NOT EVEN YEAR OF THE TIGER! NOT UNTIL I AM EIGHTY-FOUR," she said, certain that this was an achievable mark. Ma was born in a tiger year, which she brought up whenever saying she never should have married Ba, who was born in a monkey year, as were my *nainai* and I.

"TIGER AND MONKEY NO GOOD TOGETHER," Ma had explained to me once. "MONKEY SIT ON THE TIGER BACK NEVER CAN SHAKE OFF. *Houzi lao qifu hu.*" Monkeys always oppress tigers.

I wondered which monkey she was talking about.

February 2020
FaceTime Call

> MA and JAY are on a FaceTime call. Both are watching television while speaking.

MA: SOUTH KOREA GOT ONE THOUSAND NEW CASE OF VIRUS.

JAY: It's looking like epicenter number two.

MA: WHA?

JAY: It's the number two country.

MA: KOREA ALWAYS NUMBER TWO.

JAY: I guess most infections there were in that megachurch.

MA: CHURCH. YEAH. SO FUNNY.

JAY: Funny?

MA: YEAH. ALL THE PRAYING AND GOD DID NOT SAVING THEM.

JAY: Ha! That is funny.

MA: RELIGION ALWAYS WASTE OF TIME.

June 1918
Henan, China

Ma had told us the story of her mother's family's sudden conversion to Catholicism many times. And her own mother had remained a devoutly religious person from that fateful date forward. She had gotten the story secondhand from Laolao, who was just a little girl when it all went down. But it went something like this.

Laolao was only around seven or eight when she grew very ill, along with her sister, Meirong. Lying in her bed, shivering and body aching, she could hear whispered voices, like ethereal spirits outside her room and yet somehow also deep inside her ears. Two shadows fell across the gauzy drapes in the doorway, her mother, whom everyone called Madam Song, and her sister, whom Laolao called Little Auntie. Both wore their hair pulled tautly and pinned in buns. They made for slim figures, graced with draped silks even in this heat. The two women

108

checked first on Meirong, also bedridden with a high fever and far worse off by the sound of it. Laolao's older sister was almost seventeen, but she seldom went out of doors, preferring to keep to her studies and sing in her chambers. She was not hearty.

Laolao wiggled her toes to make sure she was awake and not caught in a fever dream. She longed to be up on her feet, practicing her balance with a sword in each hand alongside her father, who, it was commonly agreed, indulged his daughter's odd fancies too liberally. Girls with swords! What nonsense.

She squeezed her toes five times in a row, first the left foot, then the right, focusing in and down on the feeling with each press. Her father, my great-grandfather, had taught her this trick. Each movement was the same but also subtly different, if one truly paid attention.

She had almost been destined for a different pair of feet, ones wrapped in cloth bandages that broke the toes and the delicate bones of so many little girls, then were soaked with medicinal oils to stave off infection and hide the stench.

"BUT WHEN LAOLAO MOTHER TRY TO TIE THEM, SHE SCREAM FOR WHOLE DAY, TEAR AT CLOTH. NO ONE CAN KEEP THEM ON HER FEET," Ma explained.

"Look at this worthless daughter!" Madam Song had exclaimed. My great-grandfather, known generally as Old Song, was the grand patriarch and the object of Madam Song's ire over Laolao's unbound feet. "This is all your doing, putting fanciful notions in her head."

"Leave her feet," Old Song had sighed. "Binding is considered old-fashioned nowadays in any case."

Madam Song frowned. That comment had its intended effect. "Old-fashioned" was something she would *never* be. Why insist on such exquisite and tasteful *qipao*, from Nanjing and Shanghai, each a small fortune, if not to set her apart from their less worldly neighbors? She had a taste for western finery and company, too, it was said. Her tea set was French in design, not Chinese, and she had a phonograph from America that could play two songs.

A servant announced a visitor. Madam Song and Little Auntie scurried to the courtyard. There was a man's voice, speaking in halting Chinese. It was the German missionary priest, his Chinese name simply *Mu*. That was probably short for something like "Mueller," a word that would be such a burden on the Chinese tongue, all pulleys and ropes. Priest Mu had one of the only white faces in town. As a little girl, Laolao had spent many afternoons following behind him unseen, spying on his services, watching his comings and goings in those peculiar vestments. She had also tracked the two severe German nuns who recruited new girls for the local convent. They taught mathematics and geography, no doubt a cover for their true purposes of "saving souls," Old Song often said.

From what Laolao could gather, her father didn't care for Priest Mu. Perhaps it was because Mu came so often by the Song home and set his rheumy eyes too long upon Meirong, his stammering more pronounced as he hovered like a teenage boy around her.

"MEIRONG SUCH BEAUTY, MOST BEAUTIFUL GIRL IN WHOLE COUNTY, EVEN PRIEST NOTICE HER," Ma said to me.

"The most sought-after bride anywhere!" Madam Song so often proclaimed. Laolao would scowl. Her mother boasted of Meirong like a prized bird.

"LAOLAO MOTHER WAS CERTAIN HER TWO DAUGHTER GOING TO BE DEAD FROM SICKNESS."

With her fever still raging, Laolao quieted her breath and her heart, and she listened to the voices outside her bedroom.

"It may be the look-alike sickness everyday population acquire, in Europe and in America," Priest Mu said, his Chinese still quite poor even after years in the country. "It is name flu."

"*Fa-lu!*" her mother gasped. "No *fa-lu*! *Ay yah*, but will they survive it? Their heads are so hot! It will cook their brains!"

"They may be life," Priest Mu said gravely. "But they may be death, also higher chance."

Madame Song began to weep.

"Take faith in the Lord," Priest Mu said. "Take faith, and He will protection them safety, by grace of Heaven."

Laolao wanted her illness to end by the grace of Heaven. She wanted her big sister to get better, too. But she wondered whether the Church had other motivations. Her father had warned of the rumors: The missionaries had targeted the Song family to accelerate their work. Imagine if the most renowned family in the county could be brought into the fold! Priest Mu often came by with bibles and prayer beads, which Madam Song politely accepted.

"EVER SINCE THAT DAY, LAOLAO LIKE TO COUNT HER BEAD. EVEN WHEN HER BRAIN FORGETTING, SHE CAN COUNTING. SHE LIKE COUNT MONEY, TOO!" Ma told me.

Priest Mu would invite Madam Song and Little Auntie to Sunday services, which they politely declined each time. "Oh, you are too kind to think foolish women could learn to worship, especially in a language no one even speaks anymore!" they exclaimed. On his way out, Priest Mu would ask to see Meirong and inquire about her studies, then sit enraptured as she would sing, maybe just one more song, just for him.

"Your daughters may have more strength because others are saying this sickness coming from China first, so the Chinese have strength to stand against," Priest Mu explained. "People call it 'Spanish Flu,' but many say we did not have it until we bringing dirty Chinese labor over to work while our soldiers go off killing."

"What's this?" she heard her father shout. "You're saying we Chinese are to blame for the West's contagion? Now I've heard everything."

"Forgive me, Old Song. I mean no unkind," said Priest Mu.

"You Europeans are fully capable of destroying yourselves without our help. Look at your Great War! What a monumental waste."

"I hope only to give more promise to your family."

"Unnnh," her father grunted. "What the girls need now is rest and hot chrysanthemum tea with ginger. This is not your Spanish Flu."

Laolao could hear her father shuffling away, impatient to rid himself of the prying western priest.

"God may have put the illness back in China where it started," Priest Mu continued once her father had left. "God may have put this in your daughters. This may show His planning."

Laolao shuddered, feeling the truth of those words. In her dreams, she had seen fire fall from the sky, rivers of blood, and locusts, which Priest Mu listed among God's famous plagues. Pestilence was also among His many tools, so perhaps this bug truly was from God. What if we Chinese really are to blame for the deaths in the west? she thought. If so, then I would choose to die as punishment, Laolao pledged. A swordmaiden, she reminded herself, did not fear death, only dishonor.

112

"Your daughters are precious things to you, are they not?" Priest Mu asked in that awkward way he had of speaking.

Madam Song was still weeping. "Of course, of course, they are!"

"If I could show you how prayer will save them, will you come downstairs to church every Sunday? Will you take God into your big breast?"

Laolao giggled. Priest Mu's Chinese was truly awful.

"If your God can save my daughters from this terrible fate, then I will swear myself to Him forever," her mother cried, her penchant for drama heightened by circumstance.

"SO THAT IS HOW SONG FAMILY CAME TO JOIN CATHOLIC CHURCH," Ma said.

Priest Mu and his nuns appeared that evening, holding "holy water" in silver chalices and burning incense in a swinging lamp. The priest flicked the blessed water around the courtyard as Madam Song, Little Auntie, and a bevy of curious servants looked on. Some of the servants smiled and laughed at the bizarre procedure, but they grew serious when they saw Madam Song's face contorted in private prayer. Priest Mu droned in a strange-sounding tongue, standing solemnly over first Laolao and then Meirong, after which he slipped them each what he called "the body of Christ" to eat. They were not dry wafer crackers like Laolao normally saw him give his small number of faithful, but rather some kind of a bitter pill. She swallowed it, then went back to sleep.

When both their fevers broke later that night, Mother was tearful and overjoyed, and she ran about their compound announcing that God had come into their house and their lives. She then found Priest Mu and happily proclaimed she would begin attending services. Moreover, she ordered all of their servants to do the same. The

113

German nuns seemed triumphant over this development, and they made quick work of letting the whole town know of Madam Song's conversion.

Old Song was another matter. This turn of events distressed him greatly. When he asked Laolao about what she could remember of the mystical service, she disclosed the bitter pill Priest Mu had substituted in place of the communion wafer.

"This was not God's hand!" my great-grandfather bellowed. "This was medicine! The British devils call it 'aspirin.' You can buy it in western apothecaries in Nanjing. You have been duped!"

"I have been saved," Madam Song responded, her eyes defiant. "And you should be too, if you wish to join me in heaven. There is still time."

Old Song's complaints about their ruse soon got back to the missionaries. Villagers whispered that Priest Mu had grown concerned the patriarch would countermand his wife's decision to convert. The nuns needed to cement the Song family's bonds even more securely. And so Priest Mu announced that God had approached him with another mandate: The Song family's oldest daughter, Meirong, must join the local convent, or the sickness might be revisited upon them.

Madam Song, terrified at the prospect, quickly acceded to this new demand, but her husband was livid. He let it be known throughout the county that the Church was extorting them with threats of contagion and demanding children as ransom and that the latest victim was his beautiful daughter, Meirong. He would drive the missionaries out himself, but he was loath to cause an "international incident" that might invite reprisals.

Through all of this, Meirong had said nothing, and her little sister, my *laolao*, was flabbergasted. "How can you stay silent?" she said, stamping her foot. "How can you let them decide your life for you?"

Meirong simply shrugged demurely and said, "I stay inside here, I'll stay inside there. What does it matter where I sing my songs and do my studies?"

"As a nun, you will never marry!" Laolao cried. "You will have to wear a black dress and a head covering, and no one will ever see your beautiful arms and legs." Meirong had suffered mightily for her shapely legs, leaving them exposed to the icy winter air for long periods at the instruction of her mother, who believed it would shrink them and make them smooth as satin.

"LAOLAO TRY TO EXPOSING TO ICE ONE AFTERNOON AND GIVING UP AFTER TEN MINUTE," Ma had told me, laughing. "STILL, SHE TOLD ME TO DO IT WHEN I WAS LITTLE GIRL."

"So, did you do it?" I asked.

"ONLY TWICE. MAKE NO DIFFERENCE."

"But the convent is a prison!" Laolao said to Meirong in final exasperation over her sister's nonchalance.

Meirong laughed. "Do you not think this house is also a prison? And as far as marriage, you have read too many books. Men are stupid, and women are stupider still to bow to them, but that's the way of the world, isn't it? If I bow to a man, or if I bow to God, at least God will not care to beat me."

Laolao ran from the room, crying. She collapsed to her knees by her bed, holding her hands clasped the way she had seen the nuns do it. *Don't take my sister,* she prayed to the greedy German God. *Let her be free of your Church, and I will give myself over as a believer alongside my mother. Just not as a nun,* she added, to be sure He understood there were limits.

As things turned out, greedy German God took Laolao's prayers quite seriously. On the night before Meirong was to submit to the convent, a local warlord, who had earned the moniker "Big Tooth" owing to the size of his mouth and equally impressive stature, arrived at the Song compound on a wild steed, like a hero out of *Romance of the Three Kingdoms*. He had learned about this "deal with the devil" made by the foolish Song matriarch. The most beautiful girl in the county, traded to the Catholic Church? Never!

Big Tooth parlayed with my great-grandfather outside the compound gates and, after just fifteen minutes and in a moment seared forever in Laolao's eyes, Meirong was spirited away on the back of his steed with nothing more than the clothes she had on. She had a resigned expression as she rode off, one that hid a deep sadness. Laolao called out, tears flowing like blood from a fresh wound.

"Big Sister! Big Sister!"

She wept with her mouth agape as Meirong and Big Tooth grew smaller and smaller. Meirong was now a prisoner of a different kind. That very night, Meirong was "wed" to her new master, and Laolao would not see her sister again for many, many years.

Laolao did not forget her deal with the German God, however tricky He had been about His side of it. She had bought her sister's "freedom" with a promise, and in her intense guilt, she threw herself into service for the nuns and Priest Mu. There was no talk of her joining the convent, as she was far too rambunctious, but there was no doubting her faith. Her intense devotion to the Church impressed Madam Song, who had much to atone for after Father's scandalous, last-minute deal-making. Perhaps because of her unshakable trust in

116

Him, German God never did revisit upon their family the *fa-lu*, Spanish or otherwise.

Most distraught about the way things had gone was Priest Mu, who had wanted Meirong under his auspices. This was God's way of punishing him, Laolao was convinced. Priest Mu had lacked faith that God could cure her and Big Sister on His own, without the need for "aspirin." And God punished the unfaithful, that much she already understood. She swore that she would never allow her faith to falter like Priest Mu's. One day, she promised she would build her own church in His glory. One day, she would do such good works for Him that the Pope in Rome would request an audience.

In this, she was proven absolutely correct.

September 2020
FaceTime Call

> MA and JAY on a call. Ma is watching Chinese state-run television, a story about America.

MA: THIS COUNTRY U.S. IS NOT SAME COUNTRY I USED TO KNOW.

JAY: I would agree with that. It's run by crazy people now.

MA: I KNOW! THEY KNOWING THIS CONTAGIOUS BUT THEY STILL NOT WEARING MASK! REFUSING TO!

JAY: Do you know any anti-maskers among your friends?

MA: WHA?

JAY: People who refuse to wear masks.

MA: OH, NO! ALL MY FRIEND HERE ARE CHINESE. THEY ARE KNOWING BETTER.

August 1944
Henan, China

They formed huge clouds, shadows high as mountains that darkened the entire horizon in just minutes. The swarm of locusts—which they called *huang chong* or literally, "yellow bugs"—could strip entire fields in less than half an hour, leaving devastation that would last a whole season.

"WE LIVE IN XIPING DURING WAR, HAVING BIG WHEAT CROP EVERY YEAR. WE JUST ABOUT TO COLLECT IT ALL WHEN THE HUANG CHONG COMING. THEY TAKING EVERYTHING AWAY."

Ma was just six years old at the time—big enough to help. Wealthy landholders and poor serfs alike ran to the fields, shouting and waving blankets, shirts, scarves—anything to keep the swarm moving past. The ripe wheat were like piles of gold to the winged bandits. Ma watched in amazement as the amber square plots transformed into a buzzing, undulating brown. Farmers wailed as they failed to beat the insects back, a year's worth of backbreaking labor disappearing before their eyes.

The more closely and collectively people lived, the more exposed they were to locusts, fires, and plagues, my grandfather once explained to Ma. When a whole town depended upon crops from just a few hundred *mu* of farmland, their loss meant starvation, just as a whole village might die of thirst should its lone well fail. The more closely the people lived, the more damage nature could do.

118

We learned that lesson in New York City in 2020, too.

There was no turning back the enemy by this point. The bugs were already coating the wheat in their countless numbers, a syrupy wave of devastation. The townsfolk could only do what they could to survive, knowing that the *huang chong* had already written death sentences for half of them.

"Hurry, hurry!" Ma heard Second Uncle shouting. "Prepare ditches at the perimeters and down the center, wide and deep!"

As the town set itself to digging trenches around and across the bug-carpeted fields, my mother swatted dozens off her hair, face, and body. Each bug was as long as the gap between her thumb and index finger. The *huang chong* were efficient eaters, and after ten minutes on the stalks, their stomachs grew grossly extended. There was so much grain that they could keep eating until they could no longer fly. At that point, their own weight held them down. They fell off the stripped wheat blades and lay on the ground, hopping and twitching, their thin wings unable to lift them skyward.

"THAT WHAT DITCH WAS FOR," Ma explained.

"Deep enough, deep enough!" Third Uncle shouted, his voice now hoarse after half an hour of shouting. "Now rake the bugs towards them!"

Hundreds of humans continued their battle against millions of locusts, raking piles of their now mouse-sized, bloated bodies towards the ditches. The bugs crawled over each other in a desperate attempt to find air, but the piles kept growing, and the weight of the ones on top began to press the life out of the ones near the bottom. It was an extended dance of death. First, the locusts, distended bellies full of wheat crushing everything below them, then the humans, emptied bellies aching through a bitter winter of deprivation.

After just a few hours, the once lush fields were nothing more than dirt, straw, and carcasses from the swarm. The farmers stood in shock, bone-weary, some still sobbing as night fell. There was a somber silence at the Liu compound, too, where Ma lived with her family. They had heard reports of how the same nightmare had played out across the rest of the county and probably in all the neighboring ones as well. Who could have predicted that the locusts would deal an even more devastating blow than the Japanese?

"What will they do with all the dead *chongzi* in the ditches?"

"They will cook them, of course," my grandfather said, lighting a cigarette then rolling it in his fingers, lost in thought. Later he would learn that even their family's tobacco crops had not been spared the swarm. That meant an idle factory that winter unless they could buy dried leaves from another county. But at least the tobacco kilns could dry the grasshoppers before they rotted. That was a lot of food that should not go to waste.

"We *eat* them?" Ma asked, wide-eyed. The thought of the crawling, flapping, hopping insects already disgusted her. But the thought of crunching one in her mouth… her stomach rumbled, and her initial disgust turned to curiosity.

"We will eat them freshly cooked, then dry the ones that we cannot eat now. They will make for a rich powder when desiccated and ground up, good in soups and flour since we will have little wheat left. And you will eat them, too," grandfather said as Ma made a face. "Yes. In fact, Master Lu is already frying some up fresh. Can you smell that? It may be the last time many will have fresh meat this year."

"It's not meat," Ma said. "It's bugs."

For their dinner, Chef brought out a steaming platter of *huang chong*, dressed lightly with sesame oil, white pepper, scallions, and salt. Ma's

120

uncles and aunties all acted as if there were nothing strange about the meal as they stabbed into the pile with their chopsticks.

"It is like shrimp," Laolao said, who had spent time in Shanghai. "Think of them as land shrimp."

"The *huang chong* have devoured our crops," Second Uncle said. "And now we devour them." The family murmured at the justice of it.

Ma was deft with her chopsticks, and she didn't want to appear cowardly.

"I USED TO EAT THE BABY FROG. WHAT YOU CALLING?"

"Oh. Um, oh yeah. Tadpoles," I said, looking up from my laptop.

"YES TADPOOL. ANYWAY I TAKE OUT OF BUCKET AND EATING RIGHT IN FRONT OF BUNCH OF BOY. THEY FEELING SO DISGUST! BUT ACTUALLY NOT SO BAD WHEN I HOLD THE BREATH, GOBBLE IT DOWN."

"That's pretty gross, Ma. Why did you do that?"

"TO PROVING I AM TOUGHER GIRL THAN THEM. ANYWAY TRICK IS NOT TO CHEWING. ONLY A LITTLE WIGGLE IN THROAT. BUT WHEN LAOLAO FINDING OUT I DO IT, SHE MAKE ME DRINK WHOLE PINT OF RICE WINE TO KILLING TADPOOLS. OTHERWISE, COULD GROW INTO FROG IN STOMACH!"

The stir-fried locusts were no different than the tadpoles, Ma explained, just a bit crunchier. And she would have to chew down, as there was no swallowing them whole. She went straight for the head of the largest one and snapped it in her mouth. The now brittle chitin nearly dissolved in her mouth, and the bits of meat had a salty, lip-smacking quality to them. Her family all watched Ma taste her first bug, and, looking up at their expectant faces, she pronounced it delicious. They laughed.

It was the last time she remembered everyone laughing together that year. My grandfather laid it out plainly in meetings on which Ma eavesdropped. With Japanese troops cutting off the county from coastal food supplies and nothing but dried locusts and hard beans to eat, conditions for the poorer farmers quickly deteriorated. Within four weeks, all the remaining stores of grain were depleted, even with everyone rationing portions and being hungry all the time. No aid was forthcoming from the hopelessly incompetent KMT, the *kuomintang* or nationalist party, locked as it was in a war with Japan and the Communist insurgency.

Upriver, the KMT had blown up dams in a desperate attempt to slow the advancing Japanese troops, just as the Ukrainians would do 80 years later in the face of advancing Russians. That act had flooded what was left of the fields. Even the hated collaborationists in Nanjing had nothing but excuses to offer a poor province like Henan. The Liu family, headed by my grandfather, was among the only households with the means to stay fed, but that meant extra-armed security to ward off possible desperate mobs.

When fall ended, and winter came on, a deadly hush fell over the province. The old, the newly born, and the infirm were the first casualties, as their famine-weakened bodies failed to fight off even the commonest maladies of winter. Laolao took Ma around to visit the most destitute, delivering cooked beans and dried vegetables for making broth. During one visit, an emaciated young boy was so hungry that he stuffed a whole handful of beans into his parched mouth. His throat proved too weak to both swallow the food and breathe at the same time.

122

"HIS PARENT TRY TO GET HIM COUGHING UP, BUT HE BEGIN TURNING BLUE, NO BREATH."

"Oh God, what did you do?"

"WE LEAVING SOON AS POSSIBLE, THAT WHAT!"

One cold morning, though she was not permitted, Ma ventured into town, where she found none of the usual shops and stalls open, just one small kitchen operated by a very ancient *ayi* offering meat-filled *dianxing* at high prices. Ma hadn't eaten a bun in weeks, but she did have coins that she had pilfered from her mother's drawer. What a delicious treat some meat would make for her mother, she thought.

"Two *baozi*, to take away," Ma said. The vendor accepted her copper coin and wrapped two buns in a hot, wet cloth.

"Of course, Xiao Liu," the crone said, using the familiar diminutive. "But tell that guard behind you to bring back the cloth when you are done."

Ma hadn't noticed Xiao Miao standing ten meters away, keeping watch as was his charge. He was her favorite bodyguard because of his easy smile and pronounced dimples. He always teased her about eating the next disgusting thing, like tadpoles and snails. She seized the steaming packet and ran home as quickly as her small legs would take her to ensure the *baozi* were still piping hot when presented. Xiao Miao trotted behind.

"Mother! Mother! Look what I brought!" Ma cried as another guard let her in through the main gate.

"Where have you been?" Laolao demanded. "To town?! I have warned you, it is not safe. What if someone kidnapped you?"

"I had my eyes on her the whole time," said Xiao Miao.

"But look!" Ma said. "It's *baozi*. From the shop by the tailor. Real meat *baozi*!"

Laolao's eyes widened as Ma held out the warm treasure. Ma met her gaze with anticipation, but Laolao slapped the *baozi* down to the ground. Ma cried out in dismay.

"Oh, no! Why?"

"There is no real meat in town," LaoLao spat. "Not anywhere. What do you think is inside those buns?"

"Wait," I asked as Ma explained it to me. "Are you saying, they were actually cooking…"

"THAT WAS RUMOR. NO OTHER MEAT IN TOWN, SO…?"

"Don't frighten her," said my grandfather, who had appeared to check on the commotion. "Henan may be starving, but things have not come to that. We are not barbarians."

"No?" said Laolao. "Then tell us, Jingjian. What kind of meat do you think this is? For all we know, it is someone's dead child."

Young Ma gasped and stepped away from the *baozi*, nausea threatening to make her sick up right there.

"Throw them away," said my grandfather, indicating the now filthy dumplings. "And go ask after the seller. See where she is getting her 'meat' these days," he said to Xiao Miao.

"Of course," said Xiao Miao. "Come on, little tiger. Let's go find you something else to eat."

"There is nothing else good to eat," Ma complained. "Nothing at all!"

"Oh, but there is," he teased. "Have you tried dried *huang chong*? It's a delicacy this year."

March 1994
Phone Call

"HAPPY BIRTHDAY!"

"Thanks, Ma. I almost thought you forgot."

"WHY I FORGET?"

"I don't know. You did last year."

"I NOT FORGETTING YOUR BIRTHDAY, JUST FORGETTING TO CALL."

"I see," I said, not really understanding the difference. "Anyway, what's up?"

"JUST CALLING TO WISH YOU HAPPY BIRTHDAY. BABA IS ALSO HERE."

"Hi, Jay," I heard him say. "Happy birthday, hope you are doing well. Staying healthy."

Healthy. It was a euphemism I'd heard often lately. In 1994, I was 26 years old, and the AIDS virus still loomed shadow-like over my world, especially my relationship with my parents, ever since I'd come out on Christmas Day just a few months before. Gay people got the gay cancer. Gay people got sick. There was nothing I could do to talk them out of their worry.

"I'm fine. Bernie is fine," I added, meaning that neither my then-boyfriend, Bernie, nor I had tested positive. So much said was code now. "We're just busy with school and work."

"When do you start da new job?" Ba asked. He was still somewhat amazed that I had decided to become a lawyer. When I was little, I spent a year in speech therapy, and that had given Ba the permanent impression that my English was poor. Lawyers needed to speak very good English, he had said to me when I had brought up the possibility of law school. That's true, I had responded, wondering if he still thought I had a strong accent. We left it at that. Like many Chinese, Ba mistrusted lawyers, but he sounded pretty happy to have one now in the family.

"I start in August," I said. "I won't be sworn in until December, assuming I pass the bar."

"YOU BETTER STUDY HARD. DON'T GOING OUT TO BAR," Ma said, misunderstanding. In her mind, she assumed every gay man went out to have wild sex multiple times a week after visiting a gay bar, then inevitably caught the scary, lethal virus. Maybe if I was preoccupied with studying, I wouldn't get infected.

"I'll try to keep a balance," I offered.

"OKAY. JUST BE CAREFUL." More code.

"I will, Ma. Don't worry."

There was so much I knew they wanted to say. *Turn away from this choice! Do you see how worried you've made us? It's just the big city warping your mind. Or maybe America. Please don't get sick. We love you.*

But instead, all Ma said was:

126

"OKAY. STUDY HARD."

September 1995
Phone Call

"I need to talk to you about something legal," my cousin Elize said. She had rung me up at work, where I was an entry-level associate at a San Francisco law firm. Despite my lowly status, friends and relatives often came to me for a "sanity" check and a free consultation about their myriad legal questions.

"Okay, but I can only talk to you as your cousin, not as your lawyer," I said, deploying my usual caveats. "This isn't legal advice I'm giving you, just my own opinion."

"That's fine," Elize said. "It's actually about Calvin."

"Oh. I see," I said, getting up to close my office door.

My cousin Calvin was Elize's younger brother, and the two of them were the oldest of five children. Uncle Ken, Ba's younger brother, whom we called *er shushu* for "second uncle," had long ago married a white woman.

This was something Ma was certain had contributed to that family's many problems.

Over the years, Uncle Ken's wife had become a religious fanatic. After they divorced, she had begun instilling all manner of strange beliefs in our younger cousins still living with her. She enrolled the two youngest kids in a boarding school for blind and mentally handicapped children (even though they were neither). She would send them on religious retreats, where they held snakes, spoke in tongues, and believed that the world they saw with their otherwise

127

"blind" eyes was merely the temptations of the Devil. Things had gotten so bizarre and cultish that my brother John was preparing to form a posse and bust them out of their school just to save them from their own deranged mother. Right before John launched this questionable plan to kidnap our cousins across state lines, Uncle Ken won final custody of his children, so the scheme was scrapped.

Cousin Calvin and I had learned that the other was also gay during one memorable evening in Tucson. Calvin hadn't seen us in almost ten years, but when he moved to Phoenix, he came down to pay a visit. I was seventeen and still in high school, but the bars downtown didn't really check ID, so we all went out to a local college pub. Calvin was nerdy and thin, with round glasses long before Harry Potter had repopularized them and a stylish mop of hair that suggested MTV. He had more delicate features owing to his half-Asianness, and I often pictured him as an elf out of *The Lord of the Rings*, only with black hair. My "gaydar" activated when a good-looking guy in a letterman's jacket sauntered in, all dimples, shoulders, and casual masculinity. Both Calvin and I instinctively scoped him out before realizing the other was doing the same. He gave me a "You, too?" look and a wink that had us both busting up, with no one else in yet on our hilarious secret. Gays really do have a secret language.

After Calvin announced to his father that he was gay, word got out to my parents. Ma often cited Uncle Ken's ill-fated marriage as the culprit. Calvin had become "trendy" said Ma, and five years later had gotten sick, because he lacked a solid family upbringing, she insisted. *So what will that say about our family if I get AIDS?* I thought morbidly. After his diagnosis and announcement, Calvin didn't come down to see us as much. Ma seemed to worry I would get infected through some kind of gay cousin osmosis.

"YOU KNOW, CALVIN WAS WITH DOCTOR PARTNER, AND HE STILL GETTING SICK," Ma had said to me, as if to warn that no amount of reasonable precautions would spare me from a similar fate. At the time, in the early 1990s, many of my own friends were getting sick, and some were dying, though not in as large numbers as before the "cocktail" of AZT and other therapies had been developed. My partner Bernie's circle had been decimated, and we had become numb to the late-night phone calls, after which he would simply hang up and hold me for minutes, shedding no tears and saying nothing, as was his nature. By then, it wasn't so much a question of who had the virus as who didn't. Like most couples we knew at the time, Bernie and I had stayed monogamous. Well, mostly.

Calvin had come down with a very bad case of spinal meningitis that was likely connected with another opportunistic infection. Elize explained to me that he had gone to see his doctor, but he was greeted by someone new because his regular physician purportedly was too busy. The new doctor briefly examined Calvin and told him to go home, take two Tylenol, and report back if he grew worse. The next day, feeling at death's door, Calvin dragged himself to his doctor's office again, but the same substitute saw him and dispensed the same advice without further inquiry. Calvin went home, decided not to call and worry his boyfriend, fell into a coma that night, and never woke up. He died a few days later.

"It turns out the guy who sent Calvin home twice wasn't a doctor at all," Elize explained over the phone. "He was just a pre-med student or something, working at the office. The doctor was using students to see people, in order to collect more fees without having to do more work. He had been disciplined for Medicaid fraud before."

"Oh, my God," I said, realizing that we were probably staring at a strong wrongful-death case, at least from a liability standpoint. "That is horrible. I can't believe that happened."

"Dad is really upset about it. Calvin didn't have to die so soon," Elize said, her voice cracking. She and Calvin had been very close. We shared a moment together in silence, the last part of her sentence—

that it probably would have been just a question of time—remaining unsaid.

"Have you talked to any other doctors or medical professionals about what should have happened instead of Calvin being sent home? Would a real doctor have caught this?" I asked, suddenly sounding very much like the attorney I'd told her not to treat me as.

"My friend, who is a doctor, told me that just one look at Calvin's file would have made his HIV status instantly part of the mix. And because of his high fever and vomiting, he would have been sent to the ER, not home. Especially after the second visit."

"Well, then you probably have a good case," I said. "And this doctor probably has malpractice insurance, though you might be able to nail him personally. This is more than mere negligence."

"That's what I figured. But it's not really what I wanted to ask you," Elize said.

"I see," I said carefully. "Okay. What's up?"

Elize sighed. "It's about my dad," she began. "He's really angry and wants to sue because we could really use the money, especially after the divorce and then the funeral costs and all. But then he gets nervous. He doesn't want it to get out that Calvin had AIDS. He doesn't even want to tell our lawyer."

"Um, okay."

"But he's not being reasonable. Calvin wouldn't have cared who knew. He didn't hide his status, and he was proud of who he was," said Elize.

This was true. Calvin was out in a way I had been afraid to be. He was even an ardent and visible member of the local leather community up in Phoenix. I wondered whether my parents had known that Calvin was into some kinkier stuff. If they did, they hid it well. To their credit, they didn't appear overwhelmed or alarmed at his funeral, where a portion of the attendees were extended Chinese family, a portion were Calvin's co-workers, and the rest were leather daddies and pups from the fetish community who turned up for the services in full regalia. I asked Ma what she thought.

"DID NOT KNOWING CALVIN HAD SO MANY FRIEND."

"I heard some were quite colorfully dressed."

"NOT COLORFUL. JUST BLACK."

"But… leather?"

"BLACK LEATHER," she confirmed.

"So I gather your dad wasn't very proud of him," I said to Elize, trying to tease out over the phone what she was getting at.

"Dad harassed him constantly to change. He was sure Calvin was just messed up in the head. Nothing could get him off that idea," Elize said. "He doesn't want everyone to know that Calvin died from what he thinks of as a gay disease. He tells everyone it was a shock that he caught some other bug that came on suddenly. It's too shameful to say the truth."

So Uncle Ken would sooner pass on a million-dollar lawsuit than be humiliated, I thought. Ma would probably react the same. For her, my being gay wasn't about what it meant to me and my life but what it meant to her own standing in society. Ma didn't want people whispering about her gay son. Uncle Ken didn't want people shaking their heads about his poor boy who got AIDS from gay sex and died.

"So sorry. What's your question?" I asked Elize delicately.

131

"I want to know whether it's possible to keep that fact out of the lawsuit," she said, sounding resigned. "Dad isn't going to sue if that fact gets made public."

My mind flashed to powerful men, people like the political operative Roy Cohn and the actor Rock Hudson, who had both fought to keep their HIV statuses quiet. But the virus had a way of not respecting privacy or secrets. Often it was the KS—Kaposi's sarcoma, deep purple lesions impossible to cover—that marked its victims for an early grave in the eyes of others. With KS on display, there was little hiding the truth.

"It wouldn't have to be part of the complaint," I said. "But it's going to be part of their defense, especially on damages," I said, forgetting again not to dole out legal advice.

"So what does that mean?" Elize said. She was crying again, and I felt terrible saying the next words.

"It means they are going to say that Calvin didn't have much longer to live anyway, so any loss of income or other damages relating to what Calvin didn't get to live out would be limited. They may not win that argument, and there are liberal legal groups out there trying to change the laws around this, but the way things are now, they probably get to bring it up."

"And my dad has to answer questions about it?"

"If they depose your father, I'm pretty sure he would. He could move for a protective order, and that might limit some of this stuff getting out into the public, but it's not a surefire thing. And it wouldn't stop the defense from asking your dad about it directly."

"Then forget it. We can't go through with this," Elize said, suddenly sounding angry.

"I'm sorry that you guys have to even talk about this anymore," I said.

Elize was quiet for a moment. "I don't blame my dad. He is who he is. Maybe if there'd been enough time, he would have come around. But this fucking disease didn't give them enough time together."

It was a feeling I'd had quite often then that the plague meant less time for us altogether. There wasn't a cure, just a way to live a little while longer, knowing that your very lives as gay men caused your family to lose sleep. What an insidious thing the virus was, attacking silently at the margins of society, stigmatizing those who had it as "probably gay," rendering each instance of lovemaking both an act of courage and stupidity, death forever paired with ecstasy, sickness with release.

It was the only disease I could think of that made our families not want to talk about our lives and equally unwilling to talk about our deaths.

June 1976
Apalachin, New York

Popillia Japonica. The Japanese beetle. My brother John taught us to recognize one from a distance, based on its distinct copper back and shimmering green head and thorax. For most of human history, John reminded us, it was a humble and non-threatening native of Japan, where millennia of evolution alongside natural predators kept it largely in check. Then, sometime in the early part of the 20th century, an unwitting horticulturalist imported some, likely as larvae hitching on the roots of iris bulbs from Japan then making their way to the eastern seaboard of the United States. The journey was by ship, so they had to await the right opportunity to alight and make their new home. Bugs were patient that way.

133

Somewhere in New Jersey, the beetles crawled out of their stowaway and off their plants and found a whole smorgasbord of new American fruits, leaves, and bushes to consume. There were no natural enemies to diminish their numbers. Like many invasive species had done before, and would again, the Japanese beetles multiplied and spread. They devoured the leaves off millions of acres of trees and left behind their telltale mark like the scene of a horrific crime: nothing but bare filaments, just wiry, skeletal remains, once the beetles had chewed up all the spongy green parts and left only the veins behind.

John had read all of this with interest because, now, the journey of the beetles was quite relevant: *Popillia Japonica* presently coated Ba's beloved cherry trees in our backyard. The climes of the East Coast, particularly the warm summers of upstate New York, made for perfect breeding grounds and provided ample food for the pests. Inspecting the branches and leaves more closely, John showed us how in some places, the beetles were several rows thick, scrambling over each other in a fury to reach the edible tree parts, including the tiny cherry fruits still too sour to pick but apparently quite delicious to the beetles.

Ba surveyed the scene with a frown. Last year, after a long, four-year wait for the trees' maturity, and just as they were starting to deliver some real fruit, the Japanese beetles emerged. There had been no build-up. On the first truly warm day of the summer, they appeared quite suddenly. John explained to us that they probably had hatched from the soil beneath the trees and crawled their way up the nearest ones. We had watched as an entire row of trees was decimated, Ba's dream of fresh cherries from his own backyard destroyed chomp by bitter chomp.

The beetles, we also discovered, were quite indestructible. It was easy enough to grab handfuls of them off the branches because they didn't fly away and seemed unconcerned with any potential threat. They were just hungry. At John's suggestion, we threw them into buckets of water, but the beetles merely floated and swam around and did not

134

drown. Fire wasn't really practical, John figured, though Kaiser thought a beetle bonfire would have been very fun to watch. A magnifying glass would cook them, but the process was too cumbersome for general effectiveness. Sprays like Windex, Lysol, and furniture polish, which I tried out in various combinations because I could remain fairly far from the beetles in my attack, did not seem to penetrate their shells.

So we tried freezing them, putting several beetles into a Tupperware container and sealing it tightly, then shutting them all inside the ice box overnight. When we opened it up the next morning, the beetles looked dead, their limbs iced over and discolored. But to our amazement, after the prisoners thawed for a few hours, they began to move again.

"Whoa," said Kaiser, poking one of the beetles that seemed to be resurrecting itself. "It's still alive!"

"That's so creeeeeeeepy," I said. I hated crawly things and said John's collections of them gave me nightmares, with so many ethered and pinned butterflies, moths, spiders, and beetles in small glass paned boxes.

"It makes sense in a climate like this or in Japan," said John thoughtfully. "We could have a warm spring day, followed by an unexpected snowstorm the next. The beetles would have evolved to endure big swings in temperatures. You gotta admire their hardiness."

"So, what's gonna kill these suckers?" asked Kaiser, who was eager to begin the destroying.

Perhaps, John hoped, science would come to the rescue. Weeks earlier, he had shown Ba an ad in the back section of *Popular Science*, a magazine John devoured in his own beetle-like way, leaving nothing but the spine unconsumed. The seller had promised, for just a few dollars, a "foolproof way to destroy the Japanese beetle." His curiosity

135

piqued, and wanting to act preemptively, Ba had sent a check to the address and then patiently awaited the solution.

That solution arrived precisely in time for the beetles' spring reemergence. Ba and John inspected the modest container, wondering what magical device might lay within a package so small. They opened it and discovered two numbered wooden blocks, small enough to fit in each hand. A simple sheet of paper provided a clear and easy two-step set of instructions, which John read aloud.

1) Place beetle on Block 1.

2) Press down with Block 2.

"OH NO!" said Ma. "YOU BEEN TRICK!"

Ba began to laugh. He had indeed been suckered. When John also realized what they had paid for, he began to laugh, too. Then he ran to tell the rest of us, and everyone laughed together a good long while until little Mimi, who had been laughing just as hard with us, finally asked why we were all laughing, which only made us laugh harder. The ad hadn't lied: The method was indeed foolproof for killing the dreaded Japanese beetle!

Ba was undeterred even after being bamboozled. With beetle-killing blocks at the ready, he strode over to the trees, now an inch deep in some parts with bugs, ready to try out the blunt solution for which he had paid ten whole dollars. Ba positioned a block in each hand and, following the instructions, 1) placed a beetle on Block 1, and 2) pressed down with Block 2. The beetle squished flat and fell to the ground. We cheered, and Ba began to clap a bunch of the bugs hard, several at a time. Their bodies began to fall from the branches in large numbers.

"It actually works!" he proclaimed.

We ran to get ladders. Ba cut some hand-sized wooden blocks from his woodworking shop. In ten minutes, the whole family was clapping hundreds of beetles dead, their blocks turning coppery red as if from cherry fruit. Together, we would save the trees. The beetles were not indestructible after all.

Weeks later, Ma penned an essay describing the events from the sucker ad that Ba answered to the joy of seeing her children working alongside their father to save his beloved cherry crop. She sent it off to her editor, who called her back excitedly. How insightful it was! he said, more than once. Ma was flattered but also surprised. What was so great about a story of a family with a beetle problem?

The essay was never meant to become a hit among Chinese nationalists, who nevertheless circulated it widely. They viewed a resurgent, industrialized Japan as a threat to peace and stability in Asia, and many readers had latched onto the "Japanese" descriptor of the beetle. Xiao Xiangpo, Ma's *nom de plume*, apparently had given a vivid portrayal of the bugs' voracious appetite as a sly reference to Japanese imperialism during the Sino-Japanese War. Many readers were stunned by her deft use of metaphor: the two wooden blocks were all that was needed to crush the Japanese invaders! Brute force could repel the Japanese, and there was deep truth to that. In the post-war peacetime, and up until now, no one was willing to challenge the growing threat of Japan, so this felt like a very clever call to arms.

Perhaps, opined some, the twin blocks were the Communists and the Nationalists, who still stared each other down across the Straits of Taiwan, but truly needed to work together to keep their common enemy in check. One "block" was powerless to destroy the Japanese without the aid of the other. Or perhaps, others pointed out rather darkly, the blocks represented the two atomic bombs dropped on Hiroshima and Nagasaki, a show of overwhelming, destructive power, clapping the life out of the Japanese in an instant.

Xiao Xiangpo was amused.

I ONLY WANTING TO WRITE SIMPLE STORY OF HOW BA WAS TRICK IT WITH WOODEN BLOCK, BUT STILL WORKING OUT ANYWAY," Ma said to me decades later. "OTHER PEOPLE LIKE TO SEE OTHER THINGS IN MY STORY. SO THAT UP TO THEM."

But a memory of other pests tickled at her brain, of fields of millions of bloated bugs and legions of determined farmers pushing them towards ditches. It was the same story, with far more dire consequences. The bugs always held the sheer numbers, but the humans had their wits and their fortitude. Sometimes the solutions were decidedly primitive, wooden blocks and deep ditches. They required only coordination and collective resolve, at least as much as the invaders had. That was how you beat bugs at their own game.

Chapter Five

or

"TAKING CREDIT FOR WHAT WOMEN DO"

February 2020
FaceTime Call

> Winter. An overcast morning in New York City. JAY is staring at the bottom of MA's chin because she has again mispositioned her iPhone.

JAY: So I'm going to New Hampshire to knock on doors ahead of the primary.

MA: I REALLY FEELING SORRY FOR DEMOCRAT.

JAY: Yeah, it's been a bad week. But it looks like there are two top contenders coming out of it.

MA: BERNIE SANDER?

JAY: Him and Buttigieg.

MA: HE IS THE VICE PRESIDENT?

JAY: No, that's Biden.

MA: ALL SOUND THE SAME. BIDEN, BERNIE, BUTTI? BIDEN IS THE OLD ONE?

JAY: They're all pretty old, except for Buttigieg. He's the gay one.

A beat.

MA: ANYWAY, SEVENTY IS TOO OLD. THEY WILL BE HAVING HEALTH PROBLEM.

JAY: Bernie already had a heart attack.

MA: AND STILL RUNNING?

JAY: Still running.

MA: I FEEL SORRY FOR DEMOCRAT. HAVING NOBODY GOOD.

JAY: There are some good ones and some annoying ones.

MA: WHAT ABOUT THIS NEW YORK MAYOR?

JAY: Bloomberg?

MA: YEAH BLOOMBERGS. WHY HE SPENDING SO MUCH MONEY FOR? HE NEVER GONNA GET IT.

JAY: Maybe he thinks he can.

MA: RICH MEN ALWAYS CRAZY.

October 1980
Tucson, Arizona

It had been Ma's brainchild, after all, so it seemed only fair that she should host the fundraiser. It would be a historic first: a visit by First Lady Rosalynn Carter to the city of Tucson, with a big donor event for her husband, Jimmy, the soon-to-be re-elected President of the United States, or so Ma insisted. The dinner would be hosted by local Chinese business leaders, including, of course, the Zhangs and the Kuos. The matriarchs of the two clans agreed on at least one thing: Political connections and business went hand in hand, whether in China or America. If you wanted to be taken seriously, you needed to play the game. So, when Ma and some other friends suggested the idea of a fundraiser, her rival Millie Zhang agreed on the spot to co-host.

"We'll do it at the main house," Millie said, referring to their open and airy ranch house. The primary structure, not the guest cottages or club house, she made clear, could be used for overflow if needed. The house had been custom built, all glass and green wood rafters, with tasteful desert motifs and a large open living space that could convert easily into a reception area with cocktail tables and staff.

"YOU DO NOT HAVING TO HAVE AT YOUR HOUSE," said Ma. "I HAPPY TO HOST AT MINE."

"That's so generous of you," said Rebecca Zhang, Millie's daughter-in-law, who wore too much makeup if people were being honest, Ma sometimes noted. "But do you really think a 'suburban' setting is appropriate? It is the First Lady, after all. Your house might feel... cozy."

To Rebecca Zhang, the Kuo home was a place filled with noisy children, dropped down somewhere on the east side of town in a neighborhood filled with Mormons and their own big, noisy families. She'd been there once and never returned. Sure, we Kuos lived nominally inside of a "country club," but to Rebecca's mind, it clearly was "middle class." The Zhang family, by contrast, owned a cotton farm and had landholdings across much of Pima County, and the revenues from that business and those rentals afforded them a grand residence in a "private and secluded" area. They even had their own helicopter and private landing pad, which one absolutely needed, given the "private and secluded" nature of their lives.

"OH, WE HOST MANY PARTY, ESPECIALLY FOR VISITING CHINESE SCHOLAR." Ma said breezily. "HOUSE SET UP PERFECT FOR PARTY."

"But not *catered* parties," Rebecca said, smiling. "Making dumplings together is one thing, but hosting someone like *First Lady Rosalynn Carter* is another. It's not like she's going to sit down and have a bowl of soup dumplings."

Rebecca laughed, her perfect teeth almost too white. Ma was sure she bleached them and avoided tea out of vanity.

"WELL, SHE IS TELEVISION REPORTER," Ma said of Rebecca, making clear that the profession was a lamentable one. Rebecca was rumored to pay over two hundred dollars just to get those bangs cut by someone famous for cutting hair. "CAN YOU BELIEVING? SICKENING!" Ma had remarked.

"We'll hire the caterers, don't worry, Mary," said Millie Zhang, patting her leg reassuringly. "I have a company I use for just such things. You leave the details of the party to me, and you can focus on the more important things. I think I'll even serve my famous pecan pie!"

Ma had never hired caterers, even for her own wedding. The thought of spending thousands of dollars just to pay for people she didn't know to take over the cooking and serving of food in her own house was ludicrous. But the Zhangs were right. It wouldn't do to serve homemade food, or even to bring in food from a restaurant like Gee's Garden, to dozens of well-heeled donors and dignitaries. They were expecting a "first class" experience, and Millie could deliver that. In some ways, Millie was far more American than Ma. She even wore denim and boots when giving tours of her private and secluded property.

"THANK YOU, MILLIE," Ma said graciously. "YOU ALWAYS GIVE BIG RELIEF." Millie Zhang would now get the bragging rights now for having hosted the First Lady in her own home. But that didn't matter, Ma said. "I DOING THIS TO PROVIDE EXPERIENCE FOR YOU PEOPLE," she would tell us kids for decades to come. "TO SHOW YOUR POOR MA IS MORE THAN JUST HOUSEWIFE." Ma could make big things happen, and she wanted us to know. She could even get the attention of someone like the First Lady of America.

"Do you think she talks to the president about his job?" Ma asked Ba in Chinese over dinner, raising the subject of Rosalynn Carter for the fourth time that week. She hoped her children were also paying attention, that this was, in fact, VERY BIG DEAL, and that their mother was VERY INVOLVE.

Ba grunted. "If she wanted to, could he stop her?"

"I'm sure that they are like any couple," Ma said, ignoring the bait and looking at Mimi and me. "MAYBE TELL HER MANY THING. EVERY COUPLE HAVING PILLOW TALK AT NIGHT BEFORE BED, YOU KNOW."

"Maybe you can ask her yourself," said Ba, reaching with his chopsticks for some sliced beef.

Ba had become increasingly dismissive about the "Carter Visit," as Ma had now begun to call it, even though Jimmy Carter clearly would not be in attendance. Ba made no secret that he opposed the idea of local Chinese getting too involved with national or even local politics, deeming it a pointless show of vanity. The people in D.C. were happy to take Chinese money, but did they ever do anything to help us in return? Ba also seemed generally uncomfortable with Ma taking on

143

new roles outside the home. Within a short period of time, after we had moved to Tucson, Ma had earned her real estate license and had dipped her toe into business and now politics. What would be next?

"I wonder if they will allow photographs with the children," Ma said, thinking how wonderful that would be to show us when we were older.

"With how much we are donating, that's the least they should do," said Ba.

As the day approached, Ma grabbed every opportunity to insert us into the schedule and the event. Mimi, just seven years old, would carry and present flowers to Rosalynn Carter. "That would be so cute, don't you think?" she asked Ba, who didn't answer. "And the boys could serve drinks. Wouldn't that be perfect?"

When Rebecca pointed out that children weren't permitted to serve alcohol, Ma put her foot down. "WHO GOING TO STOP THEM, CIA?" she laughed. Rebecca backed down.

On the day of The Carter Visit, it turned out to be a good thing that Ma didn't have to worry about the party, the service, the food, or the drinks. She was nervous enough remembering all these white American guests' names and faces and being an on-point, got-it-together host. The Governor himself, Bruce Babbitt, had come with an entire entourage. He had startled my two brothers during the dinner by sneaking into the guest house where they had gone to escape, taking with them an entire plate of porterhouse steaks, a whole pie, and a gallon jug of Gallo wine. In his remarks, the governor made a point to praise Millie's famous pecan pie.

Some of Ma's friends had remarked privately that they were surprised she wasn't hosting the party at the Kuo house. They'd been to so many wonderful gatherings there, after all. Ma was gracious, saying she had to thank Millie and Rebecca for offering up their home, but she was

144

rather happy to overhear that the food wasn't nearly as good as it would have been at her home. "STEAK, GIANT POTATO, JUG OF RED WINE? ALL FOR CHINESE?" To Ma, this was Chinese people playing at being American.

When the First Lady arrived, she looked a little worn and was unusually quiet, but she did say hello to each of us Kuo children. Ma thought we looked smart in our pressed shirts, ties, and polished dress shoes. Mimi was right on cue with her flowers, though she gave them to the wrong woman at first, before Ma frantically gestured towards Mrs. Carter, who accepted the bouquet with a light smile while the crowd laughed good-naturedly at the mix-up. The much-vaunted family photograph with the First Lady went wonderfully in the end, even if we boys looked a little sullen.

"I think it's going very well," Millie said to Ma. "So far, no big mishaps."

"GOVERNOR SAY HE LOVE YOUR PIE," Ma said, pretty certain Millie didn't make it herself.

"I don't know," Rebecca said, sipping at her red wine and pursing her even redder lips. "Rosalynn doesn't seem that excited."

"*MRS. CARTER*," Ma corrected, "MUST BE SO TIRED."

"It's as if she's just being led around for show and would rather be somewhere else," Rebecca said unhappily.

She would have been much less stiff in a more relaxed environment, Ma told me later. How many of these buttoned-up events must she have to suffer through at each campaign stop?

When it came time for a toast with their honored guest, Ma called me over and fixed my tie, then handed me a platter with two champagne

145

flutes on it. "Can you handle this without spilling the drinks?" she said to me in Chinese, so the waitstaff wouldn't overhear.

"Sure, Ma," I said. But now I couldn't get the idea of spilling champagne all over the First Lady of the United States out of my head.

"Okay, then take two drinks over there to Mrs. Carter," she urged, taking a bottle from one of the servers and pouring both glasses half full. "Go on!"

Ma watched in delight as I approached the most important woman in the country. The Secret Service, as she expected, didn't seem to mind a child approaching her this way. Mrs. Rosalynn Carter looked down and smiled broadly at me as I lifted the tray up with both hands so she could take a glass.

"I have a question for you," I said after she had taken the glass. Mrs. Carter cocked her head. "OH, NO!" Ma later recounted colorfully to others as a key part of our family lore. "WHAT IS JAY SAYING TO HER?"

"Oh? And what is that, young man?" the First Lady asked me.

I blurted out the question I'd had in my head for over a week. "My mom and dad were wondering about you and the president, how you talk to each other. I want to know, do you really share 'pillow talk' with him?"

Ma quickly led me away as Rosalynn Carter tipped her head back and let out a genuine laugh, long and relaxed, probably for the first time in days.

June 2020
FaceTime Call

> Summer. A cloudless, sunny day in New York City. JAY once again stares at his mother's chin, positioned squarely in the center of her phone.

JAY: So we did a fundraiser with George Takei for the Texas Democrats. We raised a lot of money. Like one and a half million dollars, almost.

MA: WOW, SO GREAT.

> Ma's expression reveals that it was really not so great.

MA: ANYWAY, ALL DEMOCRAT EVER DO IS ASK MONEY.

JAY: Ha, that's pretty true.

MA: EVERY DAY, I GETTING EMAIL, EMAIL, EMAIL. GIVE FIVE DOLLAR! GIVE TWENTY DOLLAR! GIVE ONE THOUSAND!

JAY: I get those emails, too.

MA: SAME REQUEST, OVER AND OVER! WHAT FOR? I JUST DELETE, DELETE, DELETE.

JAY: So, do you ever make a contribution?

> A beat.

MA: NO, I EXPECTING YOU TO MAKE CONTRIBUTION, SO I DO NOT MAKING.

March 1984
Tucson, Arizona

The new Chinese ambassador was coming to our house in Tucson. Even days after hearing this news, my grandmother was still marveling at the news.

In the nine years since the death of her husband, Nainai had bounced among her three sons' families, all living in America now. She disliked feeling like a burden to anyone, but she was rather helpless under the circumstances. She had come to the States while Yeye completed his history treatises at American colleges, safe from the mistrustful eyes of the Nationalists, or the Communists for that matter. Both sides had wanted history to shine more favorably upon them through his writings. Then Yeye's heart had suddenly given out, and Nainai found herself suddenly widowed, stranded in the U.S., unable to return to China yet equally unable to function independently in America.

Ever since Washington had normalized relations with Beijing five years earlier, Nainai had talked of going back home to China. Ba had insisted it might one day be possible. In fact, Ma was looking into how to acquire a piece of land in Beijing on which we might build a house for her.

In the meantime, however, Nainai was clearly thankful she had wound up living with us. She had her own room at the far end of the hallway and a bed that could tilt into different positions at the press of a button. Although Tucson was scorching hot and bone dry for much of the year, rendering her passion for gardening moot, our home was large and comfortable. It was air-conditioned American-style year-round by something called a "swamp cooler." There was a bright blue swimming pool with a yellow slide and a "Jacuzzi" spa which she could put her feet into from time to time as we grandchildren shouted and splashed about, loud American rock music blaring through speakers and surely ruining our hearing.

To her experienced eyes, we Kuo kids took for granted everything about our very charmed lives, with such incredible wealth and abundance all around. Food came pre-packaged and could be heated up in a matter of minutes in a "microwave." Water was something you played and swam in, not something you walked for hours to retrieve from a river or well. The family's German shepherd, Wolfgang, barked at sirens at all hours, but the police were there to keep the peace, not rob or extort your family. For all this, Nainai was grateful, but she sometimes told Ma she worried it would fail to prepare us well enough for life's many difficulties.

To the extent Nainai adored our family, she couldn't muster the same for her own children. Ma was far more of a daughter to her than our *gugu*, Nainai's oldest daughter, Qian, ever was. And after a few months of living under my third uncle's roof, with his horrible and selfish wife, Lisa, who berated her nonstop as a useless old woman, Nainai was relieved to be settled in with us.

Over the years, Nainai and Ma had forged a powerful bond, as the older woman gently reassured and guided the younger in her many ambitions. Nainai especially encouraged Ma to write, even through the many years she was "just a housewife" taking care of us four children. Ma had a gift for words, and after publishing her first short story, she went on to establish herself as an accomplished writer, contributing to newspapers and periodicals across Hong Kong, Taiwan, the United States, and eventually mainland China. These days, Ma was also proving herself quite capable as a political organizer, which the impending visit of the ambassador proved to everyone except Ba.

"What do you know about politics?" Ba would ask her. Looking back, I don't think he meant it to be cruel but rather a misguided effort to spare her the humiliation of failure. Perhaps he was trying in his own way to protect her from the inherent dangers that politics carried with it. Nainai had done the same for Yeye long ago.

"I may not know anything, but I can get things done," Ma would respond tersely.

Ba's constant skepticism wore Ma down, but she told me that Nainai had stood up for her, declaring that Ma could do anything she set her mind to. Without Nainai's support, Ma wasn't sure she could have persevered.

"You should support and trust Tanlee in this," Nainai said to Ba.

"Are you her mother or mine?" Ba asked with a laugh, bewildered at being regularly outvoted by the two adult women in his life.

"I am the mother to both of you," Nainai responded. And that was that.

"THAT WAS WHEN I KNEW SHE REALLY ON MY SIDE," Ma told me.

So when Ma announced that the new Chinese Ambassador to the United States, Zhang Wenjin, would be coming to the house for a visit, Ba had been surprised and even grudgingly impressed. But Ma said it didn't surprise Nainai at all. After all, since becoming "politically active," Ma had met the state's governor and the First Lady. And even with the new leader of China, Deng Xiaoping, Ma had somehow charmed her way into a private audience when she visited China in 1978.

The ascendant mainland government appointed and sent Chinese ambassadors around the world now, with Taiwan little more than a political asterisk. And it was a mainland delegation, including the ambassador, which our family was hosting. China was still a developing power, so this was at a time when you could invite Chinese Communist Party dignitaries into your home without drawing the fire of anti-China politicians or the scrutiny of the CIA. Because of Ma, Tucson had started to become an important stop on the itinerary of many officials from China. "You have to visit New York, Washington, Los Angeles, Las Vegas, and Tucson," it was often said. "Tucson? Where is that? And what is there?" others asked. "The best home-cooked meals and hospitality you will find anywhere in America!" was the common claim.

For the visiting Chinese, especially overseas scholars, a family like the Kuos who would open its doors and make guests instantly feel at home—while seamlessly blending American and Chinese food, decor, language, and culture—was truly unique. For years I watched Ma work her magic with so many guests from so many different departments and ministries, yet somehow always remember who was who.

When the day of the ambassador's party finally arrived, the house was ready: spotlessly clean with mountains of homemade food Ma and Nainai had been preparing for days. There was even a small presentation area for a modern dance piece Ma wanted performed. Somehow, she had talked me and Anna, our exchange student from Switzerland, into displaying our school-choreographed piece in honor of His Excellency.

"It's just a piece from dance class," I protested. "It's not meant to be a big, showy thing."

"YOU DON'T WANT TO PLAY PIANO FOR PARTY, SO YOU HAVE TO DO THIS. FOR ME," Ma insisted. She never put together that her son might come off as very "trendy" to the guests in his tights and dance belt.

It occurred to me far later that what Ma was doing by playing host was remarkably consistent with her own upbringing, and she was passing that down to us kids. Both sides of our family, the Kuos and the Lius, had always been adjacent to power in China. My grandparents and their relations were advisors to and confidants of the men in charge, sometimes even secretly supporting factions with money and supplies, always just one step ahead of catastrophe. Ma's parents were politicos within the KMT apparatchik, so it was unsurprising that she had inherited the gifts of charm and gab from them. And Ba's parents were a couple whom powerful men visited to seek Yeye's advice and pay their respects.

"Li Xinyan?" said a voice after Anna's and my miserable *pas de deux* was finally over, followed by polite if somewhat awkward applause. He was addressing Nainai, and she seemed surprised by it. "Ambassador Zhang would like to thank you," he said in Chinese.

Nainai looked confused, her face for a moment betraying her thoughts. Were they speaking to the right person? How did they know her name? In the next moment, a vibrant man was clasping both of her hands, pumping them up and down with vigor. It was the new ambassador himself.

"Li Xinyan, it is such an honor to meet you. I was a great admirer of your husband and an avid reader of his work. Many of us in my generation owe a debt of gratitude toward him and to you. Thank you."

"Do not thank me," Nainai said, smiling broadly. "I did what any woman married to a great man would do. I simply supported him best I could!"

The ambassador's eyes twinkled, and he moved on, led from person to person by Ma, who recalled not only each guest's name but the drollest anecdotes about them or some obscure family relation that

152

tied them in however small a way to the ambassador. By the end of it, they would not be a group of strangers but a closely knit social gathering, with Ma at the center.

I often wondered, but never dared ask Nainai, whether she regretted that all her own years of schooling, including her studies in Germany and her deep book learning, had come to little after the war began and she had a family to take care of and protect. By comparison, Ma had never finished her own degree but could use her remarkable talent and charisma to attract important dignitaries to her circles. Ma once told me that the reason she and Nainai got along so well, the reason she thought of her as more a mother than Laolao had ever been to her, was that she saw in Ma a chance to fulfill her own dreams. Ma was the vessel into which Nainai poured her hopes, wisdom, and experience.

Many women in Nainai's own generation had been literally bound at their feet, a decidedly cruel way for the men to keep them literally in their place. But Ma could do far more than hobble forward. She could run faster than most men could ever hope to.

May 2020
FaceTime Call

> MA is in her living room in Rossmoor, California. JAY is bored at home, now in the third month of a long quarantine in New York City.

MA: DID I EVER SHOWING YOU GIFT I HAVE OF POPE? I HANG UP A SCROLL.

JAY: You have a scroll from the Pope?

153

MA: ACTUALLY, IT YOUR LAOLAO GIFT. GIVE IT TO ME AND YOUR DADDY.

JAY: Why did she have a scroll from the Pope?

MA: I ONLY HEAR ABOUT STORY MUCH LATER AFTER SHE GIVING ME THE PHOTO. THE POPE EVEN SIGN IT! HERE, I SHOW YOU.

JAY: Ma, you have to turn the camera. No, the other way.

MA: CAN YOU SEEING IT?

JAY: No, the other way, Ma. Keep moving—just turn, okay, there. Actually, that's only the left side of it.

MA: CAN YOU SEEING?

JAY: It's fine. I can see half his face.

MA: I DON'T KNOW HOW WORKING THE PHONE. DID IT GET?

JAY: It got half of it. Half of the Pope. But that's cool! He signed it and everything. "To Dr. and Mrs. Jenkai Kuo…" Why isn't it made out to Laolao?

MA: LAOLAO WORRIED DADDY NOT GETTING BAPTIZE, SO SHE GET FREE PASS TO HEAVEN FOR HIM, SO HE CAN JOIN ME AFTER DEAD. I THINK SHE MAKE HIM SIGN IT OVER TO US, GUILT ME SOMEHOW.

JAY: Did it work?

MA: WELL, I HANGING IT UP, DIDN'T I?

December 1961
Rome, Italy

I don't know many of the details of Laolao's triumph in Rome in the early 1960s. What I do know is that she somehow managed to take an entire children's choir from Taiwan to Rome to perform, and she got a surprise audience with the Pope because of it. Ma's various stories filled in some of the details.

The crowds who had gathered for the mass, mostly old Italian faces with their long Roman noses, probably never expected to see an eight-year-old Chinese boy singing in their church, let alone one backed by an entire young Chinese choir.

Uni trinoque Domino Sit sempiterna gloria,

Qui vitam sine termino Nobis donet in patria.

Amen!

Italian women and men alike wiped tears from their eyes. They may have come from half a world away, but the choir of Guangren Elementary sang in the universal language of the Church, and their faith was as strong as any of the devout here.

How far this project had come! When Laolao had declared five years ago to the archbishop that it was her intention to establish a Catholic grade school in Taiwan, he had not taken her seriously, which meant that she was given no church lands or church money to start the school.

"SHE BASICALLY STARTING FROM JUST SCRATCHES," Ma said. I imagined Laolao literally clawing and scratching her way to the Pope's notice.

Without resources, Laolao had gone in search of benefactors, whom she charmed one by one into donating property and modest funds, which she then used to raise even more funds and find even more patrons, promising them everything from plaques on the school walls to keys to Heaven's Gates if they lent their support. The school would be for both boys and girls together, and the children would receive a proper and rigorous Catholic upbringing.

Since her childhood conversion, Laolao had always felt the love and protection of God, whose missionaries had saved her and her family from sickness and damnation, except her sister, who had been traded away to a man before the Word of God could reach her. To atone for her sister's soul, Laolao had devoted herself to saving many more, from the poor girls in the brothels of Nanjing to the children who now attended her school in ever-growing numbers. Part of her success came from her musical training. In Guangren School, the light of God would reach her students through song and verse, Laolao decided. There is no greater bond than music and no holier way to honor the Lord.

Guangren had gained a reputation for being a strict school that taught in the classical style, blending repetition with discipline and European modernity with Confucian tradition. That made it a highly sought admission for the children of Taiwan's upper-class evacuees, who longed to bring order out of the chaos of their flight from the mainland. Since Taiwan's future depended on American protection, a western education made complete sense. Guangren's enrollment grew, along with its faculty. A new building was commissioned and, like many things in Taiwan, hastily built. Laolao filled it with pianos, practice rooms, and choir halls, and she selected only the best students for her elite chorus: pitch-perfect, disciplined, and radiant in their faith.

She unveiled the choir publicly before a packed service as part of the celebration of the new Immaculate Conception Cathedral in Taipei.

156

The children looked like little angels, even down to their meticulously hand-sewn garments. It was important to show what Taiwan could do, even just a dozen years after the end of hostilities.

In attendance was the now considerably less skeptical archbishop, who could not hide his delight. "They are miraculous," he said to Laolao, smiling warmly as he took her arm to walk. "And you! You are miraculous, too. What you have done with the school has earned well-deserved respect."

His praise sounded like an apology to Laolao's ears, and that was just fine. He might have underestimated and rejected her, but now he would have to respect her more.

"Respect is fine, Your Eminence. But financial support is better," Laolao said, cutting past the niceties. "Choirs require instructors, materials, and instruments. None of that comes cheaply."

"Ah, Manxi. I wondered how many steps we could take together before your hand was out for money."

"My hand is out for the *children*," Laolao corrected him.

"Well, let us speak frankly. Surely your husband and his friends can help with some of the funding? I hear he is back home now."

My grandfather had been out from under house arrest just a few months but was keeping a low profile as he rebuilt his connections and base. Laolao knew better than to ask him for help with the school at this time. Besides, these days, with most of their children in exile in America, their lives intersected less and less.

"My husband is a politician," Laolao said, smiling. "And his fortunes are those of a politician, with its many highs and lows. We are currently in the lows."

157

"My condolences," the archbishop said with a knowing smile.

"I hope you are not going to disappoint me again, Your Eminence. Did you know I am planning a trip with the choir?" Laolao asked. "And for this, we will need local church support."

"A trip?" he asked. "Where will you go? Kaohsiung? They would be so inspired by the children there."

"Not to Kaohsiung, not this time. We are going farther. Overseas."

"Overseas!" he exclaimed. "Wherever would you go?"

"To Rome."

The archbishop stopped walking.

"I have written to the Vatican about our work here, how our school has grown along with the number of faithful, and how the choir is a central part of our community. To my amazement, they issued an invitation just last week for later this year. Perhaps Christmas."

"You wrote directly to the Holy See?" the archbishop asked, trying but failing to fully grasp the audacity of this woman. "Why did you not consult my office?"

"Oh, do not fret! I credited you and your office for our success," said Laolao as she began walking again. "Our triumph will be yours as well. This will put Taiwan on the map with Rome."

And that was that. The archbishop had been checkmated, and he agreed to fund the travel.

"She sounds a lot like you," I said to Ma after she told me how Laolao got the Church's support. "Getting him to take the credit."

"MAN ALWAYS LIKE TO TAKING CREDIT FOR WHAT WOMAN DO," Ma remarked.

The choir practiced to perfection for weeks leading up to the trip. Every child's face was held in perfect position, every back straight and upright. There would be no fidgeting, no whispering, no giggling. The Latin would be crisp, not mealy-mouthed. The choir would breathe and move as a single unit. Over and over, Laolao led their rehearsals, noting any error, however slight, and making them begin again until she was satisfied. She held a tasseled toy blade in her hand as she instructed, and she would rap it down suddenly on the railing if she noted any errors, very near to hitting the young hands. The children would jump back but keep singing. No child need ever be struck. It was enough to frighten them.

Even if her own children had turned away from God's light, even if Ma had quit her schooling and rebelled by marrying Ba the prior year, Laolao believed fervently that her children's choir would redeem her.

"LAOLAO THINK SHE FAIL AS MOTHER BUT CAN SUCCEED AS SCHOOL PRINCIPAL. I THINK THAT WHY SHE SO STRICT WITH CHILDREN," Ma explained.

Her daughter may have left the church, but Rome would recognize Laolao's devotion and accomplishments. With perfect performance, those westerners would see how a modern China could lead a new era of faith.

The plane trip to Rome, paid for by the reluctant Archbishop, was tiring and long but thankfully uneventful. Laolao was certain she would lose one or two of the children in the dizzying airports and crowded hotels, but every one of them was always accounted for. Rehearsals were disappointing, but they made steady progress, even if the cheese the children ate on their pizza made them look bloated.

159

Laolao prescribed soup, fruit, and hard bread for the children for the rest of the trip.

On the day of the performance, her choir did not let her down. Laolao could find few faults in the delivery. Perhaps the altos could have been less prominent in the final hymn. Perhaps her star singer could have tilted his head up a fraction more, as she had asked, so that the light would better highlight his ecstatic visage. But Laolao knew no one but herself would notice these details. No one but God, of course.

Afterwards, as the children were being led back to their hostel by the chaperones, and Laolao was busy accepting the heartfelt praise and thanks of the assembled faithful, an official-looking young man approached her.

"You are 'Manxi Song?'" he said in both broken English and worse Chinese.

"Yes, that is who I am," my grandmother responded. She had little occasion to use English but was grateful that she knew just enough to get by.

"Would you please come with me?" he said with relief. But she also detected a bit of nervousness in his voice.

"LAOLAO WAS WORRY SHE GETTING INTO TROUBLE," Ma explained.

Laolao looked over to one of the chaperones. "I'll catch up with you in a bit. Tell the children they did quite adequately, only a few errors which I will discuss with them later." It was important not to ever praise children, she would often say, or the gods might grow jealous and curse them.

"SHE STILL HOLDING OLD SUPERSTITION EVEN THOUGH NOW CATHOLIC MOST HER LIFE," Ma explained with a laugh.

160

Laolao followed the young man back through the office of the church and into a small room, where he bid her take a seat. "Someone will be with you shortly," he said, deliberately remaining vague.

He then left her alone in the room with her thoughts for close to ten minutes. Then the door opened, and Laolao stood up and willed her mouth not to open in shock. A man she recognized instantly as Pope Pius XII shuffled in. She managed a curtsy, then checked quickly to see that her own hands were not shaking. She was surprised to see they were not.

"Sit, sit!" the Pope said. "You have come a long way, and I have not."

The next few minutes were a blur, His Holiness heaping praise upon the choir and talking broadly about the work happening in Taiwan. "An excellent opening of the Cathedral there," she heard him say, and something about building the future of the Church in that part of Asia.

"Money!" Laolao said, suddenly, in English. "Our school, our choir, it needs money. Not enough, right now."

Pope Pius XII smiled. "I shall see what can be done."

And then the audience was over, as suddenly as it had begun. Laolao was embarrassed that she had blurted out her demand, but she barely had time to blush before the younger man who had first found her entered with a souvenir portrait for Laolao. This would be proof that her meeting with the Pope actually had taken place. "What would you like His Most Holy Father to write?"

Laolao thought only for a moment. "Please write it to Dr. Jenkai and Mary Tanlee Kuo," she said. Some day she would give it as a gift to them. It would be a reminder of the faith that Laolao cherished, but her daughter seemed so ready to toss aside. She may not have stayed with the church, but Ma forever would know that her own mother was a capable woman, a woman who had impressed the Pope himself with her choir and earned a private audience with him.

Her daughter might have underestimated and rejected her, but she would have to respect her.

May 2020
Phone call

"LIFE IS SOMETIME VERY STRANGE."

"Good strange or bad strange?"

"SOMETIME YOU THINK YOU KNOW A PERSON, BUT THEN YOU FINDING YOU KNOW NOTHING REALLY ABOUT THEM.

"Are you talking about Ba?"

"YEAH, NO. SOME OF MY FRIEND TURNING OUT NOT WHO I THINK THEY ARE AT ALL".

"Is that a good thing or bad?"

"NOT GOOD OR BAD. JUST STRANGE."

Fall 2003
Beijing, China

"Hello?" answered a man, the same amiable fellow who always answered whenever Ma called.

"Hello, how are you?" said Ma brightly. "May I speak with Chen Meili?"

"Of course, just one moment."

As Ma waited for her friend to pick up, she glanced at a calendar.

"I COULD NOT BELIEVING ALREADY TWENTY YEAR FRIENDSHIP WITH HER. AND STILL, I DON'T KNOW THE BIGGEST THING ABOUT HER!"

The long association began, rather unexpectedly, back in 1983. Chen Meili, who was now a higher-up in China's State Geology Department, had caught wind of Ma's famed hospitality towards visiting Chinese delegations in Tucson. She reached out through a mutual friend and asked if she and her colleagues from the Department could pay Tucson an official visit.

Meili confessed that she had to look up where Tucson was, even though its reputation was well-known among her colleagues in the geology and mining sectors. Arizona was home to some of the U.S.'s most renowned copper experts, and Ma was always ready to help the Chinese navigate the murky waters of American industry and Western-style capitalism, even leading whole groups around town on personal tours of the university and various mining companies based in and around Tucson. Although she knew little to nothing about gems or copper, Ma knew she could provide a vital link between those who did—all in the name of better Sino-U.S. relations and commerce.

Twenty years back, China's place in the world of geology, as in nearly every field, was on the rise but not really yet on the map. Meili had wanted to attend the annual International Gem Show in Tucson, so Ma helped make the arrangements and even put the visiting group up in spare apartments that my parents owned near the University of Arizona. Casa de Kelso was little more than a parking lot surrounding three poorly lit floors of stucco-walled apartments—ones that we boys were often brought in to vacuum, scrub and refresh after a tenant moved out so our parents could save money on cleaners. Ma's offer spared Meili the cost of lodging, and this was a big deal back then. Meili had nearly been in tears because the department had failed to adequately budget for the travel and lodging cost of that week. She took Ma's hands when they met, and she shook them vigorously and with genuine gratitude.

Later, when Meili was in the market for high-quality cutting and polishing equipment for gemstones, it was Ma who helped her procure it and, more importantly, obtain the right permissions to export it to China. It had never occurred to Ma to charge for any of this, which probably made her a poor businesswoman. *We should help people out without expecting anything in return,* Nainai often reminded her.

Meili more than returned the favor years later when Ma was in the market for a plot of land on which to build a house for Nainai, who wanted to return to China in her final years. There was a property for sale right across from the Geology Museum on the West side of Beijing, and Meili even offered to front the cash for sale and took care of all the upfront zoning and title requirements. That alone had saved Ma months of time and much expense. Ten years later, the new "Finance Street" (Beijing's answer to Wall Street) began sending up skyscrapers just a kilometer away. Then the city completed a new subway line and plopped down a station right at the end of the small alleyway where the home stood. The house had become a fixture in the neighborhood that changed rapidly around it. There were regular visitors who all marveled at its Chinese exterior but western interior design. Ba inherited the house from Nainai after she passed away, and by the time we sold it in 2019, right before the pandemic, it was worth 30 times what Ma and Ba had paid to build it.

"Hi, Tanlee!" said Meili, answering the phone. "It's been a while. How come you never call me like you used to? Did I do something wrong?"

"How come *you* never come by the house anymore?" Ma laughed good-naturedly. "We've put in a new atrium since you last stopped by."

"Well, if that's an invitation, I will come by right away. In fact, I'll come by this afternoon! I have something to ask you anyway," Meili said.

"Wonderful," said Ma. "But you don't need to bring fruit again. We have plenty of fruit in the house."

Meili came by the house by bicycle, which she said was far easier than sitting in the back seat of a car stuck in traffic. Despite Ma's admonition, she brought with her a big basket of pears, which Ma by custom protested was too much, too generous, too kind, before accepting it with thanks. They sat in the dining area, enjoying a cup of tea together as old friends.

"We've known each other a very long time," Meili said.

Ma wasn't sure where this was going. "Very long. Tucson was twenty years ago."

"Ah, I still remember 'chimichangas.' And your kindness to us, a poor gemology team. Yet for all the things you have done for me, I've never done anything truly for you."

"You got me the land for this house! Li Xinyan," Ma reminded her, using Nainai's given name, "very much appreciated it while she was still alive."

"I miss seeing her. She was a formidable woman. But this house? That was just a bit of a loan, nothing important. So listen, I have a much bigger project that I'd like you to be a part of. This has been long in the planning, but I am starting a diamond business! It's a private business, so it's not in my capacity with the department. Well, not

165

officially," Meili said with a laugh. "But I got to know a number of the suppliers around the world, and they all agree the market in China is very big. Think of all the people getting married!"

"They all need to show they are getting rich," Ma agreed.

"My new company can open markets for them and get favorable prices wholesale, and with my connections, we can grow the business quickly. And I would love you to own a part of this company. Not as an investor! But as gratitude for all you've done."

Ma smiled and put her hand on Meili's and caught a glint from a large diamond on her finger, a ring too expensive for even the head of the Geology Department to have bought herself.

"PROBABLY A GIFT FROM STATE DIAMOND MINE," Ma assured me.

The hand it decorated was older than the one that had pumped hers in thanks twenty years ago. In those decades, Ma had learned many lessons, and one of them was this: Don't get involved in quasi-governmental companies.

"You are too courteous, Meili," Ma said. "And I am flattered. But I don't need a part of your company. It's exciting enough for me to watch you succeed."

Meili pressed her offer again, and Ma again declined. Meili insisted, but unlike the pears, Ma would not accept. And so, over sliced fruit and tea, they talked about other matters, about how China truly was changing so quickly for anyone to keep up with; how real estate prices were simply unsustainable but would probably still go up because people were so insane nowadays; and how the young people today were worried about things like diamond rings for their nuptial ceremonies, and not about war, revolution, famine or disease like the two of them had been at that age.

That afternoon was one of the last times they saw each other face to face. They spoke by phone a few times more, with Meili's husband always answering the phone whenever Ma called before handing it over to his wife. Then they would chat like old friends again for some time, but the calls were far less frequent than before. Meili became very busy with her new company, Diamonde, which in a short time, became a multibillion-dollar enterprise.

Ma would have been a very rich woman had she accepted a small piece of it that day. But something about how quickly Meili's company grew and commanded market share didn't sit completely right with Ma. Sure, Meili was a very capable and forceful woman, and Ma didn't doubt that she could run a business empire quite well. But still…

A year later, Ma went to visit some friends across the street at the State Geology Department. One of them brought up Meili.

"She doesn't seem to come around to visit as often as she used to," he said.

His colleague laughed. "Well, Chen Meili is probably a bit strapped for time now that she's the wife of the premier."

"Wait. What did you say?" Ma asked.

"The wife of the premier. Don't you know? He was made premier of all China."

"Chen Meili's husband is… the premier?" Ma asked, dumbfounded.

The others looked at Ma with their mouths agape.

"Wait, all this time, you didn't know who her husband was?" her friend asked. "We thought you knew! We were so impressed that you just talked to her like an equal and that she would bike to your house with fruit baskets and flowers to deliver to you."

"She never said anything about her husband! To me, he was always that nice man who answered the phone for her!"

"That nice man is now the premier," he said, and Ma began to laugh, and her friends laughed heartily along with her. Or maybe, a bit at her.

"Tanlee!" one cried. "You surely know how to pass up a golden opportunity!"

Chapter Six

REBELS

or

"MAYBE THEY JUST WANTING ATTENTION"

February 2020
New York City, New York

> JAY and MA are in an Uber, coming back with two of Jay's friends from a seven-course, vegan tasting menu downtown.

MA: HOW MUCH WAS THE DINNER?

JAY: It wasn't bad.

MA: HOW MUCH?

JAY: Don't worry about it, Ma.

MA: NO, I WANT TO KNOW, HOW MUCH YOU PAYING?

JAY: Eighty-nine, a person.

MA: A PERSON? NOT TOTAL!?! FOR THAT LITTLE AMOUNT OF FOOD?

JAY: You said you were totally full. You even asked for a card from the restaurant. You loved it!

MA: I CAN EAT SIX TIMES IN BEIJING FOR THAT PRICE.

JAY: This is New York. Things cost more.

MA: IF I KNOW, I WOULD REFUSE TO GO.

JAY: I'll make sure never to tell you the price again.

MA: HOW MUCH IS MONDAY DINNER GOING TO BE?

JAY: It's a Michelin-star restaurant. You really don't want to know.

MA: I SPEND ALL MY LIFE SPENDING NOTHING, NOT GETTING USED TO SPENDING SO MUCH.

JAY: Ma, eighty-nine dollars isn't bad. This was a seven-course tasting menu.

MA: YES. SEVEN COURSE OF VEGETABLE.

October 2017
New York, New York

We had all been meat lovers. Ba, having grown up in deprivation, raised his own family in America with a decidedly western level of animal proteins, which were always front and center. He used to buy fresh milk from a local dairy near our house in upstate New York, so creamy and rich that a layer of milk solids would form at the top of each bottle. Mimi, as the youngest, had the privilege of eating the buttery tab with a spoon, her upper lip painted white long before the "Got Milk?" ads. We would guzzle whole glasses of full-fat goodness before each meal so that we would grow big-boned and tall. Ma fretted with each chug that we were ruining our appetite, but we still cleared every bit of food in our bowls.

170

After we moved to Tucson, Ba went full cowboy on us. Nearly every Sunday, he would cook steaks: huge T-bones that he coated with garlic, salt, and pepper, then barbecued out on our patio, which he'd fitted with a 60,000 BTU gas burner and a fan strong enough to suck up small, unwary children. He would sometimes stand before the massive burner for hours, turning and drying pork shreddings in a gigantic wok fit for a banquet hall restaurant. The pork fibers were perfect for loading up a bowl of *xifan*—what westerners call congee. To this, we'd add pickled salty vegetables and red chili sauce. The hotter, the manlier in Ba's eyes, the combination creating a high-fat, high-glycemic, high-sodium but quite delectable breakfast.

Some cultures measure masculine prowess by how many shots or beers a man can drink, but for us, it was how much red pepper sauce you added to your rice. I came back from college one holiday, and Ba observed with interest as I heaped two spoonfuls of chili paste into my bowl, mixing it in vigorously so that every bite would be fiery hot. Ba nodded and grunted, his way of showing approval for both my maturity and courage.

Ma went along with the meat indulgences, happily cooking gigantic Costco family packs of chicken drumsticks that Ba brought back and threw into a giant freezer. Ba's love of Costco, especially its meat selection, was legendary. When we were living in Nainai's old house in Beijing in the 1990s, a long-anticipated Costco finally opened in the city, and Ba was so excited that he finally bought a new Jeep just so he could haul the big-box food items we would be purchasing.

When I was in grade school, Ma would take five-pound trays of Costco chicken legs and, in a distinctive nod to Chinese-Americanness, dredge them in soy sauce and milk, then coat them with crushed Corn Flakes before throwing them in the oven, where the fatty skin would crisp up. She would brag to her friends that I could eat eight of those legs in a single sitting and seem disappointed

171

if I ever sat down for less. To Ba and Ma, we were in a wealthy country now, with abundant food and fat, happy people.

Ba had suffered his first heart attack at age 47, which should have resulted in a radical change in diet, but the logical connection between what we ate and what was in our blood vessels wasn't strong back then. My brother John and I were both diagnosed with hypertension and high cholesterol in our 30s, which we treated with the latest prescription blood thinners and statins. Ba went through a triple bypass surgery in the late 1990s, which bought him another fifteen years of unhealthy eating. After he died of complications from heart disease, like his father had before him, I began to presume a shortened timeline on my own life due to my own considerably questionable vascular health. I tried to exercise regularly, especially after Ma had specifically called me out on my weight when I'd visited her in China.

"HOW COME YOU BELLY DO THAT?" she asked as she set a steaming plate of pork dumplings in front of me.

"Um, do what?" I asked, sitting up straight and trying to suck in my gut.

"HANGING LIKE THAT OVER YOUR BELT. IT NEVER DO THAT BEFORE. YOU GETTING FAT."

"Yeah, I've put on a little extra lately, I guess."

"I THOUGHT YOU EXERCISE."

"I do," I said defensively. "I even pay a trainer to keep me in shape."

"YOU WASTING MONEY THEN," Ma said. I felt my stomach from the front and sides and realized she was probably right.

"SO, HOW MANY DUMPLING YOU WANT? TEN?"

"I thought you said I was fat! I shouldn't eat ten."

"YOU DON'T LIKE IT?"

"Ma!"

Right before I turned 50, some routine blood work came back and set alarm bells ringing. My triglycerides had soared above 1000, so off the charts as to be unreadable. Ba and Yeye had both died of heart-related maladies, and I figured I was just genetically prone to such problems. The doctor switched up my meds a few times without notable improvement and with me only gaining more weight and registering ever higher blood pressure. I was ready to just feel sorry for myself and concede I would go Ba's route—heart attacks, bypass surgery, stents, then ultimately fatal heart disease.

That was when my sister Mimi reached out.

"So don't hate me, but I'm sending you a book," she emailed. "It's got a morbid title, so ignore that." Mimi and her husband Aaron had already gone "plant-based" in their diets, which was admirable and predictably on-brand for them, given the yoga, meditation, and acupuncture that defined their lives and careers. But I wasn't at all ready for a life without burgers, fried chicken, and sausage, so I was skeptical and still a little pissed off at the universe.

Mimi's book—she was right, "How Not To Die" was pretty morbid—suggested that if we ate more like our ancestors, our bodies would thank us. My own ancestors had evolved over millennia eating meat only occasionally in China's famous "green zone," getting their nutrition mostly from grains, beans, and vegetables. I read the book cover to cover in one night and made a bold pledge to honor my genetic roots and go strictly vegan, just to see what happened. It was my middle finger to Fate.

The first thing that happened was Ma. When I broke the news, it was as if I had declared open war.

"Ma, did you ever think your two youngest kids would become vegans?"

"BAAAAH!"

"Is that a no?"

"WELL…"

"Well?"

"…"

"…"

"IT A GOOD THING YOUR DADDY NOT HERE TO FINDING OUT."

Ma had a hard time understanding what was and was not part of my new diet. When out with her at a restaurant, she would try very hard to be "helpful" but really was being passive-aggressive, as if I would starve without her guidance.

"WHY DON'T YOU EAT THE MUSHROOM PIZZA?"

"It has cheese on it. I don't eat dairy now."

"NO CHEESE? CHEESE IS OK."

"No, cheese and I aren't a thing anymore. Not if I want to live."

"YOU GONNA LIVE TILL ONE HUNDRED."

"I might if I don't eat cheese."

"HOW ABOUT THE POTATO DISH?"

"It's pretty smothered in butter."

"NO BUTTER?! WHY?"

I didn't want to explain to her all the inflammatory consequences of dairy on the ancestrally Chinese gut and microbiome or how suddenly I seemed to be cured of the acid reflux and lethargy that had plagued me my whole life.

My best friends and my roommates, witnessing my sudden weight loss and health transformation in real-time and genuinely impressed by my dedication, decided they would go plants-only in solidarity. We began joking about how far we had likely fallen in the eyes of our fellow gays in New York City. Four years ago, it was, "You see those guys over there? They own that condo with the crazy hot tub party after-hours in Hell's Kitchen." Today it was, "You see those guys over there? Those are those gay vegans who live with their dogs in Harlem."

But we welcomed the change.

Despite my rapidly improving blood panels, Ma remained convinced that the new diet posed a big risk to my health and that she could curb my rebellion by stepping up her attacks.

"I DON'T BELIEVE EAT NO MEAT IS REALLY GOOD FOR YOU," Ma said.

"Actually," I said with my *I know things* voice, "it can be really good for you if you are prone to heart disease like I am." Let her try and guess which side of the family I blamed for my being prone to disease, I thought.

"HOW ABOUT FISH? THAT IS NOT MEAT," she asked me over the phone.

"Ma, I'm trying to cut out all animal proteins, at least for now, including fish. Plus, fish are in danger from overfishing, and some of the bigger fish have high levels of mercury."

"YOU CAN EATING FARM FISH. ALL FISH IN CHINA FARM NOW," she said with some pride.

"Those fish are probably full of antibiotics and all kinds of nasty stuff."

I could picture Ma scowling on the other end of the line, instinctively disliking any criticism of Chinese progress, even its suspect industrial fisheries. "ANYWAY, NOT EATING MEAT NOT HEALTHY," she said for the tenth time.

For decades, Ma had made a point of constantly complaining that my brother, John, was too fat, using every chance to needle him about it, even in front of his own children. But now that I was a healthier weight, she worried my sister and I were going too far the other way. When it was just Mimi being the mindful earth goddess, that was one thing. With me going over to the green side, Ma felt outgunned and outmaneuvered.

Ma took it out on us at every opportunity. When Mimi showed Ma her new Facebook profile picture, Ma looked at it critically. "YOU HAVE MORE LINES ON YOUR FACE. YOU LOSS TOO MUCH WEIGHT." She no doubt thought the way to convince Mimi out of her diet was to link it to vanity, which was, of course, the exact way not to persuade my enlightened sister.

"YOU MAKE TOO MANY CHANGE TO YOUR DIET," Ma would say to her.

"I just feel better not eating any meat," Mimi would respond.

"YOU DON'T GET ENOUGH NUTRITIONS."

"I actually feel great, with more energy."

"WELL, YOUR SKIN LOOK TERRIBLE."

Mimi would just laugh, and we'd exchange little "typing" gestures that meant, "This is so going on Facebook." When Mimi and I visited Ma together, she would soon launch into our disrespectful and dangerous dietary practices, as if we did nothing but nibble on grass and lettuce all day just to make her worry.

"HOW YOU GETTING ENOUGH NUTRITION?" she demanded.

Before I could get testy, Mimi interjected. "You know, there are six grams of protein in a slice of sourdough bread!" Her husband Aaron had become quite the sourdough expert, even going on later to create, in full earnestness, a meditation and sourdough bread-making class with Mimi aptly called "Awake and Bake."

"If you think about it, the cows are eating just plants, and they are getting plenty of protein," I added, shamelessly borrowing a talking point I'd picked up from some Netflix special on vegetarianism.

"YOU KNOW THE INDIAN PEOPLE?" Ma asked, ready with her coup de grace. Mimi and I looked at each other, suppressing a WTF laugh. "MANY ARE VEGETARIAN."

"Right…" I said. "See? A billion Indians can't be wrong!"

Ma looked at us sharply, her eyes carrying a dire warning.

"THEY ALL DIE EARLY."

We didn't bother to fact-check Ma on these things she had seen or read on the Internet. While we were visiting Taiwan for my cousin's wedding, and Mimi and I now had to be "specially accommodated" at every meal, Ma tried the vanity argument on me, given her certainty that I was far more sensitive about my looks than any of her other children. She was, of course, correct.

"I THINK YOU LOSE ENOUGH WEIGHT," Ma declared, looking around for support. "CAN STOP NOW. BEFORE LOOKING UNHEALTHY."

"Stop?" I said, also looking around for support.

"YEAH, YOU CAN START EAT MEAT AGAIN." Ma smiled and nodded as if the decision had been final.

John came to my rescue. "Ma, he's doing it for his health."

"YOU EAT SEAFOOD?" she demanded once again. By this point, I knew she knew the answer but was just making her own points to establish a clear record.

"No, Ma, you know I don't eat seafood when I can help it," I said. Mimi barely suppressed a smile.

"OKAY, YOU CAN STOP, THOUGH," Ma said, looking annoyed. "LOSE ENOUGH WEIGHT. YOU NEED SOME FAT, OR YOUR FACE LOOK TOO THIN." She delivered a pointed look.

Despite Ma's best efforts to derail us, neither my sister nor I went back to eating meat, and soon we had reinforcements. John's daughters decided on their own to go pescatarian, and so John cut out land-based animals from most of his home cooking. Very rapidly, there were as many meat-avoiding Kuos as there were meat-devouring ones. Ma made a point of how inconvenient this made things like ordering at restaurants and cooking meals for the family, and she had become an expert in turning our bizarre choices into her burden.

With a bit of distance, I now understand that Ma took our rebellion against meat personally. She saw it as an implicit rejection of the way we were nourished and fed by her as children, and she didn't like the implication. If eating animal proteins was killing us, then by extension, the food Ma had made and served us all our lives was suspect, too. Maybe she was even to blame for Ba's poor health.

To counter this, my conversations with Ma started including how none of us knew "back then" how bad meat and milk were for us and that American housewives had been told by the "bad" U.S. Government that milk was healthy for their kids, but this was just a cynical ploy to prop up the dairy industry. This narrative had the added benefit of being completely true, as far as I was concerned, and it put Ma in the camp of "lied to" rather than "killed her husband and her own children slowly."

Over time, as she had with my sexuality and my choice to live in a predominantly "PEOPLE WITH COLOR" neighborhood, Ma began to adapt. When we went out to Chinese restaurants, she had begun seating Mimi and my nieces with me on one side of the table and loudly proclaimed that *this* side only ate vegetables, so they had better have some good options for them with no meat in the dishes. *Not even egg.*

I even started to detect a note of pride.

October 1946
Nanjing, China

Ma was just a girl coming home from school when she saw a woman she didn't recognize standing before the Liu family gate. The figure

179

was nearly hidden in the shadows, as if she didn't want to draw any attention. The lady was attractive, but she seemed anxious, her hands moving nervously, as if they held back secrets. She appeared to be waiting for Ma, but that was impossible. Ma had never seen her before. The woman beckoned anyway.

"You are Tanlee," the woman said. It was not asked as a question, but Ma nodded. "I need you to do something very important. You are old enough now to do important things." Again, not a question, but Ma nodded again.

She was only eight years old then, but she felt she had already done important things. The summer before, her father, drunk from the news of victory over Japan, had addressed a crowd of twenty thousand people from their hometown. Everyone had gathered in the main town square to celebrate the surrender of the Japanese imperial army. Over cheers, her father had spontaneously pulled Ma onto the stage. "This is my daughter!" he cried, his breath stinking of corn liquor. "She will now say a few words on behalf of the youth of China!" He urged her toward the front of the stage.

Ma loved telling this story. "I DIDN'T KNOW WHAT TO SAYING. SO MANY PEOPLE ALL WAITING FOR ME TO SPEAK! CAN YOU BELIEVING?"

But as Ma looked out over the exuberant and hopeful faces, she knew what they wanted to hear. "I may be little, but I am powerful!" she shouted, using the same "politician's voice" she had heard her father deploy often. "Just like those two little bombs. They were little, but they were powerful! It just took two little bombs to destroy the whole empire of Japan!"

The crowd roared back its approval. "Little hero!" they cried.

So Ma was really not too surprised that someone else, even a stranger, would ask her now to do another important thing. Perhaps she would

180

begin to live a life now of doing important things. Wasn't that what heroes did?

"Take this to your San Shushu," the woman said, meaning Ma's third uncle. She pressed a letter into Ma's tiny hand. "Say that it is from Auntie Wang. Speak to no one else."

How easy! Ma thought. Give a letter to San Shushu, that was all? The woman turned to leave, then paused, smiling. But her eyes betrayed her worry. "Thank you for your help. This is a pressing matter, and you are very brave."

Brave? What could the letter say, Ma wondered after returning inside, that she might be called brave for delivering it? She flipped it around in her hands and saw that it was sealed. No way to know without breaking trust.

"I DID NOT KNOW THAT LETTER HELP CHANGING WHOLE WAR IN NORTH PART OF COUNTRY."

"What do you mean?" I asked.

Ma continued.

San Shushu was in his study, smelling of pipe and sandalwood. Ma murmured a greeting to him, and he peered up from some papers, his flashing eyes glinting through the smoke like a movie star. The rumors in hallways and servants' quarters were that Third Uncle was a Communist sympathizer. Or Second Uncle was, and Third Uncle was a double agent. There were those pamphlets someone found. The servants overheard strongly worded arguments with her father. He's with the Red Army, the maids whispered when they thought Ma wasn't anywhere about.

"This is from Auntie Wang," said Ma. "She said…"

181

"Give it here," San Shushu said brusquely. Ma handed over the letter, the seal on top unbroken to show she hadn't peeked. She backed away, pivoting to go. "Stay," he grunted. She stood very still while he finished reading the letter.

Ten thousand moments passed. Finally, he looked up, regarding her the way the cat does a cricket. She forgot to breathe.

"Are you courageous of heart, Tanlee?" San Shushu asked, squinting at her as if peering into her soul. "I think you are."

"I am courageous to the point of being a fool," Ma said, smiling. "That's what mother says. I do things even the boys won't do."

"Like what?" he asked good-naturedly.

"Like eat live tadpoles!" she answered.

He chuckled. "Well! That is unusual and alarming. What a rebellious girl. That is courageous and foolish. You are a smart little thing, aren't you."

Ma crossed her arms. What a thing to say! "Father says I'm too smart for my own good. I don't think mother agrees, though." Ma tipped her head at him, challenging him to make sense of that.

"Oh, but you are a clever girl, answering without answering!" San Shushu puffed on his pipe, his eyes now merry and twinkling. She waited for his next words, which surely were the point of all of this.

"Tanlee, you know what a chop is."

Again, not a question, but she nodded, feeling the air grow thicker in the room.

"You know where our family keeps one. You have seen where your mother keeps it." Confirming, not asking. Was this how important people spoke to each other?

"Of course," Ma said, then instantly regretted her certainty. The family chop wasn't spoken of lightly. It was unique to each household or company by design. With a chop, you could make a seal, and with a seal, a document became official. A contract became binding. A debt might be forgiven or enforced. San Shushu was asking about a powerful thing, and it made Ma feel both nervous and important.

"I need you to bring it to me."

"Why?" she asked too quickly.

"No reason," San Shushu said merrily. "I only want to see what it looks like."

"I don't believe you. You know what it looks like," Ma said, rolling her eyes.

"I need a reminder. Just for a few minutes, no longer. But do not be seen. This can be our secret."

Ma liked this game, and she appreciated that she was being lied to. It made her feel underestimated, which suited her fine. Her mother, my *laolao*, kept many secrets, so this would be hers. San Shushu was so mysterious and very often sad or withdrawn. He had a good heart, she could tell. Not like her other uncles and not even like her father. San Shushu spoke to the servants like they were his friends, not his staff. Still, he always had troubled thoughts behind those glinting eyes. This conspiracy might cheer him. Ma thought about all the questions she had for him that he might now be willing to answer, given that she was helping him "steal a look" at the chop.

"I ALWAYS KNOWING WHERE LAOLAO KEEPING IT. SHE
THINK SHE HIDE IT WELL, BUT IT SO OBVIOUS."

The chop lay half hidden in her mother's locked dresser, beneath
brushes and clips and perfumes, where only handmaidens might ever
find it, but they would never dare touch it. Laolao had taken to keeping
the chop in a locked drawer, proclaiming that her irresponsible
husband would have to get her sign-off first on any of his ridiculous
notions. The key was in another drawer, no obstacle if you know
where to look.

Courageous to the point of being a fool, Ma thought as she located the
key and opened the other drawer with it.

The chop was heavy, with dried red ink flecked on carved stone. Ma
tucked it into her pocket, feeling the weight of it swinging as she
moved through the halls, slipping past scullery girls still dusted with
flour from hours of pulling noodles in the kitchens. No one paid her
any notice, which was how she preferred it. Her mother really ought
to hide things better.

In minutes, she was back before San Shushu, handing the chop to him
as if it were nothing. He put his fingers to his lips and whispered,
"Well done, Tanlee. I will look at this now in private. And you can
pick it up from me before dinner. No one saw you."

"No one saw me," she said.

"I DID NOT LEARN WHAT HAPPENED UNTIL OVER FIFTY
YEAR LATER!"

It was a Liu family gathering, the largest ever in the forty-eight years since liberation. Ma sat across the table from San Shushu, looking at those eyes once again, now gray-blue from age, the same eyes that once peered down with interest at her five decades ago. The politics of their family were still as divisive as in those early years, Ma discovered, as he recounted her theft of the chop that day.

"What you did that day, Tanlee, was a great thing. It saved many lives," said San Shushu, his voice hoarse from years of smoking and now barely audible.

Ma had seen and done many things since that day, some of them great, but this revelation left her dumbfounded. Saved lives? San Shushu began to explain.

The rumors of his Communist sympathies were fully true, and his ties deeper than anyone had guessed. Her brief theft of the chop was the reason a whole warehouse full of rice and grain was diverted to the Communists in the north on orders from the wholesalers themselves, as authorized by the Liu family's official seal. Without that food, the young party leadership would have starved that winter. Ma's act of chop stealing may have changed the course of the war. When the subject of Auntie Wang's involvement arose, the room grew heated.

"Shame on you!" San Shushu's wife cried, drawing a sharp finger across her cheek and flicking it at him. "Shame on you, shame on you!"

"Shame on me?" he cried. "Shame on you! You nearly had me killed!"

It turned out that Auntie Wang, the woman who had asked Ma to deliver the fateful letter, had been San Shushu's mistress. His wife had reported both the diversion of grain and the ensuing long disappearance of her husband, who had followed his heart south to Guangzhou alongside Auntie Wang. They were two ardent revolutionaries in love with the cause and with each other. Arrests had been made, and then strings pulled to free them.

But San Shushu had one more favor to ask Ma, even as his wife cried "shame" about the unforgiven past. "This Missus Wang," he said to Ma. "I hear she may still be alive and in Beijing. You have connections, Tanlee. You know people at the universities. Can you find her for me?"

Decades ago, there had been a letter, you see, from a young Auntie Wang to Third Uncle, five desperate pages long, a profession of love that he could not shake, and she had sworn she would never abandon him. Despite this vow, the war had separated them, and in time she had met and long since married someone else, and he had stayed with his own wife, though she had grown more ashamed of him with each scandalous revelation. San Shushu needed to know if Auntie Wang still loved him, though he was now an old man and she an old woman.

"You can do this for me," said San Shushu.

Again, not a question. Without saying more, Tanlee closed her eyes and nodded. She would do this one last important thing for him.

Ma found Auntie Wang, but she would never tell me what she said about San Shushu or their lost love.

August 1937
Nanjing, China

"Why are you following me?" Laolao asked, swiveling to glare at the man standing several feet behind her. Her right hand rested on her sword pommel, ready to draw it if necessary. It was her father's blade,

186

but she had taken it to strap around her waist whenever she went into the "entertainment district" in Nanjing. She had already beaten back one assailant and would not hesitate to use it again.

"Ah! I meant no disrespect, Manxi. It is Liu Jingjian!" My grandfather, whom we called Waigong, was persistent.

Laolao glowered at him. "What do you want?" she asked, putting her sword back in its sheath. Waigong had courted her for many months now, taking her clear "no" as some kind of further invitation.

"Today, he would be considered a creep," I said to Ma.

"HE JUST CANNOT KEEP HIS EYE OFF OF HER," Ma said. "WAIGONG KIND OF ROMANTIC."

"Waigong was kind of a stalker."

Admittedly, Laolao would have been a bit disappointed if he'd given up so easily. Waigong was striking, tall, and charming, and she caught herself sometimes thinking about him. Laolao suspected that a dandy like him might see her as little more than a prize to win. She needed to keep a safe distance.

"I only want to know what you… what you, uh… what you do, coming so often to this part of town by yourself. This is not a place for women of good character as yourself," he added.

"And yet, you seem to know these streets well enough to follow me," Laolao quipped.

"You are hard to miss!" Waigong parried. "With your hair and those tall boots and your western-style dresses. Just like that first day, I saw you at your uncle's house."

187

"When you came to beg him for a job. I remember," she said. "That was two years ago. Are you still mooning over girls like a teenage boy?"

"A vision you were, riding up sidesaddle on that horse as if you were in the movies!"

"I *was* in the movies," Laolao said, correcting him.

"And I have seen every one of them," Waigong said without pausing. "That is why you turn every head wherever you go, causing men to fall over themselves and into big piles when they see you."

That is because men are fools and pigs, Laolao thought. *Thinking with their eyes, leading with their groins.* This man was no different, she wagered. She knew what the other men in town called her: "Mount Everest" charitably because she was tall, though more likely because of her ample bosom, which Waigong's eyes kept dropping down to appreciate.

"Don't be ridiculous," Laolao said, dismissing his absurd hyperbole. He certainly was a persistent suitor and had a remarkable ability to charm. She raised her guard further.

"I need only follow the trail of bodies left in your wake," he sang, gesturing to imaginary throngs with a smile she could neither forget nor fully trust. "And that is how I have found you here."

"So you were spying on me," Laolao said, turning back around and walking farther into the district. "That is not how you win my trust."

"I was worried! What under heaven is Manxi doing by herself, going about to houses of less-than-noble repute?"

"When a man does this, no one questions what he is doing," she said, trying to put some distance between them, but he kept pace and continued his good-natured banter.

"A fair point! But you are a woman, and so am I right to question, no?"

"You are not my father, you are not my uncle, and heaven spare me. You are not and will never be my husband, so your concern carries no weight."

"Come have dinner with me!" he said, as if announcing to the world.

"Go away!" Laolao laughed. "I have important work to do."

"Work? You are here working?"

"God's work, yes, if you must know," Laolao said, as she arrived at her first stop. "And my work is for the good of the Republic. Now, it has been nice to see you, but I must go inside now." Laolao knocked on the door.

"There is the matter of my dinner invitation," Waigong said, bowing low. "We can try French food and American jazz music! Nanjing is very cosmopolitan these days."

"I haven't an interest in those," Laolao said, but she wondered what French food was like. She still ate all her meals at the dormitory or at home.

"Then American food and French music!" Waigong said. "Though, this would be a poor pairing, as neither is renowned." He always spoke as if he was on stage, as if life was a play and he were a hired actor.

189

"Manxi!" said a woman's voice from the doorway. "We are so happy you've come again! We've been practicing!"

"Oh, yes," said another woman excitedly, pushing toward the front, where there were now several girls gathered. They were entertainers for hire, girls who sang and kept men "company" for a fee. There were strict limits to how comfortable the men could get with them, but who enforced these rules, Laolao wasn't sure.

"Wait," I said, a bit confused. "Laolao went to… a brothel? To work?"

"WELL, IT NOT REALLY BROTHEL. MORE LIKE PLACE FOR MAN TO GETTING COMPANY."

"That's a brothel."

"SOMETIME THEY ONLY WANT SINGING WITH WOMEN. BRING THEM TEA, SING FOR THEM."

"Oh, Ma, did Laolao tell you that?"

"SHE GOING TO SAVE THE GIRL FROM BECOMING MORE PROSTITUTE. THEY LOVING HER SO MUCH, EVEN WRITING LOVE LETTER TO HER THANKING HER!"

"Love letters, like lesbian love letters?"

"I NEVER SEE THEM, ONLY HEAR HER FRIEND TELL ME ABOUT THEM. LAOLAO EMBARRASS ABOUT THEM BUT DID NOT THROW AWAY UNTIL MUCH LATER. SO MANY LOVE LETTER!"

"We know *Ave Maria* and the national anthem by heart!" said one of the girls.

"Is this your boyfriend?" giggled one of the women, as they strained to get a look at Jingjian.

"No!" Laolao said a bit too sharply. "He is… an acquaintance of my uncle. A soldier."

"He's very handsome," the girl said. "You would make a very fine pair."

"Do you hear that?" Waigong cried. "They even say so! Now, what is this that Manxi is teaching you?"

"Do not pry," Laolao said.

"Music!" cried the excited girl in front. "She is teaching us how to read and sing music."

"And how to uplift our souls in praise of our Father," said another. "Manxi is very pious, and we all wish we were as devoted as she."

"Ah, so she comes down here, working hard to save your souls! How extraordinary. How revolutionary!" he exclaimed.

"I am no revolutionary," Laolao said curtly. "I am a humble servant. Of the Lord."

"If not revolutionary, then positively rebellious," he said. "I see how it drives your intentions. And you are anything but humble."

"No one else ever thinks about us singer girls," said the girl, coming to Laolao's defense. "We are nobody in society. Most of us don't even have families. But Manxi does not care about such things. She says we can be good citizens of the Republic, too. She says that God will judge us by the sturdiness of our hearts and not for working here, as we must."

There were so many adoring singer girls that Laolao could almost form her own school if only she had the resources and support of the local government. One day, she thought, she *would* open such a school. And she would admit girls because no one else will. The singers yearned for as much lesson time as Laolao could manage, split as her attention was among many such establishments. She also knew these young women needed direction, faith, and discipline.

"Let's not bore him with the details of our lessons," Laolao said. "Let's get to work. Liu Jingjian, thank you for walking me here."

"Of course. But, oh, you haven't answered my question."

"Your question?" Laolao said, genuinely perplexed.

"I have invited you to dinner."

Laolao met his gaze straight on. "Mother has the final say over whether I may spend time alone with any man, and I can already assure you, she would not approve of you. Come back and ask me again when you have a proper rank and title. I cannot even ask her if you are nothing but a pup following behind me."

Laolao turned and strode into the club through its back door, her students already warming up their voices. My grandfather stood dumbstruck, smiling idiotically as, after a few minutes, he heard the national anthem of the Republic, uplifted by voices trained to please men, now being taught to please God and country.

Positively rebellious! he thought, soaking in the raw, kinetic feeling of being hopelessly in love.

January 2021
Rossmoor, California

> MA stands up with great effort, leaning on her walker. Her health has deteriorated noticeably through the pandemic. Even when upright, she remains nearly half bent over, her back unable to bear the weight.

MA: IS MY PHONE RING?

JAY: No, it's mine. Don't worry about it.

MA: YOUR PHONE?

JAY: It's a number I don't recognize.

MA: YOU NO ANSWER?

JAY: Not if I don't recognize it. It's probably someone pretending to be the Chinese Consulate again.

MA: CHINESE GOVERNMENT CALL?

JAY: No, it's a scammer trying to pretend they're the Chinese government. If anyone ever calls you saying they're from the Chinese Consulate, just ignore them.

MA: NO I NOT RESPONDING! DON'T WORRY! ANYWAY, SO NICE TO HAVING SON LOOKING OUT FOR OLD LADY.

> A beat. MA sits back down carefully.

MA: I GUESS I AM LUCKY MA. EVERYONE IS TURNING OUT OKAY. NOT LIKE MY FAMILY OR YOUR FATHER FAMILY.

JAY: Yeah, they're both kind of a mess.

MA: MIMI CALL ME EVERY DAY. STILL VERY CLOSE! NOT LIKE YOUR NAINAI IN THE END, ONLY FIGHTING WITH YOUR GUGU. SCWEAM SCWEAM, ALL THE TIME!

JAY: I'm glad I wasn't in Beijing for that.

MA: SO SAD. ESPECIALLY AFTER BEING SEPARATE FOR SO LONG. I THINK YOU NAINAI NEVER FORGIVE HER DAUGHTER.

November 1948
Beijing, China

"Come with me!" Yeye cried over the noise of the propeller. His daughter, my *gugu,* Qian, had agreed to meet him at the airport in Beiping, later known as Beijing, but had clearly not expected to leave that day by way of a private plane.

Gugu had been studying at Beijing University, having earned a place there through her examination scores without any help from her well-connected father, the renowned professor of history. Her leftist sympathies had led her to join her more radicalized classmates, who saw socialist revolution as the only viable path forward. "How else would China ever be rid of its feudal past, its warlord present, and all the foreign powers who pulled their puppet strings from afar?" she so often demanded to know. What her politics lacked in nuance, they made up for in passion, Yeye said of her.

He had encouraged Gugu's love of books and writing, and he was terribly proud of what she had already accomplished. His daughter was proof that women were rising up in China and that they might one day have an equal say in Chinese affairs and society, perhaps even within his lifetime. That may have been naive, but it was his honest hope, and that hope now had a symbol in his headstrong daughter. That stubborn intelligence he had cultivated, however, had led her to extreme positions backed by a dangerous certitude. She was now an active member of the Communist resistance, and that meant a giant chasm had opened up between Gugu and the family. The gulf seemed greatest between Nainai and her. Gugu believed the housework her mother did was beneath an educated woman like her. Perhaps in this, she was correct, but what was a woman to do?

Gugu stood by the door of the small, squat building that passed for the Beiping airport, the rain forcing her back to the awning. Or perhaps she held back because of the roar of the propellers, which sounded angry and impatient. The Communists were advancing on the city, and the plane's pilot refused to wait much longer to take off. The final push to take the city was on. Should it fall, the entire north would be in the hands of the rebels.

This seemed an inevitability now. The disarray of the Nationalist forces was evident, and they were now in full retreat. For two years, in fact, the leadership had been making contingency plans to pull back to Taiwan and regroup after losing key urban centers along the coast. Yeye had even accepted a teaching position in Taiwan the year before.

"YOUR YEYE WANT TO GO NEGOTIATE WITH GENERAL CHEN CHEN FOR LAND TO BUILD NEW NATIONAL UNIVERSITY. THEY PROMISING TO MAKE HIM PRESIDENT, BUT THEN MAKE ALL KIND OF EXCUSE," Ma told me. After all, students everywhere were already too vocal, too violent, in opposition to the Nationalists, Gugu included. No one wanted to build a university where zealous ideals could run rampant and where students could easily come together to plot further sedition.

"Come with me!" Yeye shouted again, gesturing to the plane. "I can take us both to safety. It is the only opportunity we will have. The city will fall!"

"I know it will, Father," shouted Gugu over the din. Then she said, with some pride, "I am part of the reason the city will fall!"

"Guo Qian," said Yeye, his eyes filling with tears. "I know how much this all means to you. But your family wants you, too. We are leaving for Taiwan from Nanjing tomorrow. We cannot be separated!"

"It is you who are separating from me by running away!" Gugu responded, still more stubborn than seemed possible in a young woman. "You could stay and help build a new China!"

Yeye had heard this before from her, so full as she was of hope and faith in the great Mao Zedong. While Yeye respected what Mao wanted to accomplish, he used to tell Ba that he believed it simply went too far. "Mao wants to change the human heart through his socialism," Yeye opined. "And this is why he cannot succeed." People were not angels, and appeals to their better natures were not sustainable. People would always act in their own interest or the interest of their family or clan. If Mao really could convince them to act in the interest of a whole nation, it would come at a cost no one could predict.

"Professor, we must leave," the pilot said, the rain starting to come down harder. "If the storm gets much worse, we will not be able to take off."

"Come with me!" Yeye implored yet again. "Guo Qian! Don't do this. Please!"

"I'm sorry, Baba," Gugu said, her own tears welling. "Please come find me when we are reunited as one China!"

He wanted to tell her that she was his light and joy. He wanted to tell her how proud he was of her and how scared for her he was now. He wanted to hold her and tell her how much he loved her. But all he could manage was, "But... we may never see each other, not ever again!"

When she turned to leave, he felt a stabbing in his chest as if his heart would give way. He nearly fell to his knees from the pain, but the pilot grabbed his arm and helped him back into the plane. Yeye kept looking out the window, hoping his daughter would change her mind, even as the plane lifted up into the storm and flew out over the positions of the advancing Communist army, which would take the city just days later, sealing him off from his daughter, smashing their history together with a hammer, slicing their family bond with a sickle.

August 1975
New York, New York

It had been twenty-seven years since Yeye had any word of his beloved daughter, my Aunt Qian. As a former Nationalist, he was not permitted back into China, even after it opened its doors to some foreigners after Nixon's historic visit in 1972. But with every chance, at every conference, and every occasion he heard someone he knew might be returning to China, he asked people to inquire after her, to find out if she had survived the war, the famine of the Great Leap Forward, and the Cultural Revolution. He had so many different nightmares about what might have become of her, willful as she was. Gugu was still the daughter of intellectuals and descended from landholding families. It was not a safe legacy in a society bent on destroying its feudal past and everyone with any ties to it.

Yeye finally heard from an Indian professor at Columbia, where he was now guest lecturing, about a woman named "Qian" who lived and taught at Beijing Teachers' University under his same surname. She was the right age, too. Yeye grew excited, and he began to write letters to this Qian, who might be his daughter, telling her all about their lives since that day, how he had gone to Taiwan with the family and helped set up a new university, but how troubles with the students had materialized as expected.

His letters were long. He told her about how he had been writing a new Modern Chinese History text, but that the government in Taiwan, now under martial law, did not like what he was suspected of writing, so he had taken leave and exiled himself to America, where he taught at Harvard, then Columbia. He was careful not to say anything negative about the current government in Beijing lest the censors catch it and stop his correspondence from reaching her.

He wrote about his grandchildren, including us, four children of his son Jenkai, to whom he gave each the character *yi* 怡 as part of our names because it comprised both an elongated heart symbol *xin* 心 and the *tai* 台 from Taiwan 台湾—showing how his "heart" still was in "Tai-wan," the beautiful tropical island he had called home for so many years. He worried any talk of loving Taiwan might not get past the censors, but he risked it anyway.

And he asked many questions about her life, whether she had married, whether she had children, whether she still read as many books as she once loved to do. He was careful not to discuss politics, but even with this precaution, he never received a response from this Qian at Beijing Teachers' University. He checked and rechecked his postbox regularly. Weeks turned to months, and Tingyi wondered if she really was alive and teaching in Beijing, as rumored. Or if it was really her at all. Surely if it were someone else receiving so many letters, they might at least write back to say he had the wrong woman?

198

Yeye had begun to despair of ever knowing more about Gugu when Ba was suddenly invited to return to China. Yeye became very emotional. This was the chance they all had been waiting for, and his son could do what he could not. Yeye provided long lists of names and descriptions of people with whom he had lost touch, old colleagues who had stayed there to help rebuild China, and many ideas on how to reach each of them through friends, relatives, and work. His heart brimmed with the hope that he might receive word back, especially from his daughter. Did she ever get his letters? Was she in good health?

Ba returned from China with so much news that it took days for him to tell Yeye about everything he had seen and everyone he had met from that long list, having hardly any time at all to rest during his entire trip. But most importantly, Ba told him that Gugu was indeed alive and was teaching in Beijing at the address they had for her. She had run off during the war with a revolutionary and married him, and she had a daughter that everyone called Xiao Guai—the "behaved one." Gugu had fallen out of love with her husband over political differences, and she seemed very disappointed with how New China had turned out, especially after the Cultural Revolution. She held a great deal of bitterness towards the world and the empty promises of Mao. She had indeed received Yeye's letters but didn't dare to answer them because the crime of *haiwai guanxi*—foreign-related influences—was still a punishable one, and she could lose her job.

Yeye was elated to hear that Gugu was alive, and he found the next month to be a buoyant and productive one. Relations with China were improving, and perhaps in time, he would be permitted to return, or his daughter might come to the States to visit. He spoke so often of her that Nainai began to tease him about it. With this optimistic new energy, he poured himself into his latest text, a sprawling and comprehensive history treatise that would become one of his most celebrated works. He still wrote everything by hand, late into the night, smoking alone and hunched over his desk, as he had for decades.

When he wrote the final words of the book, he let Nainai know. "It's finally finished," he said with a bone-weary smile, putting down his pen.

"Good, good. Very good," Nainai said. "But you look terrible. You must rest."

Yeye nodded and threw himself into their bed, dreaming of his daughter, who was so like him, separated by war and by political forces far beyond their control. The world could be so cruel, splitting families apart for half a lifetime.

That night, Yeye suffered a heart attack, and he succumbed a few days later in his hospital bed, finished with his great treatise but deprived of the very thing he had most wanted: a chance to set eyes upon his favorite child one last time.

June 2020
New York City, New York

It felt like a war zone around my apartment building in Harlem. For ten straight days, the city, along with the rest of the nation, had been rocked by protests, at first in the form of riots, then in an outpouring of marches for Black Lives Matter.

Ma had called me repeatedly, worried that what she was seeing on Hong Kong television about the unrest in New York would soon engulf me, especially given that I was in a majority-minority neighborhood.

"Don't worry," I told Ma, not sure I wasn't also concerned.

"YOU PROMISE TO STAY INSIDE? YOU ARE CHINESE, AND THEY WANT ATTACK YOU."

"People aren't attacking Chinese, at least not right now." There had been dozens of random assaults on Asians in New York after Trump had doubled down on his "China Virus" rhetoric, and now it seemed we had both a pandemic and racial unrest all across the nation. *Please turn to page 400,566 of your History Books on the year 2020,* said a meme I shared with friends. Historians would probably one day have to specify in which quarter of 2020 they specialized.

"WHO THEY ATTACK? NOT CHINESE?"

"Well, the police are attacking the protestors, and some of the protestors are attacking back, but it's mostly peaceful, with a few exceptions." The Hong Kong news Ma was glued to loved focusing on those exceptions, having had some experience in what drives viewership during their own pro-democracy protests.

"I WORRY YOU NOT SAFE IN YOUR NEIGHBORHOOD," Ma reiterated.

"There's a police station right across the street."

"MAYBE THAT EVEN WORSE! THEY COME ATTACK POLICE STATION!"

Ma nearly turned out to be right. The very night after her warning, large crowds of demonstrators approached the precinct across the street from us in Harlem, where a line of cops guarded the entryway. "NYPD KKK!" and "No justice, no peace, no racist police!" they shouted. My bedroom window looked down on the crowd of protestors directly. From where I watched, it wasn't clear whether they intended to escalate or whether the police might push back and start an incident. They were demanding justice for George Floyd. For Breonna Taylor. "If we don't get it, shut it down!" they shouted. Not knowing what else to do, I went live on Facebook, so my friends at least could be in the moment with me. Many commenting on the live feed sounded like Ma. "Stay safe!" "Are you okay?" "Are they wearing masks?"

Ma knew that it was in my nature not to stay out of things for long. So she tried to lay it on thick in our next call.

"PROMISE ME YOU WON'T GO OUT. TOO DANGEROUS!"

"I won't go out after curfew," I offered.

"WHY YOU WANT TO PROTEST?"

"Ma, the whole world is protesting right now!"

"NOT CHINA."

"Well, in Hong Kong, they are. For different things, but still. Anyway, this is right here. And it's important."

"IT TOO MANY PEOPLE, COULD GET SICK."

She was probably right about that, and it gave me pause. I had tried to judge the distance between protestors below us in the streets, and there was essentially none. Certainly not six feet from each other.

"If I go protest, I'll do it on the side, from a distance."

"JUST DON'T GO OUTSIDE WITH THEM. PROMISE YOUR MA."

I hedged and promised her I'd be safe, and she seemed to accept my concession. But after two more days of watching the police overreact and instigate violence, I'd seen enough. I wanted to get out there, observe firsthand what was going on, and experience what our city looked like from the ground level amidst the unfolding chaos, and not just above it from my window. I imagined what my brother Kaiser had experienced when he was in Beijing in the middle of the Tiananmen uprising 31 years ago. We were both finally rebels with causes, even if they weren't really our own.

The next weekend, I headed out to the Black Lives Matter protest march that began from Frederick Douglass Circle and wound its way down to Washington Square Park. My roommates had both bailed, citing the heat, so I went alone. It was in the high '80s, and the march was over one hundred city blocks. I put on sunscreen and a disposable mask, and I resolved to make it all the way downtown with the marchers.

I was feeling energized but also a tad guilty over going against Ma's directive. I would just tell her after the protest was done, I reasoned, so she wouldn't be scared.

Because the march began in Harlem, I had expected the protestors to be mostly Black, but it was a sea of faces of all different colors. I felt buoyed by this; I wasn't the only one who had decided that the cause was also my own.

A demonstrator called out, "SAY HER NAME!" and the crowd roared back, "BREONNA TAYLOR!" A young Asian guy threw me a greeting with this chin, and I nodded back at him. It was a brief moment of solidarity. I wondered if he also had a Chinese mother who didn't know where he was.

I saw a young white woman on the side of the road talking to her child, who couldn't have been more than five years old. He was clearly confused about the protest, and she was explaining it as best she could. I eavesdropped shamelessly.

"Why are the people shouting her name?" the boy asked.

"She was a woman who died," the mom explained.

"How?" he asked.

The mother took a deep breath, and I felt myself take one with her. "The police came to her house, and they shot her. They had the wrong house, and they shot her inside her own house."

The boy's eyes widened. "Could they come to our house?"

My heart thudded, and the young mother's eyes teared up. "They could, but they probably won't, sweetie. But that's because, well, it's because we're white. And Breonna Taylor was, well, she was Black, and that's why this happened to her."

"But," the boy said, trying to process that. "But that's not *fair*."

Now my own eyes filled up with tears. I thought of Tahira, my grand-niece, whose father was Black. Would someone have to explain to her that the world was more stacked against her dad than her mom? I suddenly wanted to talk to Ma very badly. I wanted her to understand that this wasn't an abstract thing for our family. I wanted her to know that there was nothing to be scared of and that this was important to me. So I found myself FaceTiming her right from the protest.

MA: WHERE ARE YOU?!

JAY: I'm marching, Ma.

MA: OH, NO.

JAY: Don't worry, it's peaceful. There are lots of people here of all races and ages. Even people with their kids, see?

MA: WHERE YOU MARCH TO, POLICE?

JAY: No, down to a rally downtown.

MA: DOWNTOWN? THAT FAR?

JAY: It will take us hours.

MA: IT NOT SAFE. YOU SHOULD GET INSIDE. WHY YOU HAVE TO PROTEST?

JAY: Because, well, because what happened isn't right. It isn't fair. Do you know what happened with that man, George Floyd?

MA: THEY KILLING HIM, TERRIBLE.

JAY: Right. And so I just wanted to come out and say I think it's terrible, too. I don't want to just be online saying it. I want to be out here saying it.

MA: EVERYONE WEARING MASK?

JAY: Yes, everyone I can see is wearing one. And I'm staying on the side of the road, away from people if I can.

MA: NO NEED FOR YOU TO GET INVOLVE!

JAY: Ma, remember you took me to my first protest, though? It was outside the White House. You wanted Jimmy Carter to normalize relations with China. You wanted it so bad you took us, kids, there. I remember it so clearly.

MA: (laughing) YOU BOYS LEARN TO PROTEST. NEXT TIME WHEN TIME FOR HAIRCUT, YOU MAKE PROTEST SIGN, THEN MARCHING AROUND, "WE DON'T WANT A HAIRCUT! WE DON'T WANT A HAIRCUT!" I WISH I SAVING THAT SIGN.

JAY: I remember that, too! So this is just like that, but way more important. It affects all of us. Even our family directly now.

MA: I SO WORRY ABOUT YOU. CAN YOU CALL ME WHEN YOU GET HOME SAFE?

JAY: I will. I promise I'll be fine, Ma!

Ma's eyes looked troubled as we hung up, and I wondered if I'd made a mistake. As I walked those 100+ blocks, I tried to feel the importance of this moment. We knelt in front of Trump Tower with our fists up, silently condemning the racist in the White House. Someone handed me bottled water and another gave me a placard, which came in handy to shield me from the sun.

But for all the excitement, something felt wrong. I felt deeply guilty for having made Ma worry, just to prove my point to her, just because I was feeling self-righteous and emotional at the moment. It had been a selfish act, really, because it would only worry her, not actually change how she saw the world. I couldn't stop thinking about her and feeling like I'd let her down.

Just as we approached Washington Square Park, I received a WhatsApp message alert. It was from John. Ma was experiencing very bad dizzy spells, and he had called the hospital. She was headed to the ER.

June 1989
Phone Call

"Ma, it's Jay. Are you watching this?"

"YEAH, WE WATCHING FOR MANY HOUR NOW."

"I just woke up, and people were in the TV lounge with the news on. I can't believe this."

The tanks had finally rolled into Tiananmen Square on June 4th. For the last few weeks, my dorm had been glued to the reports coming out of Beijing. When one of the party reformers, a man named Hu Yaobang, suddenly died, his funeral blossomed into a full-throated cry for greater freedom and democracy, led by the college students in Beijing and joined by the professional and working classes. It was a grassroots movement that quickly morphed into an occupation of Tiananmen Square. To everyone around the world, the possibility of freedom from Communist rule felt within reach. China was the biggest prize of all. We imagined one billion Chinese claiming a democracy that was theirs by right, their true potential finally unleashed.

But that day, the footage we saw on the loop was grainy and dark, images of fires and crowds rushing about chaotically, the sound of gunfire and the roar of armored personnel carriers. A makeshift statue erected in the square, the "Goddess of Democracy," toppled over and over on our screens. Reports of hundreds, maybe thousands dead, making our heads spin.

"I KNOWING THIS GOING TO HAPPEN," Ma said. "THE POOR STUDENT." I couldn't tell for sure, but it sounded like she was crying.

"Jay," my father said. "Dis is Ba. Ma said you were calling. Ask me to talk to you." Maybe Ma really was crying. She always pulled Ba in when she wasn't able to hold it together.

"They really did it," my voice quavering. "They really just opened fire. They didn't even bother with tear gas or going in with just batons? It's not like the protestors were armed."

"Dey want to make a show of force," Ba said matter-of-factly. "Dey do not want to give anyone a second chance. Dis is as much about who is in charge as it is putting down de protest."

"I'm sick to my stomach," I said. "Who would fire on innocent, unarmed people? I thought China revered its students."

"This day is going to change a lot of things," Ba said, a sadness in his voice, too.

I stared at the images a bit longer, then a sudden realization struck me, overwhelming me with dread.

"Wait. Ba, have you heard from Kaiser?!" I asked.

June 1989
Beijing, China

My brother Kaiser had gone to China to play rock and roll. It was a young musician's dream: a nation just waking up to the idea of heavy metal, with almost no one else from the West able to navigate the budding rock-music landscape. Two years earlier, after Ba had pulled some strings, Kaiser's college band, Freefall, had been improbably invited to headline venues around China, including huge arenas like Workers' Stadium. But his bandmate had been reluctant and had thrown so many obstacles in the path of the performance that they'd had to cancel. Furious but undaunted, Kaiser set out on his own right after graduating from Berkeley.

It hadn't taken him long to find a music store and some actual gigs in Beijing, even though he had, as yet, no band. While jamming with his new friends in the storefront, a curious crowd of dust-covered workers gathered to gawk and experience the electric, pounding energy of Western Music. Most found it unsettling, but the owner of the store was impressed and invited them to dinner across the street to talk business.

That was when Kaiser met Ding Wu, his future partner in music, who would go on with him to form one of China's first and most popular metal bands, Tang Dynasty. Kaiser liked that Ding Wu, like him, was tall and wore his hair long like a rocker. He was also knowledgeable, having listened to Led Zeppelin and even heard of Kaiser's favorite band, Rush. He suggested they play together, and they held their first rehearsal in a factory next to the Beijing Shangri-La Hotel, falling instantly in love with each other's musical stylings. They began playing gigs around town.

Together they made an unforgettable pair, lead singer and lead guitarist. Their black clothes, imposing height, and wailing melodies seemed to herald a new kind of China, one that borrowed stylings from the West but made music that was distinctively and irrefutably Chinese. Along with Tang Dynasty, Kaiser formed a second band with some expatriates called STG, which stood for "Short-Term Gratification." They played album-oriented rock, souped-up versions of classic Chinese songs like "The East Is Red," and even a rock version of the *Star Trek* theme. The rock scene was fledgling, and nobody could have guessed its importance. Kaiser was hanging out regularly with artists who would go on, as Tang Dynasty did, to become famous throughout China and sell millions of albums.

When Kaiser went home to America for a spell, he brought back more gear—amps, effects pedals, and another guitar—doubling down on his career as a rock musician. He convinced his drummer from his college band, Bruce Yarbro, to join him in China for an adventure like nothing he'd ever get a chance to experience again.

Kaiser was right about this, but not for the reason he assumed. At the time, he was living with our *nainai* in Beijing's Xisi district, a normally quiet part of the Western side of town now rocked by constant street protests and marches. Bruce arrived on April 15, 1989, the very day that the reform-minded Hu Yaobang died, and overnight, the country went from calm to chaotic. Throngs of mourners pressed into the main thoroughfare in Xisi, and Kaiser and Bruce were amazed that so many people could fit in them and still move forward at all. The outpouring turned into a second day of street occupations and then a third. The central leadership was caught off guard. The crowds were so packed in that Kaiser and Bruce sometimes feared for their own safety, genuinely worried they would be trampled in a stampede. In one harrowing moment, a packed crowd suddenly surged toward them, and Kaiser and Bruce ran for their lives, stopping only when they were a good safe distance, then turning around to see people laughing and pointing at the two odd Americans who had bounded away like scared rabbits.

Nearly every day, Kaiser and Bruce went out to Tiananmen Square, where the student protestors had set up a makeshift city, with the command center located at the obelisk known as the Monument to the People's Martyrs in the center of the square, concentric circles radiating out from it: Beijing University and Tsinghua University students in the inner circle, then students from other universities in Beijing in the next, then students from other Chinese universities, then out to professional classes, and finally to the workers' circle. As the students settled in for a longer encampment, the number of protestors grew. A carnival atmosphere took root, with the locals distributing box meals to the student protestors, along with bottles of water to help cool them from the unforgiving summer sun.

I was following all this on our television set in my dorm lounge, where all the Chinese Americans and some of our friends gathered each night to listen to the news and see China transforming, we thought, into the next great democracy. I called Ma often during this time. She was far more skeptical than I was.

"I NOT SURE STUDENT KNOWING WHAT THEY DOING. MAYBE THEY JUST WANTING ATTENTION. I DON'T KNOW."

The festivities reached a crescendo on May 4, when a million people flooded the square, calling on the spirit of the May 4th protest of 1919. Seventy years before, students in Beijing had rallied to give voice to the anti-imperialist sentiments of the people, who were outraged over an agreement granting former German territories not back to China but to Imperial Japan after World War I. To most Chinese, this had been a symbol of China's continued weakness against the west, even eight years after the Qing had been deposed and the new Republic of China was established. Thousands of students had marched on the Forbidden City, setting off a chain of protests across the nation and strikes in places like Shanghai, paralyzing the country. The student protestors in Tiananmen in June of 1989 saw themselves as the heirs to that May 4th political movement.

During the huge rally, Kaiser chatted up a Western news crew, apparently from ABC. Some Tibetan monks had raised a banner calling for a free and independent Tibet. But the student protestors quickly surrounded the monks, snatching the banner from them and throwing it to the ground, their nationalist sentiments overcoming their supposed desire for democratic freedoms.

"Why aren't you filming and reporting on that?" Kaiser asked.

The news producer laughed. "This isn't what we're here to show."

"Don't you want to report what's really happening?" Kaiser pressed.

"Do you understand what it means to stick to the narrative?" the producer responded.

For Kaiser, it was a heady time. During the weeks that followed, STG and Tang Dynasty played gigs regularly, and because the protests had authorities occupied, without the need for any pre-approvals from the police. They appeared in venues that were usually wholly off-limits, like the ancient observatory of Beijing and Ritan Park, within the zone of occupation by the students. It was near anarchy, and there were no limits on what might be changed or done.

Kaiser and Bruce witnessed remarkable sights around the city as well. Near the outskirts of town, out by the Military Museum, troops in armored personnel carriers were now stalled, barred from rolling down main thoroughfares by rows and rows of civilians who had laid down in the streets. Protestors walked up to soldiers and, in scenes reminiscent of the Vietnam protests in the U.S., placed flowers in the barrels of guns.

As the government began to warn that its patience was wearing thin, hunger strikes by the student leaders added to the stakes. A visit by General Secretary Gorbachev of the Soviet Union drew the world's eyes—and a May 18th declaration of martial law its condemnation.

"CHINA LEADER GETTING VERY SERIOUS," Ma warned.

"But they won't actually attack the protestors, will they? I mean, students are revered, right?"

"MAYBE JUST ARRESTING THEM," she said. "CANNOT HAVING *LUAN*." Chaos.

Kaiser also knew that violence was now a distinct possibility, but like me and many others, he believed that the government would never open fire upon its own people.

It turns out Kaiser and his friends were incredibly lucky. On June 3rd, one day before the deadly crackdown, the band members of STG and Tang Dynasty departed Beijing to play a gig in a small town called Baicheng on the border between Jilin Province and Inner Mongolia. The producer of this tour, however, had not been fully forthright, and he informed them mid-tour that they would also be traveling a long distance to Manchuria for their next engagement. Kaiser tried to mollify his pissed-off bandmates, one of whom nonetheless bailed on the rest of the tour and headed back to Beijing. Kaiser was left with Bruce and a bunch of Chinese musicians. He worried audiences would not believe they were a Western band, especially with the only white face positioned way in the back, playing drums.

When they finally arrived in the city of Qiqihar on June 6, they checked in at their hotel, where they met a Swedish couple who seemed desperate to get out of China. Kaiser watched as they placed frantic calls, and he finally asked them what was going on.

"Haven't you heard?" the Swede said. "There has been a massacre in Beijing! The military has taken back the square. Everyone is getting out!"

"That can't be true," Kaiser said. "We were just in Beijing. Things were fine. It's still a stalemate."

"Turn on the television and see for yourself!" he said before rushing off.

Kaiser ran to his room and flicked on the hotel room TV, where state media was running reports. His stomach dropped. There were images of fire and of grim-faced soldiers marching on the city. A video of a soldier strung up, set alight, and left to hang from the bridge at Fuchengmen, very near to our Beijing home, was a favorite go-to clip for the government. The newscaster was speaking vaguely about counter-revolutionary forces being quelled.

The state-run news was only showing the deaths of soldiers, with no reports on civilians. But years later, the foreman of our factory in Beijing, who had been on the west side of town and had witnessed the brutality of the clampdown firsthand, relayed to me what he'd seen.

"A group of young people were waving the Chinese flag, back and forth, on the end of a long pole. They stood in a triangle, singing the national anthem. I saw a commander order a soldier to fire on the flag-bearer. When the soldier hesitated, the commander shot the man in the head, then ordered the man next to him to fire on the flag-bearer. The soldier did so without hesitating. Cha! But then a remarkable thing happened. A terrible thing. Someone behind the fallen flag-bearer stepped forward and picked up the flag, and she continued to wave it, the people behind her only singing more loudly. The commander ordered the soldier to fire on her, and he did so. Cha! But then another person stepped forward, and the order was given again, but the soldier hesitated this time, so the commander shot him, Cha! Then he picked up his rifle and began to shoot whoever picked up the flag. The street was running red with blood. I must have seen two dozen people killed in a row."

Back in his hotel in Qiqihar, Kaiser went down to the lobby and made a call to Nainai.

"Don't worry," she said. "I am okay. There is still gunfire, but I am safe in the house and have not left. I have told your family and the U.S. Embassy that you left town the night before it all happened."

Kaiser phoned the consulate, and they seemed to be expecting his call.

"Glad you got in touch with us. You musician types were going to be the first up against a wall, you know," the consular officer said.

Kaiser still had gigs to play in Qiqihar. That night, still numb about the news out of Beijing, or perhaps because of it, things got even crazier. Apparently, the ticket buyers had been told by the promoters that STG was the backup band for Michael Jackson, and they had expected Caucasian or at least Black musicians. The crowd, feeling duped, promptly rioted in a decidedly Manchurian fashion, burning down the ticket booth and forcing Kaiser and his band into hiding. By the next day, when they were set to play their second gig, the producers had smoothed things over. They moved Bruce with his white face to the front, and the band faked its way through the set with made-up lyrics to a bunch of cover songs like "Hey You" and "Comfortably Numb" from Pink Floyd.

Kaiser hid out with his bandmates in the city of Dalian on the coast, getting high on the beach and waiting for an opportunity to leave China. Within a few days, he was on a plane back to the United States, his dreams of playing heavy metal in an increasingly open China ground to dust beneath tank treads, at least for the time being. He would wind up returning a year or so later, reuniting with Ding Wu to make Tang Dynasty China's most celebrated heavy metal band.

One of the most popular songs from their first album, which gave local authorities everywhere ulcers and was banned from being performed, was "The Internationale," which was a tune often sung by the Tiananmen protesters. That a glorious socialist anthem was itself now *verboten* was only one of many ironies to come, but this was China post-crackdown, where dreams of a free China would go into a long deep freeze.

Ma as a young student giving a speech

Ma in her college years

Early 1960s

Ba and Ma, Berkeley, California, 1960s

Ma and Laolao, in the Kuo home in upstate New York

A rare picture of Waigong (Ma's father)

Nainai and Yeye (Ba's parents)

One of my favorite photos of Ma.
(She didn't really know how to ride one.)

Ma and Ba, Tucson Arizona, 1980s

The Kuo family, celebrating Ba's 80th birthday

Ma at Mimi's wedding in Beijing

Ma making "lion's head" meatballs

Ma at her 80th birthday celebration,
holding her great granddaughter, Tahira

Chapter Seven

TRAITORS

or

"NONE OF THIS IS YOURS!"

June 2017
Beijing, China

My ex-boyfriend, Zhang Yan, had gone to live with Ma in our family home in Beijing after Ba had died three years earlier. Zhang Yan had an easy smile and an infectious laugh that had stayed with him even into his forties. Appointing him as Ma's primary caretaker had been my idea after it became clear that she was spending too many nights in the house by herself. None of us American kids with our busy lives and jobs could realistically pick up and move to Beijing to be with her. Without someone there, though, should anything happen to her—a fall down the slippery marble staircase Ba had installed or a stroke like Laolao had suffered—it might not be discovered until the following day or longer.

In truth, Zhang Yan was also the only one I could think of whom we could entrust with Ma's safety. He was honest to a fault and would be willing to put up with her for long periods of time without going totally insane. I had been impressed with how he had handled Laolao during her dementia years earlier, so I figured living with another old lady with only slight bouts of fantasy and memory loss would be breezy by comparison.

As a child, Zhang Yan was raised by various relatives in various villages in the south of China. Every day on his way to school, he would pass a billboard with the pouting face of the dashing Cantonese actor and singer, Guo Fucheng, encouraging the purchase of "555" brand cigarettes. Zhang Yan would imagine Guo Fucheng's arms wrapped around him, and the thought made life in his small farming village both bearable and isolating.

Zhang Yan had only achieved an eighth-grade education before going to work and live full-time in a factory. Over a few years, his rising "debts" for things like water, food, and electricity, for which the company charged exorbitant rates and kept meticulous ledgers, meant he was effectively an indentured servant, going further into the red with each pay period. There were guards armed with shock sticks posted at the gates of the factory, and they had instructions not to allow him or other "deadbeat" workers to leave. Zhang Yan found an unlit spot near the factory wall where he might dig himself to freedom, working under cover of night with a small gardening spade. After weeks of secret excavating and before the spring rains came to wash his efforts away, he tunneled his way out.

Not knowing anything about the Chinese capital, except that there were millions of undocumented migrants like him there, Zhang Yan hopped on a grain-filled railcar heading north and found himself in Beijing with only a few yuan in his wallet. He used ten of those— nearly all he had—to hire a taxi to take him up one of the new superhighway on-ramps, just so he could experience it first-hand. It was his first brush with modernity, besides the "555" billboard.

In time, he found a job singing at a karaoke bar, then selling flowers illegally by the roadside (a period during which he came to despise the local police, who harassed anyone who didn't pay them off). A kindly owner of a fledgling purse company took pity on him and gave him a chance with a real job. Zhang Yan worked hard on his way up from street vendor of purses to store clerk, to assistant manager, to store manager in a few more years. That was around the time I'd met him, in one of China's first gay bars in the Sanlitun District of Beijing, his infectious joy making it impossible not to fall in love with him.

When I first wrapped my arms around him, he told me that I bore a resemblance to a pop star on the billboard of his childhood.

That was twenty years earlier. After we'd broken up, mostly because I had always planned to leave Beijing to return to the States, Zhang Yan had gone on to successfully manage Destination, Beijing's first big, gay discotheque. With money finally in his pocket and a job that revealed bits of the outside world to him, he decided to travel abroad, heading to The Netherlands to watch the Gay Games and even vacationing in Thailand. He took me out to lunch and paid with his own credit card when I came back to China to visit. I was so proud of him, considering the cards he'd been dealt as a child.

But after a falling out with the owner of the club, a return home to bury his father, and a series of bad choices in romantic partners, Zhang Yan started drifting from job to job. He found it increasingly difficult to manage his life, particularly after his health deteriorated from HIV, and he had to obtain and pay for medicine all the time. Traveling around the country by rail or plane was also more challenging because his "social score"—a new way the CCP was tracking and controlling citizens—had been lowered, in part because of his medical status but most likely also because of his frequent interviews with the press about the need for greater protections for gay people in China. (To get around the travel ban, Zhang Yan once even biked his way across the entire country, from Beijing to Tibet.)

With my job offer to take care of Ma, I hoped to solve both Zhang Yan's financial woes and Ma's lack of live-in, trustworthy help. Zhang Yan was happy to be back in Beijing with a roof over his head and a steady job that was, at least on paper, objectively easy to perform. He was hired to be Ma's personal assistant but ended up being a form of a therapist, a sounding board, and even a stand-in son. Ma certainly treated him like she could dictate his every move and emotion.

"HE NEED TO BE HAPPIER AROUND ME. AFTER DINNER, HE JUST WANT GOING TO HIS ROOM, NOT TO TALK TO ME. WHY?"

"We're not paying him to talk to you, Ma. He's there to make sure you're okay."

"HE SHOULD BE MORE GRATEFUL, HAVING ROOF OVER HEAD. HOW MUCH YOU PAY HIM?"

"Enough to live on, don't worry yourself about it."

"HOW MUCH?"

"I'm not going to tell you. And don't ask him either! I told him not to talk to you about his pay."

The truth was, his decision to withdraw from her presence once night fell hurt Ma's feelings, though she would never admit it. Just as he had experienced after being around me for a few years, the stress of caring full-time for a person as demanding as Ma began to wear on him.

By year three, Zhang Yan quietly indicated that he was ready to move on and that the following year would be his last. While this gave us over a year and a half to plan, it was a source of considerable consternation for me and Mimi. We had become spoiled with Zhang Yan always around to look after and, more importantly, occupy Ma. The arrangement had allowed us to go about our lives in London and New York without worrying too much about her. With Zhang Yan setting an outside timeline and making his own life plan, we would have to come up with a new one for Ma.

First, we needed to figure out what notions Ma had, if any, for her life in 2018 and beyond.

"So, who is going to take care of you after Zhang Yan leaves?" I asked casually, as if inquiring about what the weather was like or what she had eaten for breakfast. For Ma, the idea of Zhang Yan leaving was painful, like he had betrayed her in some way, his loyalty to her daring to have limits.

"MAYBE LAUNDRY LADY," Ma muttered.

"Oh! Really? Her?" I asked, trying not to sound too judgy. "Why her?"

"SHE WORK TEN YEAR FOR ME," Ma said, meaning if she were going to quit, she would have already.

"Is she trustworthy?" I asked.

"VERY HONEST. SOMETIME WE GONE FOR DAYS, COMING HOME AND NOTHING MISSING!"

"That seems promising," I said, imagining Ma arriving home and flying about the house to see if Laundry Lady had taken anything of value, her skeptical eye missing nothing and her equally skeptical heart ready to accuse.

"EXCEPT FOR MY OLD CUP," Ma said, pointedly qualifying her statement. "I DON'T KNOW WHAT HAPPENING TO OLD CUP. MAYBE I SET DOWN, LOSE IT, BUT NOW LOST TWO CUP, VERY STRANGE."

In Ma's peculiar vernacular, "VERY STRANGE" meant someone had done something wrong, possibly criminal. "KIND OF STRANGE" meant unusual or noteworthy, but usually carried negative judgment anyway. "STRANGE" by itself meant Ma had not yet formed an opinion but was wary per usual. Mimi got into a good habit of clarifying Ma's intent. "Good strange or bad strange?" she would ask, to which Ma sometimes, surprisingly, replied, "Good strange!"

"I don't think anyone would steal old cups from you, Ma," I said. I wanted to be sure Ma didn't also suspect Zhang Yan, whose heart was too pure to even consider theft an option. Happily, Ma seemed focused on Laundry Lady as the only potential traitor.

"NO, I DON'T THINKING SO. ANYWAY, I ASK HER WHERE OLD CUP IS, SHE SAID SHE DID NOT SEE."

"Maybe she broke them?" I said, trying to guide her thinking to something less nefarious.

"YEAH, SHE PROBABLY SMASH IT, AFRAID TO ADMIT. SHE WOULD NOT STEAL…"

Ma did not sound convinced. After all, though the cups were old, they were still valuable, at least in her mind.

"She would steal something better if she wanted to steal," I said. "Not just a cup."

That seemed to register with Ma. "YES, PROBABLY, SHE DID NOT STEAL, SAID SHE DID NOT TAKE."

"Do you believe her?" I said, hoping to close the chapter. If Ma said yes, that was that. She wouldn't contradict herself later, at least not intentionally.

Ma could sense I was trying to wrap this up nicely, so she gave herself an out. "WELL," Ma said, her voice still dripping with skepticism. "I STILL MISSING MY CUP."

I sighed. "And?"

"AND SO I WARN HER."

January 2021
Rossmoor, California

MA: DID I EVER SHOW YOU PICTURE OF ME JUST BEFORE I LEFT FOR UNITED STATE?

JAY: Maybe? I don't know.

MA: I GIVING TALK BEFORE WHOLE SCHOOL. MANY PEOPLE ATTEND, EVEN PRESIDENT OF TAIWAN. HE HEARING ME TALK, THEN TOLD ME HE WANT TO JOIN THE PARTY.

JAY: Yeah, I remember that. You said he really wanted to hold you as a kind of hostage to earn your father's loyalty.

MA: THAT WHY I LEAVING SO SOON AFTER SPEECH. HAD TO GET AWAY. MY FATHER KNOW THAT HE IN TROUBLE AGAIN WITH HIS BOSS. COULD NOT TRUSTING HIM.

JAY: This seems to be a recurring theme in your family.

MA: WHY?

JAY: I mean the whole "trust/treason" split. It was always just one or the other for them.

MA: WELL. MY FATHER SUCH A POLITICIAN.

233

July 1930
Northern Plains Expedition, China

"HE SHOULD HAVE STICK TO POLITICAL."

This thought might well have occurred for my grandfather, as he stood blindfolded with bound wrists. He was never much of a tactician, and while war presented many opportunities to an ambitious young man, it also had its risks—among them being blamed for a disastrous military campaign and ordered to be summarily executed by firing squad.

Waigong tested the bindings again, but they held firm. Where would he go anyway, even if he got them loose? He had seen other prisoners piss themselves, and he didn't want to go to his Maker, whoever that was, with his drawers soaked in his own shame.

There were so many other paths that could have led to a better ending. He could have married the "Dummy" and stayed on at his uncle's compound, for example. Perhaps all of life's choices, the ones that didn't result in being tied to a stake and shot, ran through a condemned man's head.

"HE THINKING CAREER IN MILITARY WORKING OUT BETTER FOR HIM. BUT HE NEVER WAS GOOD SOLDIER."

"I was just thinking," I said. "If he really had died that day, shot by firing squad, none of us would be here. Maybe a lot of life is like that. One of your ancestors makes one different choice, the whole timeline changes."

"MAYBE TRUE," Ma said, pondering. Then a furrow. "OR MAYBE TURNING OUT SAME."

A career in the new military class of post-Imperial China sounded like so many better, finer adventures to Waigong. But apart from excessive

234

drinking and frequent visits to brothels, military life mostly had been long periods of boredom, not enough to eat and now, apparently, a pointless and violent end.

One could understand if incompetence had led him to this moment, standing for four minutes now, awaiting the roar of rifles. Bad military choices led to bad deaths all around. As a new convert, my grandfather ought to have been praying to the One God. The "Christian Warlord" whom he served, Feng Yuxiang, as China's most devout and second-most-fearsome servant of Heaven, required faithful conversion by all his men. If that meant a quick promotion and greater opportunity, it would not have even been a close question for Waigong. The world was run by people who bowed to Christ, so why not him? People like the warlord Feng and Generalissimo Jiang followed Christ. For a prophet of peace, Jesus seemed to attract the most bloodthirsty of champions.

But it was not incompetence for which he stood accused and tied to a stake, blindfolded. Waigong certainly thought he would die that day, but not because he had just lost a decisive battle in what would come to be called the Central Plains War. Feng actually suspected that he'd actually lost it on purpose. A traitor, that's what they had said of him. How badly must it have gone that everyone simply assumed he must have thrown the fight?

Perhaps he should have stuck to politics.

"Personal Secretary" once had a nice ring to it. Waigong had bluffed and lied his way into the ranks of the military, then jostled, romanced, and charmed his way into Feng's inner circle. It had taken years of careful planning, dangerous plots, and more than a few personal betrayals and bribes before the *former* personal secretary had been sent packing. My grandfather had learned how to manipulate people by watching his own mother, who had shown how to control his bear-of-a-father well enough to become the de facto head of the Liu

235

household. Applying that art, Waigong had become the right hand, the Personal Secretary, to Feng! The very warlord who had led the coup in Beiping, deposed the last Emperor Puyi, and invited Sun Yat-sen himself to return and preside over a New China. These were heady, historic times, and he had had a front seat.

Waigong's good looks, charms, and wit had gotten him far. But Feng had mistaken his charisma and political sensibilities for actual strategic talents. Feng had needed men he trusted in charge of his wayward Christian forces, so he made Jingjian a formal commandant and sent him into battle, as if a wily fox could defeat a pack of hounds out in the open.

There he stood for his crime of incompetence. Five minutes had passed now. How long could one man keep on like this? Any longer, and his bladder would burst, and he really would piss himself.

"What have you to say, Liu Jingjian?" a voice barked again. "Why did you lead us into failure? How much did the KMT pay you? What position did they offer? Confess your treason, and you might still live."

My grandfather's mind raced. Speak a word, any word at all, and the order to shoot will come for certain. Even if he had been a traitor, only a fool would utter a sound now. Was Feng testing his loyalty or his backbone?

Death by the sudden heat, and then nothing. Painless and quick, if he was lucky. But some men didn't die right away and had to bleed out.

Another minute. A true Christian would be praying by now. Waigong only shifted his weight and tested his bonds again.

"Prepare!" boomed a voice. So this is what the last moments of life are like, he must have thought. So pointless.

Seconds ticked by. Maybe if he gave them what they wanted to hear? A lie could still save his life. A lie could…

"Fire!"

"Wait," I said to Ma, interrupting her story. "They actually shot him?"

"NOT HIM. THEY SHOOTING UP INTO AIR."

The sound was deafening, like cannons in his ears. But then, the ground was still beneath his feet, and his heart still pounded like a scared rabbit. Death felt so much like being alive.

"Bah, let him go," spat a voice. Feng Yuxiang, that scoundrel, had been there this whole time, watching. It took Waigong another moment to realize the line of soldiers had shot into the air, probably on Feng's orders. A guard ripped his blindfold off, and another cut his bonds. Feng was standing not two feet in front of him. Waigong had managed not to piss himself from fear.

"Liu Jingjian, you may be a useless dandy. And you may be the worst commander in my army. Maybe the worst commander China has ever seen. But you are no traitor," Feng said. "So I warned you just now. Do you understand?"

My grandfather nodded, his throat unable to form any real words.

"Come see me when you've had a bite to eat. We have much to discuss."

As Feng turned to go, Waigong knew right then that the Christian Warlord's reign was ending. A more fearsome and ruthless general would have shot him dead as punishment for his failure and a real warning to others. Feng's enemy Jiang Jieshi, whom the west called Chiang Kai-shek, the future president of the Republic of China, would have killed him, even though Jiang was also a Christian. Jiang would go on to kill so many more.

No, Feng was soft. In a cockfight, it was important to bet on the right bird.

A year later, after improbably surviving yet another of Feng's trial-by-firing-squad scenes, Waigong was on his way to exile in Germany. He would study professional military strategies and learn the strange ways and vulnerabilities of the Europeans, the knowledge that he and many others would use one day to thwart their colonial ambitions in China.

"BECAUSE YOU WAIGONG A CHRISTIAN AND ALSO SPEAKING OKAY GERMAN, HE CAN DOING OKAY," Ma explained. "NOT MANY CHINESE CAN DOING."

On his return, Waigong bided his time and angled for favor in the new regime. He decided to head to Beiping to see about a job. My grandfather still had friends in the old Beiyang army. Generalissimo Jiang could use his talents, and Waigong would prove that to him. He just had to figure out how to get into Jiang's good graces, even after openly declaring for and fighting under his chief rival. The Christian part would help, he knew. He still spoke all the Latin he needed.

If Waigong could have known that, decades later, he would become a wealthy and powerful senator in Jiang's KMT party, married to the most beautiful woman he'd ever laid eyes upon, that he would raise three tall, strapping boys and two beautiful, clever girls, who would all go to America one day, he would have said that the Christian God is good, indeed.

But if he could have also known they would lose the civil war to peasant revolutionaries, who would sweep his kind out to sea across the straits to an island that he would never fully think of as home, and that his family's wealth and influence would fade to nothing as the

238

long cold war with the Communists drew to a stalemate, he would have converted to a better religion.

None of the children he would later sire would ever place much faith in Christ. The soulful prayers of his future wife, my *laolao*, would repeatedly fail to make things any better for them. By the end of the century, all the smart money in the new Republic of China was on Buddhism, so after just one generation, most of the family had abandoned the Catholic Church in favor of burning incense and paper money offerings in temples of the fat sage.

My grandfather understood that switch. It was important to bet on the right bird.

December 2018
New York City, NY, and Chapel Hill, NC

Even before Donald Trump was elected, Ma saw everything America did through the lens of how it would harm China. When the U.S. formed a trade pact with Canada and Mexico, it was to exclude China. When the U.S. attended G7 meetings, it was to thumb its nose at China. It didn't seem to matter when I pointed out that China wasn't in the G7.

It was a kind of national insecurity, bordering on cultural paranoia, that drove this. I'd noticed from watching Chinese-language television with her that the Chinese news media, even the state-aligned outlets, reported on the U.S. far more than Western media reported on China. They even reported on the state of our elections and the candidates running. I would have been surprised if most Americans could even name the Chinese president.

Western media had grown increasingly critical of China, picking up on some of the tensions from the ongoing trade war. This put Ma and other good Chinese patriots on the defensive. It had gotten to the point where any criticism her offspring made of China, even of the CCP, was a bitter betrayal of where our loyalties should be. My arguments about human rights and democracy were, no doubt in her mind, the result of long exposure to western-media bias. The irony of Ma, the daughter of two KMT Nationalist politicos, defending the Communists who had routed her family from China and taken everything they had, was head-spinning.

Ma's blood pressure tended to rise whenever we argued about politics, so when she came to visit, the subject of politics—particularly Chinese politics—was strictly verboten on orders of my sister. But that didn't stop my roommate Blair, who adored Ma but loved to get her goat, from stirring that pot.

BLAIR: All these leaders are getting "lifetime terms." Even China!

JAY: (Hissing, beneath breath). Oh no, you di'n't…

MA: WHAT ABOUT CHINA?!

BLAIR: Xi Jinping. He's president for life now!

JAY: Blair, I hate you.

MA: YOU KNOW, PEOPLE REALLY LIKE HIM.

JAY: Ma. The party's papers say the people like him. The people don't really like him.

MA: ALL MY FRIEND LIKE HIM. HE IS WHAT CHINA NEED.

JAY: Well, now they better need him for life.

MA: ANYWAY, IT JUST TEMPORARY TERM.

JAY: Temporary. Really.

MA: YEAH. TEMPORARY FOR LIFE.

Even though she was a U.S. citizen and had spent most of her early life in America, after being immersed in CCP state-run media for the last twenty years, Ma had come to believe the following:

- China has freedom of the press and total freedom to practice religion, as evidenced by the many channels on TV and in the small places of worship permitted in the cities;

- The fact that you can't get YouTube, Facebook, Twitter, CNN, or *The New York Times* inside China isn't a problem because the West just wants to say bad things about China anyway;

- There couldn't be one million Uyghurs in detention camps in the "autonomous" and mostly Muslim province of Xinjiang because her friends in the capital of Urumqi say things are fine there, and in any event, she herself didn't see any camps during her last visit back in the 1990s;

- Chinese people need to stand up for China no matter what because eight nations ganged up on it more than 100 years ago after the Boxer Rebellion and robbed China of its future; and

- Everything being done to suppress rights and freedom in China is necessary to make China strong and repel Western influence.

Ma was not alone in believing this. She didn't need Facebook to create her own echo chamber of Chinese patriots deeply suspicious of U.S. motives. It was common for her to circulate emails from her friends that boosted the latest bizarre conspiracy theory, and I started to better understand how American cable news viewers, over time, might come

241

to hold their wacky and anti-factual views about our own country. It also made some kind of perverse sense out of the Russian populace's seemingly unwavering support for Putin's war in Ukraine.

Trump's ascendency and a long trade war with China only solidified her views. The U.S. was out to destroy China, because it was jealous, because it was afraid, because it did not like to share power. As a result, it had become impossible for me to say anything remotely critical about China without Ma becoming very agitated and spouting all manner of state-sponsored talking points back. She used to think far more critically, so much so that other Chinese Americans accused her of being a revolutionary.

The most recent kerfuffle was over the company Huawei, a rising Chinese telecommunications company and darling among China's social elites, which also made it an easy target in the simmering trade war. Trump's Justice Department had just upped the ante by arresting Huawei's charismatic CFO, who was also the daughter of the company's founder. To put this in context, it was as if Ivanka Trump had been taken into custody by the Chinese government. Ma was glued to the coverage, the outrageousness of the tactics only confirming her worst suspicions about America and reinforcing China as the victim in all of this.

"POOR HUAWEI. WHY THE U.S. HATING IT SO MUCH? JUST A COMPANY. SUCCESSFUL CHINESE COMPANY."

I really didn't have any answers for her. Trump kept making everything more difficult to explain.

"Huawei will be just fine," I said, hoping not to get into it with her.

"THEY STILL HOLDING HER? THE LEADER?"

"Their CFO. Yes, she is still being held in Canada."

242

Ma was pretty certain that, back in the 1980s, our phone lines had been tapped because the government somehow knew to search her luggage. She even pointed out that "THEY MAKE ME TAKE MY SHOE OFF" once when she alighted in Tokyo while en route to Beijing. No amount of explaining about random searches, or pointing out that static on the phone lines did not necessarily mean someone was listening, could assuage her suspicions.

"I DON'T KNOW HOW THE U.S. BECOME LIKE THIS."

In her mind, the U.S. used to be a place of decent, polite people who asked decent, polite questions about China, not some place that would actually arrest the scion of one of China's most famous families.

"What, arresting people for political purposes? Sounds familiar."

"HAHA. BUT CHINA IS GETTING BETTER, LITTLE BY LITTLE. U.S. GOING THE OTHER WAY."

"That is a fair view of things," I agreed.

"MAYBE THEY MEET IN THE MIDDLE, RUIN EVERYTHING."

My brother Kaiser and his wife had a good way of dealing with Ma's politics. After she'd left New York and flown down to North Carolina to see them, she still hadn't managed to let the Huawei incident go. Unlike me, Kaiser had a more objective view of Chinese politics, and he generally used this to keep Ma from blowing up about it. But even her jingoistic parrotings of the CCP's party line had gotten on his last nerve, and he was on edge and done talking politics with her.

On their way to the Raleigh-Durham airport to drop her off, Ma once again brought up the way Huawei had been so ill-used by the U.S. and how the arrest was really about wanting to keep China down. Rather than argue, Kaiser suggested that it was a tactical blunder by the U.S. to detain her because it looked like obvious revenge. Beijing could

243

have had something of the moral high ground. He posited and won its case in at least the court of international public opinion.

To his surprise, his wife Fanfan started laying into him with a textbook aggrieved-nationalist argument, something about hitting back and the futility of making any kind of moral case and about how strength determines everything. She appeared to get pretty heated. Kaiser offered lukewarm resistance, "two wrongs don't make a right," and that sort of thing, but she kept at it.

Ma went silent during this whole tirade before quietly suggesting that they maybe not talk about politics if it was going to make them fight. As they got out of the car, she couldn't resist adding, "BUT I TAKE FANFAN SIDE IN THIS."

They checked Ma in, quietly upgraded her cross-country flight to California, summoned the whalechair assistant to get her to the gate, and said their goodbyes. As they strolled back to the airport garage, Fanfan took Kaiser's arm and was noticeably happier.

"Were you faking that fight?" he asked her.

She smiled slyly and said, "Maybe a little."

Fanfan truly possessed high-level mother-in-law management skills.

June 1946
Jiangdianjie, China

At age 14, my father stepped off the narrow ledge of the train car at the Luohe railway station and onto a platform far too small to handle all the people shoving and pushing. With the war against Imperial Japan finally won, the family regrouped at the Kuo compound in Jiangdianjie in Henan Province.

Disorder still reigned in China, with the civil war starting up again more or less where it had left off, the KMT Nationalist government only nominally in charge but losing ground steadily to Mao and his insurgency. Ba's father, my *yeye*, had ordered his children and my *nainai* to Henan Province, where they might find safety and refuge behind the high, guarded walls of their family compound. It would be a critical stopover on their journey to the restored capital in Nanjing. Ba's siblings—my aunt and my two uncles—were already in Jiangdianjie. Ba was the last of the Kuo children to arrive, along with my grandparents.

Ba had not seen a modern city like Luohe since they'd fled Nanjing seven years earlier for greater safety inland. The wartime capital of Chongqing, which was chosen in part for its inaccessibility, had produced barely any manufactured goods: no glass, no cement, no metal that wasn't destined for guns or ammunition. There were also no trains, no motorcars, and no telephone wires. Luohe was like stepping into another world.

Ba scanned the station for any sign of his own grandfather, whom everyone called Sanye because he was the third of three brothers, all grandfathers now. Ba had never met Sanye, only seen a faded photograph from long ago. There would be no placard with names on it to greet them because Sanye was totally illiterate. He couldn't have made a greeting sign unless someone else, like Daye (the eldest of the three brothers), had thought to write it out for him.

"Isn't it strange, Ma?" I asked as I wrote down Ba's account of his time there best I could. "Ba was one of three brothers, Yeye's father was one of three brothers, you had three brothers, and I'm one of three brothers."

"ALWAYS THREE," Ma agreed. "WAIGONG ALSO, ONE OUT OF THREE."

"It's strange."

"NOT SO STRANGE," Ma remarked. "HAVING MANY BOY IMPORTANT, IN CASING SOME DIE."

The chatter from the gathered humanity on the train platform in Luohe was nearly unintelligible to Ba, who spoke common Mandarin and some Sichuanese, not the Henan dialect of the area. He stood staring about as my grandparents patiently negotiated the busy platform with their belongings. That's when an old but very energetic man began waving at them, standing far taller than the others around him. He had a rough face, crew-cut hair, and a broad smile, and he still looked like the man in the faded picture.

"Ah! You made it, you made it!" Sanye cried, gesturing for Nainai to let go of her luggage. Behind Sanye was a guard armed with a rifle standing next to two mule-drawn carts. A bored driver absently chewed a piece of straw. "Come, come, come, let's get away from here. Cooler on the road! So many people, no? Give Xiao Jun your bag, and he'll put it in the cart! How was your trip? Are you hungry? I brought some *shaobing*. The sesames are grown right on our land!" Sanye handed my bewildered father and each of my grandparents a cold bun wrapped in a cloth.

"Now, you must be the oldest boy, Guo Kai," Sanye said, using the plain name originally given to Ba. "Get in the back. Go on, just hop up. It's a long trip out to Jiangdianjie. Three hours, if we set a good pace."

"Aren't you getting in, too?" teenaged Ba stammered, finally saying something in response to the flurry of questions and information.

"Me? No, no, I'll jog alongside. It's good for the health. Have to keep fit!"

The cart had no seats, just a flatbed platform, so Ba pulled himself up and sat with his skinny legs dangling off the side, my grandparents climbing awkwardly into the other. Nainai still had on shoes with heels, even if she was reduced to riding in a mule cart. Ba marveled as the driver urged his fly-pestered animals forward, and the carts lurched to life behind them. Sanye kept a brisk pace beside him, talking excitedly and waving his dirt-crusted hands constantly, as if they were crows ready to fly off. The guard trotted behind them all, not saying a word. Every few miles, though, he would fire a shot into the sky as if to warn any others that they were armed and not to try anything.

Sanye was nothing like Yeye would later become, meaning a quiet scholar with a cough from smoking too much, one who never exercised except to push his pen around a page and to stretch his back from hunching over his desk, chest concave from years of bad posture. Sanye, at nearly 70 years old, was strong enough to jog alongside for the full three hours, putting everyone to shame. He made the trip back to Jiangdianjie pass quickly as he regaled them with tales for which he was famous. He may not have been able to read, but his memory was like no other. The world was a big, magical adventure around Sanye.

Ba had heard the story of Sanye and his two brothers: Daye, the oldest, and Erye, the second. Many generations ago, the family had been rich, with ancestors in Shanxi Province who were rumored to have ties to the Ming court. They had come to southern Henan Province in the late 18th century. But by the end of the next century, the Kuos had fallen into hard times, with their land holdings divided so many ways. The three brothers had begun their lives in poverty, with only 40 *mu* of land to their name. Despite humble beginnings, the three brothers made a strong and successful troop. Daye was their leader, with great plans and ambitions; Erye was organized and prudent and kept good books; Sanye was daring and charismatic, though something of a playboy.

247

Daye constantly reminded them that, with three brothers working, they were a lot stronger together than apart. Like fingers in a fist, bunched together, they were unbreakable, an image Ba carried with him and later demonstrated memorably to us sons. Daye had hatched a plan to collect hogs from the farms around their county and ship them to Hankou, which was part of a tri-municipality known collectively as Wuhan. They bought hogs at low prices and put them onto boats up the Louhe and the Shahe rivers, then walked the final 400 kilometers to the city. There, they sold the hogs at a considerable profit then made their way back downriver or hitched a ride on the train and used the money to buy even more hogs. The cycle repeated, and their profits grew.

Daye used the money to become an influential member of the growing merchant class, which had arisen from the ruins of the Qing dynasty to form the core of civil order and society in Republican China. Daye had gotten an education and had even stood for the Confucian Civil Service Examinations, which he had "almost passed," so the legend went. Because of this, Daye was held in high regard by the town, and he did not suffer fools. When one of his nephews had cheated their neighbors in a business deal, Daye gave him a very public beating for it, calling him a good-for-nothing lout who brought shame to their family. That incident became instant Kuo lore.

Under Daye's leadership, the family had grown wealthy over the three decades, diversifying from hogs into the production of sesame and soybean oil made the old-fashioned way, with dozens of manual laborers working nearly naked in the heat of the late summer, twisting and hammering a huge press made of giant planks of wood and steel wedges that squeezed the oil out of millions of sesame seeds. The Kuos also now owned the county's only cigarette-rolling machine, a foot-operated contraption that could turn out finished, perfectly-rolled cigarettes at the rate of three per second. With the considerable profits from that one machine, the brothers had also begun to buy up huge tracts of farmland. As the mule cart passed through the county, Sanye pointed to parcels and said, "That is our land over there. And that, over there!"

As they approached Jiangdianjie, Sanye urged Ba to stand up tall on the back of the cart. Sanye threw out his arm wide, his hands sweeping and pointing off in different directions. "As far as you can see, all of this is yours! All of this is yours!" It was a moment Ba would remember his whole life, and he retold it frequently to us as Ma scowled. Once upon a time, the family had been fantastically wealthy, with over 30,000 *mu* of prime farmland in their name. That was about 5,000 western acres, he explained, but the sheer size of it could not be conveyed by words.

Closer to the Kuo compound, Ba noticed guards both on the ground and in the *zhuanlou*, whose spiraling stairs led up three stories to gun emplacements, where they could get a clear shot at any intruders. The gray, somber walls were pockmarked with bullet holes. They had fought bandits, Sanye explained, which was why they kept fifty guns on the property, including ten German lugers, which they called *heizipao*, or "box cannons," due to the shape of the magazine. Sanye himself was in charge of the militia. "We have a hundred people eating at the house every day," Sanye boasted. "Many distant relatives, plus the guards and servants. Sometimes when the bandits come, all the villagers crowd inside. A whole village! Can you imagine? Well, they overstay their welcome. But all the Kuos are gathered here now. You should treat it as a vacation!"

My aunt and uncles, still children at the time, were waiting outside. The boys had grown, but Gugu looked paler and even more withdrawn. She was a member of the CCP, and her strong proletariat convictions had bristled at the wealth and extravagance of the Kuo family estate in Henan. My uncles didn't seem to care.

"Jenkai! Mama, Baba!" the littlest shouted. "Wait till you see! We are in the main compound! It's as big as the entire dorm in Chongqing."

249

"And they serve us four dishes at every meal!" Ba's other brother added.

"That food belongs to the people," said Gugu, scowling. "We take it from their starving bellies and waste so much of it."

"Good to see peace hasn't changed you," Yeye said to her.

"If you don't want your food, I will eat it," Ba offered.

"Come inside," Sanye said. "Or the bandits will come to kidnap you, put a chain through your collarbone. These KMT scoundrels will shoot you dead just to take just coppers off of you," he warned.

During the war, they had fought off Japanese soldiers and even killed two of them, dumping their bodies into a local well to hide them. The villagers normally liked to drop watermelons down long ropes into the village wells to cool them during the hot summers, but they knew better than to use the well where the soldiers' bodies were decomposing.

After the war, the danger was now roving bandits, deserters from the KMT army who had come through Jiangdianjie and attempted to extort local merchants. When a pack of them arrived at the compound, they met with surprisingly fierce resistance. The battle had gone on for more than a day, but the former KMT soldiers had been beaten back, with many of their dead comrades dumped into the river by the Kuo militia. They had not expected an armed defense, and they never returned again.

The largest city in the region was Wuyang, some four hours by buggy. Sanye took my father and his brothers around to the villages and even as far as Wuyang, where Sanye hosted parties and big banquets. Ba was impressed by how much respect his grandfather received, treated as if he were royalty everywhere they went. But Ba also saw that this respect was largely bought, and he felt both thrilled and a bit ashamed.

That summer, as Ba told it, he felt like he was the master of the world. No more would he wake up to air-raid sirens and have to run for the shelters. He was the favored heir to the Henan lands, a role he threw himself into. He felt confident that he knew everything and could do anything that anyone put in front of him, including driving mules to plow the fields and cracking a whip expertly. All that summer, he went off with his grandfather to the countryside, watching as Sanye performed every task with method and precision. There was so much he wanted to learn from him. At night, they slept in granaries on the threshing floor, with Ba dozing off to sleep as Sanye spun his fantastical tales.

His summer nearly ended tragically, however, when Ba suddenly grew gravely ill from typhoid. He could neither eat nor walk, and he felt his strength draining away. Typhoid killed most who contracted it at the time, and there were no doctors in Jiangdianjie who could provide any medicine or relief. Instead, they resorted to folk remedies. They cooked a turtle shell in salt, then dropped it into a bowl of vinegar to dissolve, and forced the noxious liquid down Ba's throat again and again for several days. He took opium ash for his diarrhea and the innards of beetles for his flagging strength. Despite these horrific remedies, Ba recovered.

Before he left that fall, Ba traveled once more to Wuyang to see his mysterious San Shushu, or third uncle, who lived in an even grander courtyard complex. His uncle's house had even more guards than the ancestral complex in Jiangdianjie. They had positioned themselves around the outside of the house to protect it on three different sides. Gigantic ceramic barrels, big enough to hold some forty gallons each, lined the walls of the entire courtyard, two or three high and two deep in some places. When Ba asked San Shushu what was in them, his uncle simply shook his head and growled, "Nothing that is your business."

This was probably the wrong answer to give my father, whose curiosity burned during their entire visit. On the night before they were to depart, Ba crept out into the courtyard and, using a long piece of bamboo, pried the lid off one of the barrels. Inside he could make out the unmistakable thick, viscous paste of opium. The same held true with the second barrel. If all of the barrels held opium, it was an enormous sum.

Ba told us he was appalled, so stunned by his discovery that he sat down in disbelief. Nainai had drilled into her own children the story of how her family was once very well-to-do, how she was a *Da Xiaojie,* the eldest daughter in a prominent household, but her father had become an opium addict and had sold off all of their possessions, all of their gold, and eventually even the very bricks of their house to pay for his habit. That drug left him and many in their house in a state of hazy incapacitation for days on end. Opium had been foisted upon the nation by the western imperialists in order to keep the Chinese down. And now it was here, on their family's property.

There in the courtyard, surrounded by barrels of opium, Ba suddenly understood why his mother had steadfastly refused all of the gold that the family had tried to send to them during the war. Opium had already destroyed her father's family, and she wasn't going to let it destroy her own.

"What are you doing?" San Shushu said. Ba had not heard him come into the courtyard.

"I should ask you the same," Ba responded heatedly. "What are you doing? Are we selling this? Are we merchants of death?"

"Children should not ask these questions," San Shushu said. "Little children should not pry into adult matters."

"I am no little child. But I am a young man who is ashamed," Ba said, his voice steady. "Older sister was right. The wealthy are the true

252

traitors of this country. It is bad enough that we take the peasants' food and profit from their hard labor. But to learn we also deal in *this*, this *poison* that has crippled our whole country and made us beggars at the feet of the Europeans, how can our family ever hold our heads up when we have done this? How can we call ourselves Chinese?"

"Be careful what you say," San Shushu warned. "Do not think to question my patriotism."

"Mao is coming," Jenkai said, parroting the words he'd heard from the many left-leaning student leaders, including his own sister. "And he will sweep all of this corruption and decay away. You will see, and you will regret it!"

San Shushu took out a cigarette and then lit it, slowly puffing while regarding his hot-headed nephew. "You are a boy. You understand nothing. Put the lids back on, and go inside."

After that night, Ba didn't see San Shushu for many decades. The next time they met, some forty-five years later, China had reopened its doors to the outside world, and San Shushu had become a professor in Inner Mongolia. He was, in fact, now a dean at the Inner Mongolia Animal Husbandry Institute and was a leading expert in, of all things, the raising of chickens. San Shushu threw a feast of chickens and freshly roasted lamb leg, served in a *hothot* tent, in honor of his now very American nephew, Jenkai, and his entire family. Apparently, San Shushu's former status as a landholding capitalist and drug-smuggling kingpin had cost him neither his life nor his freedom, even through the anti-rightist campaigns and the Cultural Revolution itself, when so many who had committed much lesser crimes of capitalism had suffered and died. San Shushu was always wily that way, but Ba had thought to himself that the Communists must indeed be experts at reforming people to have turned a dangerous criminal into a peaceful teacher.

After the splendid dinner, San Shushu pulled Ba aside, his eyes still bearing the same searching quality he recalled from so long before. "We left things on bad terms back in Wuyang," he offered. "Do you remember?"

Ba nodded. That argument had haunted him for many years. "I do. It was a bitter moment for us both."

"You questioned my patriotism. You said Mao would sweep me and other bad elements away. You were too young to understand. I told you that at the time. But you are old enough now to know the truth."

Ba suppressed a smile. He was in his 60s, an old man himself now, but San Shushu still saw him as the angry young man he'd been. "Okay, then. Let's hear it."

"We were trafficking in opium, that is true. But I was a patriot. In fact, I had joined the Communist underground. I wanted the KMT gone and wanted a new China to arise. So I decided to help out. I helped Mao."

Ba blinked back in surprise. "You helped *Mao*?"

"Mao had the people, but he didn't have a way to arm and feed them. He needed financial backers, rich ones, for his peasant revolution to succeed. It's really ironic if you think about it."

"You backed Mao with drug money?"

"Where do you think the money we made from the opium went?" said San Shushu, a final twinkle in his eye. "It went to Mao. We gave it to him for his revolution."

Those were the last words he ever heard from his uncle, the man who had helped fund Mao Zedong, the revolutionary, the hero, the egomaniac, the monster. Opium, the weapon of the West, had crippled the wealthy classes of China and then had funded the very revolution that undid them. Ba would live just long enough to see the West begin to face its own opium crisis, with millions of Americans addicted to the numbness offered by corporate pharmaceutical peddlers. A different kind of revolution, but one built on resentment and despair nonetheless, would start to take hold. San Shushu's revelation changed the way Ba thought of the world, and he wondered how much else he had failed to understand.

"I remember when we went to Jiangdianjie to see the old family home," I said to Ma, as I pressed for more details about San Shushu and the incident with Ba. "I remember the peasants lining the streets to watch our car entering the town."

"THEY NEVER SEEING CAR BEFORE. COW ALSO SCARED OF SEE CAR," Ma said, laughing at the memory.

"Ba told us so many stories about the family's land, but all I can remember was how poor everyone looked. There were still children running naked in the dirt street and carts pulled by mules."

Then, the strongest memory of all washed over me. Ma had spied an old, rickety wagon and urged me to climb up on it. I was about the same age Ba had been when he first arrived in Jiangdianjie. Ma told me to try to stand up straight. She looked triumphant as I shakily locked my legs and held my head up, as if she had waited for this very moment for years.

"LOOK AROUND," Ma cried. "AS FAR AS YOU CAN SEE. *NONE* OF THIS IS YOURS! *NONE* OF THIS IS YOURS!"

October 2015
New York City, New York

> JAY and MA are seated in Union Square Park. Ma is expertly judging the appearance of the people passing them.

MA: LATELY, SO MANY CHINESE MEN GOING BALDY.

JAY: You think they're suddenly losing their hair more?

MA: YEAH. MY FATHER FRIEND ALL HAVE THEIR HAIR. BUT CHINESE MEN TODAY LOSING IT ALL. SO SAD.

JAY: I don't think there's more baldness than before historically.

MA: MEN HAVING TO USE THEIR BRAIN A LOT MORE TODAY.

> A beat, as Jay considers whether this has any validity.

MA: SO THEY LOSING THEIR HAIR MORE.

JAY: So, are you saying your father's generation didn't use their brains?

MA: WELL, LOOKING WHAT HAPPEN TO CHINA BACK THEN.

August 1970
Taipei, Taiwan

"Hurry, Senator. Hurry!" the nurse said to Ma's father—my *waigong*—while holding out a patient's gown and some footies for him to slip on. "They are only minutes away!"

"Yes, yes," said Waigong impatiently. "Someone tell the doctors to stall them!"

"There's no stopping the director if he wants in," the nurse said, referring to Director Zhang, the feared deputy head of the Secret Police. "Hurry, now! Down the hallway, first room on the right!"

"I know where my own room is," Waigong growled.

"Hurry, hurry!"

They scurried down a dimly lit hall into a small corner room, where two other nurses were frantically pulling in equipment and setting clean linens on the bed. Waigong's butler, Lao Fan, was there, putting half-fresh flowers in a vase and arranging half-eaten tins of food and stained teacups as well. Nice touch, he thought.

The assembled team knew the drill and had practiced and run this very exercise successfully before. My grandfather was technically under arrest after publicly opposing President Jiang's plan to appoint his own son as vice president. Waigong hated the nepotism that coursed through the Republic's veins, even in exile on the tiny island of Taiwan. Fortunately, he wound up only serving two days in the horrifying central prison. Through some clever advocacy from his friend—the Chief Administrator at Taiwan General Hospital—and a few generous bribes to the local police, Waigong was permitted to serve out the balance of his sentence in his own private hospital room, under a medical exception. The doctor's fabricated report indicated tuberculosis, but truth be told, granddad was in radiantly good health.

257

The upside of being at the hospital was that it was only a few minutes' walk from his home, and after a week of being stuck in the dank and depressing room and already tiring of flirting with the nurse staff, Waigong had worked out with the hospital how he could stay at his own home most of the time. Should any official visitors arrive to see him, the staff would ring him at home, and he would speed over and head up the back stairwell while the visitors were still downstairs waiting to be let up. The staff and his Lao Fan would make it appear as if my grandfather had never left the room.

"That really worked?" I asked Ma.

"ACTUALLY, NURSE PREFER HE NOT AROUND BECAUSE HE SO DEMAND THIS, DEMAND THAT. SO THEY GOING ALONG WITH PLAN."

Waigong was still a striking figure, his hair still full and black, and his posture strong and upright. To play the part of the invalid, he slipped into the bed, and a nurse stood over him as if taking his pulse when Director Zhang entered.

"Ah, Senator," Zhang said, his eyes hard and sharp. "I hope I'm not disturbing you."

"Director Zhang," Waigong said. "What an honor to lay eyes upon you again."

"You certainly look fresh and well-rested," Zhang remarked.

"And you look tired and overworked," Waigong responded.

Zhang snorted and walked about the room, his eyes surveying the details, two bodyguards standing sentry at the door with others no doubt down the hall. Ever since the attempted assassination of the president's son, the secret police had been busy rounding up, arresting and, rumor had it, torturing the president's political rivals and their associates.

"I trust your health is improving then," Zhang said. "But not so much that you should return to prison."

"There are good days and bad," my grandfather said. "Today has been a good one, capped off with a visit from you."

Zhang smiled too broadly, the gold on a front tooth glinting. Waigong's butler broke the awkward silence that followed.

"May I offer you some tea, Director?" Lao Fan asked. Zhang held up a hand, dismissing him.

"We may have been remiss, charging you only with subversion," Zhang said. "But the President can be sentimental. He doesn't like seeing his old friends suffer. Especially those who have long served the country, as you and your wife have."

Ma's parents were the first married couple to both win an election to represent their home province in the Chinese National Legislature. They were the celebrated "ten thousand-year" lawmakers—the implication being that they would never step down. Laolao had thrown her hat in without thinking she would actually win anywhere near the top number of votes, but she wound up securing more than anyone, including her husband. Rather than present as a powerful and celebrated couple, which might draw the political jealousies and suspicions of others, Laolao graciously declined her seat, saying it was enough that her husband loved Henan Province and would serve it loyally.

That was almost more than twenty years ago before the entire legislature fled along with President Jiang to Taiwan. There they set up a makeshift chamber in exile, still claiming to be the rightfully elected representatives to a land now run by the Communists, while

Jiang ruled them as a de facto dictator under martial law. Efforts to reform the political system were routinely and ruthlessly quashed. As expected, no new elections for their seats were held.

"I only think and act for the good of the nation," said Waigong simply. "Perhaps I am sentimental as well."

Director Zhang smiled. "You might find it of interest to know, then, that we are holding your eldest son."

"What's that?" my grandfather asked, heat suddenly welling in his chest.

"Oh, yes, he is quite the troublemaker for someone so young, don't you agree? Star basketball player, top student, but spends too much time around leftist student groups. They are a poor influence on him."

"Why are you holding him?" Waigong demanded, his voice rising, forgetting completely that he was allegedly weak with tuberculosis. "On what charges?"

"Conspiracy."

"Conspiracy of what?"

"To assassinate the President," Zhang said simply as if speaking of the weather.

Waigong scoffed. "Nonsense. My son is no traitor and has not a violent urge in him. He's an honor student. You have made a mistake. You have the wrong person."

"We have his confession already," Zhang said, still smiling. "He gave it earlier today. It only took four unpleasant hours."

"What have you done to him?!" Waigong cried, as the nurses, and Lao Fan held him from leaping out of bed.

"He is fine, don't concern yourself. He had no need for a doctor or hospital."

"ACTUALLY, MY BROTHER NEVER SAME AFTER HE COME OUT OF THERE," Ma said to me sadly. "HE LOSING LOOK IN HIS EYES, ALWAYS LOOKING SCARED. BEFORE WAS SO CONFIDENT YOUNG MAN."

"Where is he now? How dare you do this to him and to our family?!" Waigong's eyes burned with rage. He wanted to strangle Zhang, close his fingers around his throat and watch that smirk turn to terror.

"Young Liu apparently has been very angry about your arrest," Zhang continued, his words dripping with false concern. "He has been telling other students he would seek revenge for it. Very brave. Very foolish. We have many witnesses."

"He's a boy! Just seventeen years old, maybe just trying to prove he's a man. How can you take such boasts seriously, even if he ever made them? This is an outrage!"

"We take every threat on the president very, very seriously," Zhang said. "And it is my job to ensure no further violence is ever directed again at the president or his family. You don't wish to see me out of a job, do you?" Zhang leaned in to speak more quietly. "You would do well to support the president and his son in his new role. Don't you see? We can't allow Beijing to believe we are weak and splintered. Be a loyal partisan and we will let your son out, perhaps after a few weeks, once he has learned his lesson."

Waigong's mind raced. He thought of his other children. His eldest daughter, my mother, was already in America, having been spirited out of the country as soon as the KMT had tried to recruit her as a

261

party spokesperson. His two other sons and younger daughter were still little, but that might not stop Zhang from using them as further pawns in his games. Grandfather needed time to get them to safety, but he could not appear weak, or he would have no bargaining power left.

"Don't pretend you are making a deal with me," Waigong said, his own voice now edged like a dagger, a skill he had learned over the years dealing with bullies and thugs. "You think you hold a trump card with my son? But if you wanted me dead or disappeared, that would have happened already." He began to see the game more clearly, even as he spoke the words. "No. What you actually need is my voluntary cooperation. Jiang needs the support of the ten-thousand year Congress and the United States. There is talk in Washington of playing China against the Soviets, leaving Taiwan exactly nowhere. Jiang is scared he will lose support, and that is why you are here."

He could see the thoughts turning in Zhang's head as the director's eyes shifted almost imperceptibly. It was time to press his advantage and call the bluff.

"But you have a problem, don't you?" Waigong asked, his voice steady as a monsoon rain. "You don't know how to win my support, so instead, you seek to frighten me into giving it by roughing up a boy. I wonder what the president would say if the American embassy were to hear of this? Eh? Quite a mess you would have, beating up family members of loyal parliamentarians. It would only confirm what the White House believes, that the future isn't with the tyrant of a tiny island, but with the tyrant of a mighty mainland."

Zhang snorted, regarding him coolly. Waigong felt the familiar rush of having pushed all his bets in, the firing squad again at the ready, his hands and eyes bound, gambling everything on another gut call. Zhang broke the moment with a laugh.

"You are certainly a fox and as difficult to hunt," Zhang said. "We'll let your boy and this misunderstanding go. I hope you won't disappoint us again, Senator."

Waigong waited until Zhang and his guards were gone, then pulled Lao Fan over, speaking in his ear. "Go see that my other children are safe. Then get them out of Taipei and to America as quickly as possible. Don't tell my wife what has happened, only that for their safety, the children must leave."

"And your wife? Will Manxi be going as well?"

"No," he laughed. "Manxi has never run from a fight in her life. She will stay. Zhang won't touch her, and she's too high-profile. If something were to happen to her, the Pope himself would probably hear of it."

Lao Fan bowed, and he was out the door. As he left, my grandfather saw how his family would soon be scattered, exiled even from their current exile. Decades of his life and his work were evaporating quickly, like mist before a burning sun, the last hope for a Chinese civil society dissipating with each baton blow to his son's body. He had long since lost faith in the future of the Republic. That faith had been dealt a mortal blow by the *Baise Kongbu*, the White Terror, begun by Jiang with the slaughter of thousands of Taiwanese civilians on *Er Erba,* the 28th of February, 1947, even before the KMT evacuated to the island. A brutal crackdown on dissidents and intellectuals followed, leading to a permanent state of martial law in Taiwan.

Grandfather had kept his head down and his mouth shut as colleagues accused of being communist sympathizers disappeared forever, leaving so many widows and orphans.

"HE KNOW HE CAN BE CRUSHED, JUST LIKE ANT," Ma explained. "GOVERNMENT CAN BE LIKE THAT."

Waigong's mistake had been to even question the right of the president to appoint his own son to political office. That hubris had cost him his freedom and nearly cost him his son.

He saw it clearly and personally now. Jiang was no better than Mao, a despot ruling through fear and violence, as so many Chinese would-be emperors had before. He had served under other men like that, and he had survived them all. Eventually, their own power and ego would undo them. He only had to wait and outlast them.

That was the thing about emperors. They were just ordinary mortals, stupidly believing they were demi-gods bearing the Mandate of Heaven. But the world turns and turns yet again, and Heaven laughs at their many schemes and plans. And in the end, empires and emperors always crumble.

Chapter Eight

BUSINESS

or

"THAT IS CHINA"

April 1998
Beijing, China

"What do you mean you are 'keeping' my lawyer?" I asked the man on the phone.

"I am saying we have your lawyer, and if you don't agree to our demands for payment, then we will not release him!"

I heard a number of others murmur their approval behind whoever was on the phone. His Beijing accent was very thick, making him seem gruff and uncouth, the linguistic equivalent of a strong English cockney. Ba poked his head into the office, and I put my hand over the receiver.

"I sent Victor over to talk to the construction crew, and now they're holding him hostage!" I explained. Ba closed his eyes and took a deep breath. I wasn't sure if he was tired or trying to think. Perhaps both.

"Chinese see lawyers as troublemakers," he explained. Most of the world does, I thought.

"So what am I supposed to do?"

"WHAT HAPPENING?" Ma said, nosing in on our conversation.

"I got Victor into a mess with the old construction crew, and now they won't let him go."

"WELL. THAT IS CHINA," Ma said simply.

Ba shrugged. He had warned me against trying to reason with the men and specifically against this particular legal escalation. He turned and walked away, his version of an "I told you so."

"We don't want to hold him here, but you have left us no choice!" the man yelled. "You have not acted fairly! We want to talk to Mr. Kuo. The older Mr. Kuo."

The man holding my friend, Victor, whose Chinese name was Wang Qin, was part of a work crew that had been hired by a local construction company. Many years back, Ba had paid that company a considerable sum to complete my grandmother's house on the west side of Beijing. But like many things in China, the project hit complications and delays, and the original builder vanished not long after Ba had paid the deposit, the house remaining only partially completed. Ba had to find a second construction company to come and finish the job.

But as it turned out, like so many projects in China, the first company had never actually paid its construction crew for the work that they had done, so after their boss disappeared with their wages, they turned their ire on Ba. He tried to explain that he was also a victim since he had shelled out twice for the same house and that if the workers had a problem with anyone, it was with their boss, not him.

This explanation, though facially logical and fair, did nothing to tamp down their anger. Their efforts to locate their old boss had ended in failure, so the workers had started sitting outside our house, banging pots and pans and shouting, "Mr. Kuo took our money! Mr. Kuo is a cheat! Our money is in this house!" Sometimes, the banging and shouting would go on for hours. The neighbors understandably were less than happy with the ruckus, and while the local police had already come twice to clear the workers away and had even cited them, the former construction crew simply came back the next week.

"THAT JUST HOW CHINESE CAN BE," Ma explained. "LIKE OUR OLD NEIGHBOR, REMEMBER? SO ANGRY THAT WE BUILDING TALL HOUSE NEXT TO HER DINKY HOUSE. SHE CANNOT STOP OUR BUILDING, SO SHE SIT IN MIDDLE OF CONSTRUCTION ON A STOOL, NOT MOVING, SO STUBBORN!"

I remembered seeing a similar story on the Chinese news of a homeowner who had refused to yield his property rights to an indifferent construction company, no matter how much he was paid, so they had dug an entire pit, many stories deep around the house, cutting him off entirely. But still, the owner refused to move. The national viewers saw him as something of a martyr.

The situation outside our house in Beijing had worsened to the point that Ba armed our maid and her live-in husband with small cattle prods, in the event the workers tried to break past our gate. I asked them if they had ever used them before, but they just laughed nervously. I suggested to Ba that we try instead to pay off the workers so they would go away. He listened skeptically to my plan but, in the end, agreed that Victor could go meet them, if only to relay our position as our lawyer, then try and find out what settlement offer might mollify them.

"Do not let dem know you are nervous, always show strength, or at least no emotions," Ba had advised several times on doing deals with the Chinese. "Dey will be dis way, too, very calm and polite until near to de close of negotiation, den dey will get suddenly angry or upset, and dey hope dat will push you towards a final deal."

"That's crazy!" I protested. "It's just theatrics."

Ba laughed. "Dat is China."

I had already gotten used to several cultural differences while doing business in China alongside Ba. By the late 1990s, our family had interests in several heavy industries: a concrete-pipe manufacturing plant that supplied water mains to China's burgeoning cities, a copper-mining operation that used American block-caving to improve their low yields, a factory making agricultural drying equipment for all manner of crops from ginseng to tobacco. It was as if Ba was driven to restore the Kuo family name to its former success back when his grandfather and two great-uncles owned 40,000 *mu* in the county.

But Ba didn't have the business savvy of his forefathers, being too forthright and honest a man. Ma often complained that he had a mind that was great for science and technology but not so great for business. Ba had brought me in to untangle the legal and financial messes these businesses were now in after years of corrupt government partners, and he hoped I would assume the helm of the family business when he was ready to retire. After two years in China, I had grown accustomed to transacting business there, but found it so frustrating that I had no interest in taking over from Ba. A contract in America might be dozens of pages long, laying out every term and accounting for every possibility. But in China, a contract was often just a page or two, more of a memorandum or a term sheet, not a contract as I knew them. Anything longer than that, and the Chinese might balk, viewing any complicated agreement with all its conditions and terms as an insult that questioned their very integrity.

But a kidnapping to start negotiations off? That was new. *Don't let dem know you are nervous, always show strength.*

"Put my lawyer on the line. I want to hear that he is okay," I said.

268

Moments later, my buddy, Victor, picked up the phone. He spoke in perfect if uniquely singsong English, breaking longer words into two parts with different tones, which always delighted my ear.

"Jay, I did not know when I ac-cep-ted this re-quest that you would be sen-ding me into a pit of the viiii-pers!" Victor said, humor leaping into his melodious voice, despite the tense circumstances.

"I'm really sorry about that," I said, not knowing what else I could convey. "But quick question: What do they know about your relationship with me and my family? Do they know we're friends?"

"Oh no, not at a-ll," Victor sang. "I just con-veyed that I was your lawwww-yer. That is all they know."

"Okay," I said, thinking hard. "Okay, don't hate me, but I'm going to call their bluff."

"What is that?" Victor chirped. "Oh, yes, of course! From the po-ker game. I saw it in a mo-vie! You are a gam-bler! I do not think that their threat is real here. They look more scared than de-terrr-mined. They have made a dannnn-ger-ous bet."

Ba came back into the office as I spoke with Victor. I saw a chance to prove to Ba how steely I could be. This could be great, or it could be disastrous. I told Victor to put the guy back on.

"Listen," I said, dropping my voice to as butch a one as I could manage. My halting Mandarin was no doubt as grating to them as their guttural dialect was to me, but I wanted to sound as serious as I could. "You can do whatever you want to my lawyer. I owe him money anyway, so if you get rid of him, you'd be doing me a favor."

"Pay us what you owe us!"

"You know that we don't owe you anything," I said. "You know that your old boss is the bad guy here. But I'll tell you what I will do. The lawyer you are holding is very smart, and he's good at finding people. Instead of holding him, why don't you work with him to find your old boss? He has connections at the Public Security Bureau and can help track him down. I'll pay for his time to do that."

They conferred amongst themselves. I could hear them arguing and talking to Victor, his perfect Mandarin a sharp contrast in class and education to their own. It took two more minutes before they put Victor back on. "So, I am sup-posed to help them now, after they took me cap-tive?" he laughed.

"Just tell them you can help, and they'll let you go."

"Well, it is pos-si-ble I ac-tu-ally can help," Victor said. "And they are wor-ried after you said 'PSB.' Well, it is true, I do have some con-tacts there. In China, it can be very hard to hide for long."

After the call was over, Ba seemed both amused and alarmed. "You are a risk taker," he said.

I laughed. "Oh, you mean when I said how they'd be doing me a favor if they got rid of Victor? Yeah, I guess that was a risky bluff."

"You lie so easily," Ba remarked, his eyes studying mine.

"I'm a lawyer," I said, with a laugh that sounded a bit too casual.

"Hmm," Ba said as he walked away.

JAY lies on his bed, making his daily video call to MA. She holds her phone too low, and JAY can only see the top of her head, where he spots many more gray hairs than were there just months earlier.

MA: I HAVE MANY FRIEND IN HONG KONG THINK THEY ARE GLAD TO BE BACK UNDER CHINA. YOU KNOW ENGLAND TAKING HONG KONG FROM CHINA BEFORE, I WANT YOU CHILDREN TO KNOW THIS.

JAY: Yeah, we know.

MA: EIGHT NATION GANGING UP ON CHINA, TAKING DIFFERENT CITY. MACAO GO TO PORTUGAL. TSINGDAO GO TO GERMAN. AND ENGLAND TAKING HONG KONG. SO NOW THEY TRY TO MAKE DIFFICULTY GIVING BACK?

JAY: It's a bit complicated.

MA: ALL MY FRIEND THERE ARE PRO-CHINA. EXCEPT FOR LI SHU SHU, REMEMBER HIM? HE IS ANTI-CHINA. I FEELING SORRY FOR HIM.

JAY: Imagine that, a journalist who is anti-China.

MA: I KNOW! HE JUST MAD THEY TAKING HIS BUILDING.

JAY: Yeah, that would probably make me mad, too. Anyway, I guess there's not much anyone can do now. China is going to have its way. Just like Putin in Russia. Did you see they are clearing the way for him to rule until 2036?

MA: I DON'T THINK HE WILL MAKE IT THAT LONG. HE WILL BE IN HIS EIGHTY.

JAY: He'll never give up power. He could wind up in prison.

MA: MEN NEVER WANTING TO GIVE UP POWER. LOOK AT YOUR DADDY. HE NEVER BELIEVE I CAN DO ANYTHING. I AM JUST A HOUSEWIFE, SO HE CANNOT GIVING UP POWER TO ME.

JAY: (considers this a moment) That's probably a fair statement.

MA: ANYWAY, YOU BABA ONLY THINKING HE HAS POWER. NOT REALLY EVER HAVING IT. ALL THE PROJECT HE GET IN CHINA? HE GET BECAUSE OF ME. HAHA.

JAY: Haha.

MA: NOT BAD FOR POOR HOUSEWIFE.

February 1984
Tucson, Arizona

Another disaster, Ba reported, as he read the quality control report from the hospital buyer. It was the same storyline as usual: Ma had met someone, who had introduced her to someone else, who had set up a meeting with a manufacturer, this time of rubber and latex goods in the south of China, and they had indicated a strong interest in breaking into the medical-supply business in the United States and Europe. Then Ma had come back to Arizona full of ideas and had asked around for weeks before finding a potential buyer at a local hospital, who indicated he wanted a cheaper source for surgical-grade latex gloves.

In earlier days, Ba would have tried to dissuade Ma from moving forward, to remind her that she didn't actually have any experience in latex products, medical products, manufacturing, or even importing or exporting. But he had learned, after several bitter arguments and days of stony silence, that it was better to say nothing, wait for things to go awry, and then see what could be done to fix the situation. His prior naysaying had only angered and emboldened Ma further, and so he was resigned to endure yet another costly business mistake. Ba was mostly there now to make sure she didn't commit too much of the family's savings towards any one idea.

It had been a similar painful lesson after Ma started dabbling in real estate. Around three years ago, she had been keen to buy tracts of land on which she envisioned large residential developments, and she had talked Ba into the idea. In theory, it could have, it ought to have, worked. Tucson was a mini-boom town in the new American sunbelt. Companies like IBM had put down local roots. The University of Arizona attracted talent to its medical school and its astronomy department. Property values were rising. Ba had agreed with her that real estate sounded like a good play. Or perhaps, in retrospect, it was some unconscious drive, passed down through generations of Kuos and Lius, to create wealth through landholdings. The money came and went with governments. Gold could be stolen out from under you, but land? Land was permanent. Land held the key to security.

To finance it, they had gone to good friends to pool their resources. This made getting the money a lot simpler, but it also made it personal. Ba didn't want to lose his own money, but he wanted even less to lose his friends' money along with their faith in him. And so, after getting home from the IBM plant each day, he spent long nights preparing spreadsheets with vast arrays of financial calculations and contingencies, meticulously and even conservatively planned out. Ma's instincts *looked* correct when mapped out. Even if property values grew only at half the current rate, they would do very well. The

273

partnership would flourish, and all their friends would thank them for a handsome return.

Or so Ba thought. That was before the U.S. Federal Reserve, in a bid to fight back inflation, slammed the brakes hard on the economy and drove up interest rates by ten basis points to over 20 percent. It was an outcome that none of his charts and sheets ever came close to predicting. For months, he sat helplessly watching their financing costs shoot up while demand cratered, the beautiful multi-building complex they had planned now reduced to a single sad, completed structure in the middle of nowhere. There was no saving the project; it would fail, and they'd lose all their money. Correction: They'd lose all their friends' money. So Ba made the calls, one after another awkward one, apologizing for the loss. It was a deeply humiliating and painful experience. Even though everyone outwardly said that none of it was his fault, he couldn't convince himself of it.

From that point forward, Ba was more cautious with any business idea and assumed any given project could go belly-up, no matter how carefully he planned. He also decided never to go back to his high school and college friends for investment funds. He couldn't bear to lose their trust and confidence a second time. Besides, he thought morosely, who would trust him again with their money?

Ma, however, seemed to spin in the opposite direction. She somehow parlayed her real-estate failures, along with a growing but mostly untapped list of overseas manufacturing contacts, into a spot on the Sunbelt World Trade Organization, based in Tucson, where she touted her knowledge about and experience in China. It was an audacious claim in Ba's eyes, but his attempts to rein her in had been met with angry and stubborn responses.

"All you ever do is criticize me," she said, arguing in Chinese with Ba. "I am the one out making contacts, generating opportunities, and thinking about new business. Without me, we wouldn't be doing anything at all."

"If you hadn't talked me into this, we wouldn't have lost everyone's money," Ba replied bitterly, but this wasn't totally fair. He had agreed to the venture and been key to its planning. It was as much his failure as anyone's.

But the damage had been done. He had said the terrible thing out loud, and Ma resented him more than ever. She was even more determined to prove her own worth and value. He didn't want to stand in her way, but he also didn't want to gamble on everything again. She tried her hand in all manner of schemes now. Freshwater pearls from China? Why not? Even if it meant setting up and personally staffing a table to move inventory at the Tanque Verde Swap Meet, the local flea market in Tucson, Ma's somewhat random jewelry business made them some good money—apparently, women loved to wear necklaces made of lavender strands of freshwater pearls—at least until an unscrupulous saleswoman named Georgina took possession of $70,000 worth of inventory and promptly disappeared. Ma was very quiet after explaining to Ba what had happened, saying not much more at the end besides, "SOMETIMES, I AM JUST TOO TRUSTING." Ba knew better than to press the matter. She was hard enough on herself about it. He did make sure their business insurance policies were updated, though.

My parents' real estate properties were only a hair above low-income housing units, and they skimped on costs wherever they could. This meant that when tenants moved out, my brothers were sent in to clear and clean the apartments, which were often left in a disgusting state. To manage their properties, they relied on overseas Chinese scholars, like Xiao Li, the rocket researcher, who quietly supervised the Casa de Kelso apartments for them. (Xiao Li was an unassuming and polite man who, to everyone's surprise, later went on to lead China's national rocket program, holding the number two spot at China's equivalent of NASA.)

The surgical gloves were their latest albatross. An entire container's worth was now in a warehouse in Tucson and couldn't be sold because many of them, it turned out, were defective. A spot quality check revealed tiny pin-prick-sized holes in the palms for a large percentage of the gloves, which was only evident after they were inflated with air. The hospital buyer rejected them outright, and Ma had been on the phone with the Chinese supplier for hours, ultimately unsuccessful in negotiating their return with a refund.

"What are we going to do with a bunch of defective surgical gloves?" I asked during an emergency family meeting.

"Same thing we did with that container worth of white T-shirts," Kaiser said flatly, referring to another failed endeavor that bore no easy resolution but inflicted continuing psychic and financial pain in the form of unsold white tees.

"Why didn't we test the gloves before they shipped?" I asked.

"GLOVE WERE TEST, PASS OKAY," Ma said with annoyance. "ONLY WHEN ARRIVE DISCOVER PROBLEM."

"But…" I began, and Ba shook his head. Better not to dwell on what might have prevented this, for everyone's sanity.

"But… if the gloves can't be used for surgery," I said instead, "Maybe someone else can still use them, even with holes in the palms."

"Use them how?" John asked with his usual exasperation.

"Maybe cleaning companies would want them?" I offered. "Or painters?"

"That's a lot of gloves to sell piecemeal," said Kaiser.

"OH! I HAVE IDEA!" Ma said suddenly.

"You do?" Mimi asked, hope in her voice per usual.

"GLOVE HAVING PROBLEM IN PALM, OKAY. BUT WE CAN CUT OFF FINGER FROM GLOVE!"

"Why would we do that?" I asked.

"TO TURN THEM INTO CONDOM!"

I instinctively shot Mimi a look. Her mouth was agape.

"Mary!" my father exclaimed.

"Ma! You can't just cut the fingers off gloves and use them as, well, like that," John said. "They're too small."

"MAYBE NOT TOO SMALL." Ma said slyly. "AT LEAST FOR SOME PEOPLE." She pointedly did not look at any men in the room.

The pain and frustration of the moment dissolved instantly into belly laughs. The children doubled over, and even Ba found himself laughing, which was what everyone really needed.

August 1998
Beijing, China

"LOOK ON THE NEWS!" Ma said, calling me into the living room.

"What's going on?"

I stared at our television and, at first, couldn't make out what I was watching. The broadcast was showing what appeared to be a line of monks in robes, armed with staves and nunchucks, fighting off a group of men armed with machetes. "Where is this?"

"ZHENGZHOU," Ma said. "THAT IS MY COUSIN BUILDING."

The news was breathlessly reporting the melee in front of what looked like a modest office building.

"A group of men representing the bank came armed and ready to seize back the building and its assets inside," the reporter relayed, "when they encountered defenders of an unusual nature: Xiao Lin temple priests, hired by the borrower, who insists that the building cannot be reclaimed extrajudicially in this manner."

"Wait, that's our building?"

"YEAH. MY COUSIN WHO WORKING WITH US ON TOBACCO DRYING, HE RENTING THE BUILDING, BUT BECAUSE OF TRIANGLE DEBT CANNOT MAKE PAYMENT." Triangular or "three-angle" debt was a common phenomenon in China. Borrowers frequently claimed they couldn't repay loans because they were owed money by third parties, and so they were not to blame for their default. If you wanted to collect the money, they would refer you to those third parties.

"BANK DON'T WAITING FOR MONEY, INSTEAD SENDING PEOPLE TO CHASING HIM OUT OF BUILDING. MY COUSIN HEARING THEY GOING TO SEND ARMED PEOPLES TO TAKING IT BACK, SO HE HIRE MONK TO GUARD."

"He hired Shaolin monks to defend the bank building?"

"YES."

"That is probably the coolest thing I have ever heard."

When we were little, Ba had us learn a bit of martial arts and even had us live for a few hard days of training at the Shaolin temple in Henan, not far from his ancestral home. Our only other connection with the Shaolin had been watching the television series *Kung Fu*.

An armed thug on the TV went down under a rain of blows from a very determined monk in a tan robe. Apparently, the reporter said in all seriousness, this was the third unsuccessful attempt by the bank to retake the building by force. Crowds had gathered, which had alerted the press to the fight.

"Where are the police?" I wondered.

"PROBABLY PAID NOT TO BE THERE," Ma said matter-of-factly.

The assailants, bloodied and staggering, retreated. The crowd cheered. Ma looked pleased.

"CHINA REALLY IS THE WILD EAST."

June 2020
FaceTime call

"YOU PUTTING MONEY INTO STOCK?" Ma asked.

"We have only a little bit in stock right now. We're mostly cash," I responded absently. Like her mother before her, Ma had begun to bring up money frequently in her eighties, seeking assurance that we had enough for her to live on. No matter how many times I told her that things were fine, that she had plenty now in the bank and owned her house outright, she still couldn't stop fretting.

"I SEEING MARKET FALL REALLY FAST. DOW DROPPING EIGHTEEN HUNDRED POINT."

"That's actually good for us, bad for other people," I said.

"GOOD FOR US?! DROPPING?"

"We bet against the market. It's called a hedge. When the market goes down, our hedge index makes money. If it goes down a lot, it makes a lot of money."

"GOING DOWN MAKING MONEY?" Ma said skeptically.

"Sometimes," I said, not wanting to explain.

"ANYWAY, SO GLAD WE BUILDING THE HOUSE IN BEIJING, CAN SELL IT MAKING MONEY FOR YOUR POOR MA TO LIVE."

"It was a good investment, Ma." For all the ways Ma had mismanaged the family's money across the decades, the house she had insisted on building in Beijing in the early 1990s made up for all of it many times over.

"WELL, IT A GOOD THING YOU LOOKING OUT FOR IT. WE STILL HAVE MONEY IN CHINA?"

"We moved a bunch of it out," I said for the twentieth or so time.

"MY FRIEND CECILIA CALL ME, TELL ME THAT AFTER JULY 1, THEY WILL BE WATCHING MORE CAREFULLY ANY MONEY MOVING OUT."

"We don't actually move the money out of China," I said, trying both to reassure her and not dump a can of worms in her lap. After we sold Ma's house in Beijing, we had a classic problem of how to get money out of the country. Chinese RMB was not freely convertible, but it had a set value both inside and outside the country, which made moving large sums of it both interesting and challenging.

"YOUR FATHER DID NOT UNDERSTAND WHY I WANT TO BUILD IT. HE THINKING IT WASTE OF MONEY, TOO MUCH TROUBLE. IF NOT FOR ME, WE WOULD NOT HAVE DONE."

There was a hint of pride in her voice. And some pain. For more than three decades, Ma and Ba had fought about money and business, with Ba concluding that Ma took foolish risks for no return and Ma concluding that Ba was too careful and didn't know how to charm his way into a deal or a sale. They were actually both correct, and if they could have worked together as trusted and equal partners rather than tearing each other down non-stop, the results might have been spectacular. Yet, for all their quarreling and recriminations, they had still managed to launch several successful projects in China, to keep from going bankrupt and to provide a comfortable middle-class lifestyle for their children. Long after Ba's death, though, the fallout from those clashes still drifted like floaters in her mind's eye.

"WHEN YOU FATHER LOSS HIS JOB, DO YOU REMEMBER? HOW TROUBLE HE WAS?"

"I remember," I said. "How could I forget?"

"HE PICKING UP THE PLATE, AND BANG!"

I had rarely seen Ba lose his cool before. After twenty-one years working for IBM, he had never expected to find himself in a long unemployment line, waiting for hours just to receive a check for a couple of hundred dollars and change. That same day, he had stood in line, and a credit-card bill arrived showing I had charged more than the amount of his check for some items that I didn't even remember buying. Being a worthless and self-centered teenager, I asked, "What's the big deal?" Ba became so angry he slammed his dinner

281

plate down on the table, shattering it into four pieces. Ba stood up and strode from the table, leaving us staring at the broken plate. It was the first sign he'd ever given of the pressures he was under to provide for us. It was the most vulnerable I had seen him since Yeye died.

"YOU ASKING, HOW ARE WE GOING TO HAVE CHRISTMAS?"

"I was a brat."

"THAT WAS SAME YEAR I FINALLY SOLD MY FIRST PIECE OF LAND AND GET THE BIG CONTRACT FROM CHINA."

"Yeah, you saved Christmas."

"I SAY, WE CANNOT MISS CHRISTMAS! SO I CALL UP THE COPPER MINE PEOPLE IN CHINA, ASKING THEM TO PLEASE PAY US BEFORE CHRISTMAS. THEY SAY, NO PROBLEM! AND I MAKE ENOUGH FOR ALL OF US TO HAVE BIGGEST CHRISTMAS EVER." Ma had a way of tipping her head and jutting her chin out when she made a strong point, but I had to imagine she was doing that now because her camera often only showed the top of her head again. Some of my Asian American friends confirmed that their mothers did exactly the same on video calls.

"You saved Christmas!" I said again, not really listening to the rest of what she said. We had cycled through the exact same conversation two days ago, but I let it go. I was just happy she could recall things and tell her stories at all. This way she could relive and reshape her triumphs, even in a business where she had failed more often than not.

"AND FOLLOWING YEAR WE MAKING MORE MONEY THAN BABA EVER MAKE WORKING IBM, SO WE TAKE YOU CHILDREN ACROSS ALL ASIA ON TRIP. YOU REMEMBER?"

"I remember. It was a great trip." Well, parts of it.

"YOU KNOW, IF IT WERE NOT FOR ME, YOU DADDY NEVER WOULD HAVE CHANCE TO DO BUSINESS IN CHINA. HE SAYING ALL MY IDEA ARE NO GOOD, BUT SOMETIME THEY PRETTY GOOD."

"You were more the idea person, and Ba was more the execution person," I said, offering a familiar yet intellectually lazy parse.

"YEAH, YOUR BABA ALWAYS HAS TO MAKE 'EXECUTION.' I JUST HANGING IN BACKGROUND, KEEPING QUIET."

"I don't think you ever kept quiet, to be honest," I said, laughing.

"HE PREFER I SAY NOTHING, ALWAYS TELLING ME TO 'SHHHH' DURING MEETING. ONE TIME, OUR PARTNER EVEN SAY, 'HOW COME YOU ALWAYS TELLING TANLEE TO BE QUIET? WE ARE HERE BECAUSE WE WANT TO HEAR WHAT SHE HAVING TO SAY!' OH, HE GOT A LOOK ON HIS FACE!"

"Ba liked to mansplain a lot of things, it's true."

"WHA?"

"Mansplain. But I can't tell you what it is without me doing it."

"ANYWAY, SOMETIME I MAKE THE BEST DECISION FOR ALL OF US."

"That's true, Ma."

"SO GLAD WE BUILDING THE HOUSE IN BEIJING," Ma said again.

"I am, too," I said, though with some sadness. I had visited my parents in that house for twenty-five years. And I had lived in that house in

283

Beijing for two full years with my boyfriend, Zhang Yan. Together, we had thrown Beijing's first big gay, non-public gatherings there, with over seventy local guys and a few gregarious lesbians. Everyone had been amazed at how "open" Ma was about having a gay son and socializing with his friends, whom she referred to as "butterflies" for a reason I suspect related to David Henry Hwang's play, *M. Butterfly* (which she had heard about but never actually seen, despite her many opinions on it).

The Beijing house held troves of memories like this, and it was further graced by my father's and my two grandmothers' spirits. Selling was a difficult emotional process, one that I had dealt with—even if temporarily—by making the deal all about numbers and conditions and timetables for payments. Within a year, the buyer—a wily lawyer from Ma's home province of Henan who never wound up making the final payment on the house, so it technically remained in legal limbo—had transformed the property into an upscale coffee house. No one would ever know that it had once been at the heart of China's nascent gay-liberation movement in the mid-1990s or that two incredible matriarchs who had met with popes and presidents spent many of their final years there.

"YOU FATHER THINK I WAS CRAZY FOR WANTING TO BUILD IT. YOU THINK IT WAS A GOOD IDEA NOW?"

"You made more money with that house than Ba ever made in business," I said, grasping for words that might reassure.

How many nights of sleep had Ma lost worrying whether she had ruined us financially, especially with the way Ba had talked to her? She deserved to know she had provided for her family in the end, that she had regained the lost wealth of her own family. We wouldn't have obtained the land for the house without the help of her business contacts at the Geology Department. And it was Ma who had found a buyer willing to pay cash up front and cover all the back taxes Ba had neglected to pay. The profit from the house sale would ensure that her five grandchildren and one great-grandchild all had the money for college and beyond. It was now my job to not lose the money Ma had remade for us.

"YOU BUYING STOCK NOW WITH THE HOUSE MONEY?" Ma asked again.

"Stocks aren't a good bet right now," I said. "They're really overvalued, plus there's a pandemic, and there's just so many people unemployed.

"HOW MUCH WE STILL HAVING LEFT?" Ma asked for the third time that week.

Ma was only a bit younger than Laolao had been when her brain started to betray her, and I worried that she was exhibiting some of the same obsessive behavior around money. We had collectively decided not to tell Ma how much things cost or how much she still had left in the bank. Better that she did not dive into details.

"You have more than you ever will need since you don't spend it on anything," I said.

"NO, I DO NOT SPENDING MUCH AT ALL," Ma said. "REALLY NOTHING TO SPEND ON HERE. KIND OF BORING HERE, TO TELLING THE TRUTH."

I was relieved we were back to complaining about her move to California. Business and money never made Ma very happy, and it brought up bad feelings about Ba, even long past his passing.

"You should make some friends," I said, as I'd said many times before. "Go to the clubhouse or to some of those activities."

"I WENT ONCE TO CLUBHOUSE FOR LUNCH. FOOD REALLY TERRIBLE."

"Sorry to hear that."

"LUCKY FOR MANY OLD PEOPLE, THEY CANNOT TASTE DIFFERENCE. MY TASTE BUDDING ALSO NOT WORK LIKE THEY USED TO."

"Do they charge for the lunch?"

"JUST THREE DOLLAR. FIVE FOR NON-MEMBER."

"Well, then, it sounds like you got what you paid for."

Ma centered her camera and looked right at me.

"SHOULD NOT HAVE TO PAY FOR THAT FOOD."

October 1998
Shenzhen, China

"It is as we suspected," said Mr. Gao, our factory manager. He sat Ba down and offered him some tea.

"No, thank you," said Ba. "Tell me what we learned."

Ba had devoted many years to this project, a concrete pipe factory in the South of China. It was a joint venture between western companies that supplied the technology and Chinese partners that supplied materials, labor, and land. They had made headlines when the venture was announced, heralded as a solution to China's growing water shortage issues. These steel-wrapped cement pipes could supply millions of Chinese with fresh water from reservoirs hundreds of kilometers away. But soon after the project got underway, the realities of doing business in China, especially in the very corrupt south, quickly dampened everyone's enthusiasm.

Gao looked nervously over at me. I was sitting separately from them and had a notepad out.

"Maybe he shouldn't write any of this down?"

"It's okay. Think of him as our lawyer," Ba said.

We were vigorously pursuing a case for fraud in the Chinese courts, but as with most things in China, it wasn't going well. We had lost at the trial court, and it was now on appeal.

Gao cleared his throat. "As we discussed, our investigators began quietly tracking each member of the judicial panel as soon as we knew who was going to hear the appeal. At first, there was nothing out of the ordinary. But then, after the date of the hearing was set, things began to look suspicious. A lawyer for the defendant started making contact with one of the judges at his home. We have photographs of him coming and going."

"I see," Ba said, furrowing his brow.

"Wait," I said in my halting Chinese. "The lawyer met with the judges without us there?"

For all its problems, this sort of behavior would never have been allowed in the U.S., I thought. In America, laws were enforced, and rules of conduct were followed. Sure, in China, it also was also technically against the rules for the defendant to meet secretly with a judge, but it happened all the time, and no one did a thing to stop it. In fact, it was nearly expected. Ba motioned for Gao to continue.

"It gets much worse. A few nights ago, all three judges went to a karaoke bar. They ordered liquor, women, cigars, whatever they wanted. The construction company picked up the tab."

"You've got to be joking," I said, putting down my notepad.

Ba's frown deepened. I knew what he was thinking. The appeal would be heard in just under a week, and already those judges had been bought and paid for. It didn't bode well for our chances.

For over a year, our company had been embroiled in a bitter dispute with the construction company that had built our new factory. The costs of construction had come in far higher than budgeted, and this had strained the finances of the operation from the get-go, rendering the end product more expensive and less competitive.

In response, the factory, at the urging of our foreign partners, had begun a quiet investigation. Ba wondered privately whether our manager at the time may have been cheating us.

"PROBLEM WITH DOING BUSINESS IN CHINA IS ALL THE CHINESE," Ma once said to me.

"The biggest risk to any business comes from dangers on the inside," Ba's grandfather, Sanye, had taught him. "Partners will squabble, managers will betray, accountants will pilfer. To do business, you must first understand this."

Sanye's ancient advice was prescient. Our investigators quickly discovered that the factory manager had purchased an apartment in Shanghai, leased two cars, and kept a mistress on the payroll. An internal audit showed he had signed off on fake cost overruns and taken a cut of each of them. With the help of the Shanghai authorities, the factory seized the apartment and the cars, cut the girl from the payroll, and eventually sued the construction company for fraud.

It should have been an open-and-shut case. While our manager refused to provide any details, the accountant and the secretary who had worked with him agreed to testify in detail about how the scheme worked. But the construction company had ties to dangerous criminal elements in Shenzhen and Hong Kong and wasn't afraid to escalate. On the day the two witnesses were due to appear in court, a bomb exploded in the accountant's car. It didn't kill or injure anyone, but it frightened the two witnesses into silence.

We requested a trial delay, but the judge refused the request, despite the car bomb scaring off their witnesses. The judge then dismissed the entire case for lack of evidence, a stunning pronouncement that caused a rare ruckus in the court and shouts of shame from the factory management.

Ba had deep suspicions about the motivations of the judge, so he also had her investigated for corruption. It had taken all of one day to unearth the truth. "This is too much!" Gao had said, reading the report. "This judge who dismissed the case? She is married to the lawyer for the other side!"

Ba had grown up witnessing the effects of government corruption in China firsthand, where those with power simply bent or broke the rules to suit them, and average citizens paid the price. During the war, KMT soldiers would scour through every town, extorting merchants and families and taking all the best food, lodging, and goods for themselves. Small wonder the Nationalists had lost the faith and trust of the people, opening the door for someone like Mao to come to power. Back then, as Yeye would say, Mao was so arrogant as to think he had changed the human heart, stamping out greed and official corruption forever through his peasant revolution. But after Deng Xiaoping reopened the nation for business, the old and familiar patterns reemerged quickly. Now, we were victims of grifters and crooked officials once again.

Going to the press wasn't an option. The media was loath to report on corruption cases unless they had been directed to do so by party officials, which defeated the point. Plus, the parent company of the Chinese partner had recently landed in the headlines when its chairman was found dead in a brothel in Bangkok. Ba didn't say so, but it was probably because he knew too much about the books. Running any story about corruption, even when we were the victims of it, risked putting that history into public view again, and the Chinese partners were dead set against it.

Our only other option was an appeal from the trial court ruling on the grounds the judge was married to the defendant's lawyer. That should have been a slam dunk, but this was China, after all.

"So we're going to lose again," Ba said. "Then what?"

"If the panel rules against us, that's it," Gao said. "So we can't let the panel move forward."

"How do we stop that?"

Gao set his teacup down. "You and I both know China isn't a country of laws. Not yet, anyway. We see it here so plainly. Two things count in China: money and power. Down here in Shenzhen, we are on the losing side for both. The defendant has all the money and all the power, so it controls the outcome."

"You're not making me feel better about our prospects," I said.

"But outside of Shenzhen, we might have stronger cards to play."

Ba liked manager Gao. He was a creative thinker with creative solutions. That had kept the company going, even through the fallout from the cost overruns. How Gao had sold so many kilometers of concrete water pipe to local buyers despite their much higher price was something we didn't ever ask.

"You have my attention," Ba said.

"You and your wife know a lot of people in Beijing. She told me she often gets invited to the People's Congress. I've seen her photos with Deng Xiaoping in the early days."

Ba looked uncomfortable. Ma often spoke casually of her connections and was always seeking more of them, sometimes on very thin pretenses. Admittedly, those connections often led to business deals, but Ba frequently had to downplay her many careless promises and exaggerations. Yet Ma had puffed her way into countless contacts and deals, leaving Ba to clear things up and get them on a reasonable course. Some people saw through Ma's charms immediately and didn't take her seriously. Ba counted himself among them.

"Tanlee might sometimes overstate her connections, but they have sometimes been useful," Ba said diplomatically. "What were you thinking?"

Gao pulled out a clipping from a newspaper. "I saw this earlier in the week. There is a focus this month on administrative corruption, including concern about the judiciary. It looks like they are taking a hard line in Beijing, at least for the moment. We couldn't get this case heard outside of Shenzhen normally. But because there is evidence of corruption, perhaps we would catch their attention."

"I'm heading back to Beijing tomorrow. I'll talk to my wife and some friends we have. But honestly, I think it's a long shot.

"Perhaps so," said Gao. "But at this point, what is there to lose?"

Two days later, in Beijing, Ma asked us how the case in Shenzhen was going, and Ba realized he had completely forgotten to raise Gao's idea. He relayed the report of the investigator to her. She scowled, particularly when Ba said there were call girls involved.

"I have a good friend who knows people close to members of the legal committee. Can you have Gao fax the report up here?" she said.

"Is that really going to get them to act?" I asked skeptically. "That sounds like a pretty remote contact. A friend of a friend?"

"THAT DEPEND ON FRIEND," Ma said, switching to English.

The next day, Ma called Ba down to her office.

"Look!" she cried. "There is a notice here! From 'The National People's Judiciary Committee' regarding 'the subject of claims of corruption in Shenzhen' and our case file!"

"What did they say?" Ba asked, genuinely surprised.

"They said, 'Effective immediately Case Number. etc. etc., in the matter of Shenzhen Taiyang PCCP etc, etc, is hereby the jurisdiction of the Committee in Beijing on the grounds of suspected corruption...'"

"They removed the case to Beijing?" Ba asked.

"They did! I guess my friend pushed it through."

The phone was ringing. It was Gao.

"I just received a call from our lawyer," Gao said incredulously. "The other side wants to talk settlement. What just happened?"

"I guess you might say," Ba said, "that it pays to know the right people."

October 2019
New York City, New York

> JAY serves MA a bowl of noodles in his apartment, on the third day of her visit.

JAY: So what do you think?

MA: FLAVOR IS GOOD.

JAY: Even without any meat?

MA: I GOT TO KNOW GOOD FOOD BECAUSE EVEN THOUGH WE LOSE ALL OUR SERVANT, COOK STILL STAY AND WORK FOR US. VERY LOYAL.

JAY: So, I never got the full story on how your family went from riches to rags. Well, not rags, but—

MA: OH WE GOT RIP IT OFF.

JAY: Oh, right, but how?

MA: WHEN WE FLEE TO TAIWAN ALL RICH FAMILY BRINGING GOLD. YOUR GRANDPARENT TOO. WE HAD SERVANT AND CAR AND BIG HOUSE. BUT WE NEED INCOME, SO WE POOL TOGETHER AS FIVE FAMILY AND BUY A STORE.

JAY: I didn't know the Liu family had a store.

MA: GOLD STORE. BUT THEN THE GUY WHO MANAGE STORE TAKE IT ALL.

JAY: Wow. Why did you trust him with all the money?

MA: I DON'T KNOW. ANYWAY, MAYBE TOO TRUSTING. I ONLY KNOW WHAT I HEAR FROM EAVEDROP SINCE I WAS IN THIRD GRADE.

JAY: So we lost all our money to some scam artist? How much did we lose?

MA stares out the window.

MA: ANYWAY, MAYBE JUST TOO TRUSTING.

January 1952
Taipei, Taiwan

"What do you mean Chen is 'gone'?" Laolao asked. "Gone where?"

"We don't know," said her feckless husband, my *waigong*. "We are trying to find him. He left very suddenly. And… it seems he took gold and money with him."

"He did what?" she asked, her voice rising in volume and pitch. Waigong shrunk before her, which only encouraged her to press harder. "Are you saying he stole from us?"

"It would appear so," he replied, his eyes failing to meet hers. "We are doing our best to track him down."

"Stole how much?" She asked. When Waigong didn't answer, she cursed under her breath. "How bad?"

"Bad."

It was an inside job, like so many before it. Five families, who all had managed to escape the mainland with most of their wealth and

294

possessions, had come together for a business venture at Waigong's urging. Gold was still king, even in exile in Taiwan, which implied that a reputable gold exchange could do a thriving business. The wealthy couldn't exactly use their gold to buy food, so at some point, they had to exchange it for the new paper currency. The banks refused to act as glorified pawn shops for gold items, so that's where Waigong saw an opportunity.

The new exchange would have to maintain just enough capital to float and then pocket the difference between what it bought and sold, he had explained to Laolao. To seed the business, he suggested they pool their resources with others. His good friend, Xiao Chen, would manage the store.

"LAOLAO OPPOSING TO IDEA THOUGH. SHE DID NOT WANT MAKE ANY BIG INVESTING IN TAIWAN, BECAUSE NO ONE KNOWING HOW LONG THEY STAY."

If the optimistic, if rather belligerent, reports from the Generalissimo were to be believed, they might very well be back and in charge of Nanjing by the spring. *Then what would become of their gold exchange shop?* Laolao wondered.

In Taipei, their family was counted among the lucky ones, with enough resources for a fine home full of servants, two cars, and even bodyguards. My grandfather's position as a senator provided little salary but more than enough new financial "opportunities," particularly when the government contacts were lucrative and could go to one of his well-connected friends.

"Let others make the investments on this little island," Laolao said. "We can just take a piece of the deals for our introductions and help. There's no risk in that!"

But Grandfather was eager to leverage the economic uncertainty, and he waved off her concerns. The harder the government struggled to stabilize the economy, the more the people would seek safety in gold and the more business they would do, straddling the gulf between those that needed to sell their gold possessions and those that needed cash to live on.

And so, he and four of his buddies from the military and the legislature put their collective fortunes into the gold exchange. To Laolao's surprise, within a few months, it was doing a robust business, driven in part by their many connections. The business was flush with profits. "You see?" Waigong said to her. "We bet right. In uncertain times, there is a great opportunity."

He celebrated their success with lavish feasts, copious amounts of liquor, and all-night card games with the heads of the five families. They toasted to their good fortune, to Waigong's business acumen, to their brilliant manager Chen, to the KMT that helped send more business their way, and even to the island of Taiwan itself, which after a few years had begun to feel like home, even with its sticky heat and frequent rain. Some mornings, Laolao would often find her husband unconscious on the floor of the parlor after a night of too much liquor, and she would have to wake their manservants to come to haul him back to a bed before the children saw him.

All the success had begun to turn Waigong careless. He stopped looking over the business's books each week, a task that bored him anyway, and began simply accepting Chen's reports and signing off on them. Had he opened his eyes wider, he might have discovered that Chen had begun skimming from certain transactions, paying out more than he should to certain regular buyers, who then kicked back a piece of each exchange to Chen. Had he listened instead of boasting, he might have heard that Chen himself was deep in debt to some unsavory characters and should never have been entrusted with the ledgers, vaults, and security of the gold exchange. And had he not turned his nose up at his wife's caution, he might have smelled the rat right under it. My grandfather's mistrust of banks and depositories meant that nearly all of the venture's gold and cash was kept physically on the exchange's premises, under guard night and day against would-be robbers. What he never expected was that the thief would already possess the keys and could simply send the guards home on his orders, which is precisely what came to pass.

"The biggest risk to any business comes from dangers on the inside," I said to Ma, repeating the words of Ba's *sanye*.

"LAOLAO NOT KNOW WHO IS BIGGER DUMMY, YOUR WAIGONG OR HERSELF FOR MARRY HIM!" Ma said.

"So you have lost all our money!" Laolao cried. Well, not all, it turned out. Alarmed at her husband's lackadaisical attitude and dearth of common sense, Laolao had opened another account, into which she had regularly moved some of the profits from the business. Women everywhere, for all of history, have been stashing money because men are fools, she once told a bank teller. That Waigong didn't notice her activity at all was further proof he had no idea what was actually going on with their finances. It was just as it had been in Nanjing, where she had to take the family chop away from him. She knew better than to let him know about any side accounts, or they would soon be emptied, too.

"We will find him," he promised. "We believe he has gone to Hong Kong. His sister so much as blurted it out when we confronted her."

"If he has already left the island, what hope do we have of recovering what is ours?" Laolao asked.

"Leave that to us men," he responded with impatience. "Trust me on this. We know some people there, some old secret police types, who will help us find the scoundrel. We'll tie him up and put him in a crate on a ship back to Taipei if we must!"

Laolao was about to say more when she noticed her daughter in the entryway.

"What are you doing, skulking about?" Laolao shouted, glad to have someone besides her husband to yell at.

"Did we really lose all our money?" Ma asked.

"That isn't your concern," my grandmother said. "Your father created this mess, and he will clean it up, or heaven help me. I will hang him by his collar and beat him until he does!"

"Manxi," Waigong said. "You are upset. But I will make this right."

"Go on back to your studies, Tanlee," Laolao said. "And not a word of this to your brothers or sister or any of the staff."

But Ma persisted in her questions. In that way, she was very like her own mother.

"What are we going to do if we can't get it back?" Ma asked her father.

"We will get it back. We have been betrayed, but we are not beaten yet!"

"I thought you trusted Uncle Chen," Ma pressed.

"Yes," Laolao said bitterly. "He trusted him. The fault is not just with Chen. It is with your father's judgment."

"Easy to say after the fact," Waigong said with a shrug. "It's not a betrayal without trust, and a strong bond isn't broken until it is."

Laolao scowled. "Do you hear that, Tanlee? Your father thinks he is a philosopher, but in fact, he is a dotard. A wise person knows what bad things might happen and prepares for them. Let that be a lesson."

Over the next days and weeks, Chen continued to go missing. That's when the recriminations among my grandfather's circle of friends began. How had it been so easy for Chen to do this? Why should they suffer because of disastrous mismanagement? Was he going to make them whole?

So our family has been losing its friends' money for a while, I thought as Ma continued with the story. But I didn't bring that up.

Animosity grew among the families. Would they have to sue? How did they know this wasn't the plan all along? Perhaps Liu has the money himself now in Hong Kong?

The last accusation stung because, for all the things he was, my *waigong* was an honorable man, even if easily duped. He redoubled his efforts with his contacts in Hong Kong at considerable personal time and expense, but Chen had simply vanished, as if he had sunk into the sea itself with all their gold.

Laolao had been the one to break it to the servants. "You will be leaving us at the end of the day," she said to shocked gasps. "We can no longer afford your services. This house will be put up for sale. You will be paid through the end of the week. Thank you for your many years with us. I'm sorry to have to bear this news."

Only the cook remained because, truth be told, they would all starve if Laolao made their food. When Waigong dared to ask how they would continue to afford him, Laolao said simply, "Let me take care of that. You go find Chen."

There were no more banquets, no more card games. The five friends never met together as a group again after that, only in separate pairs where suspicions and accusations flew. Laolao stopped visiting shops and markets for fear of being seen and to avoid the whispered gossip. She found comfort only in attending church and in making Waigong more miserable.

"Don't ever go into business with your friends," Laolao told Ma over dinner in front of her father. "Do you know why I say this?"

Laolao knew that Ma hated to be drawn into their fights, but her child idolized her idiot father too much, in her view. She would need to see him for the weak and stupid man he was.

"When things fail," Ma said after a moment, reluctantly drawing out the thread. "You will lose both your friends and your business."

"Quite right," Laolao said with a look at her husband. "And tell me, Tanlee. What happens in a business among friends when things succeed?"

Ma looked at her father.

"Look at me, Tanlee, not at him. He has no good answers," Laolao said as the weight of the question pressed out all the air in the room. "You are correct that when things fail, you will lose both your friends and your business. Very good. But what happens when they succeed? What happens when things soar beyond your wildest dreams, and gold spills from your coffers faster than you can count it?"

Ma's eyes brightened as she guessed the ironic answer to her mother's riddle.

"When gold spills out faster than you can count it, it makes everyone greedy and jealous. Your friends will betray you, or you will betray them. And you will still lose your friends and then the business."

"You see, Jingjian? Our daughter has never earned a coin in her life, but already she is wiser than you," Laolao said. "There is hope for us yet."

Chapter Nine

LUCK

or

"JUST ONE STEPPING AHEAD OF JAPANESE"

June 2020
FaceTime Call

"WHEN YOU LITTLE, DO YOU REMEMBER, JUST THREE YEAR OLD, WHAT YOU ALREADY KNEW?"

"Why don't you tell me again?"

Three months in lockdown had begun to take its toll on Ma. Her brain drifted more frequently to old, familiar stories, ones that comforted her and validated what she wanted to believe about herself: her decades as a good mother, her devotion as a wife, her occasional wild success as a businesswoman. I wondered if her octogenarian friends did the same around each other, at least before the pandemic, their limited gatherings defaulting into a repeating loop of the same trusted conversations.

"YOU ALREADY KNEW ALL YOUR SQUARE ROOT AND CUBE ROOT BY HEART. YOU COULD RECITE THEM. YOUR DADDY TEACH YOU ALL OF THEM, AND YOU CAN SAY THEM ALL BY AGE THREE!"

I don't have any memories of myself at three, my brain having overwritten itself sometime around age five in my haste to grow up, but Ma had burned my alleged math superpowers into our family lore, insisting that she had "genius" children who could read and solve problems far earlier than we should have been able to. For the first part of my life, her confidence and pride lifted me to absurd levels of show-offiness, greeting complete strangers with exhibitions of my supposed math prowess. My brothers hated it, and for good reason. I was, in a word, insufferable. Once I gained an awareness of my own obnoxiousness, though, for most of the rest of my life I grew keenly embarrassed any time Ma told these stories, now worried they would easily see through her boasts about me. I was also uncertain whether I had let her down by not "doing" anything in my life with these fabled math abilities, something she frequently backhandedly implied.

"YOU FATHER ALWAYS WONDER WHY NONE OF HIS CHILDREN BECOME SCIENTIST SINCE HE IS ENGINEER. BUT YOU ALL STUDY OTHER THING, HISTORY, POLITICAL SCIENCE."

Ba had insisted that I enroll in the engineering program in college rather than in liberal arts. I walked into my assigned vector calculus section, saw all the Asian faces, pictured the class curve, and immediately transferred to another section where at least half the students were white. Even with this desperate move, I disappointed Ba. It seems a trope, but Ba was truly livid when I only managed a B+ in the class, berating me for "goofing around" and "wasting tuition money" and threatening to take back the car he had loaned me. The sad truth was I had worked my ass off for even that grade, so to avoid similar heartache and conflict going forward, I laid it on the line: I would be switching to something I really liked and understood. My degree would be in Political Science, and I announced after I'd already switched it all officially. Ba let a painful ten seconds of silence pass before saying, "That is not science."

"Maybe science skips a generation," I said to Ma. After all, Yeye was a historian, but his sons had studied science. And among Ba's grandkids, two were interested in the hard sciences, and one was even studying to be a doctor.

"MAYBE LIKE MUSIC, ALSO SKIPPING GENERATION," Ma said. "YOUR LAOLAO WAS FIRST GIRL TO STUDY MUSIC AT NANJING UNIVERSITY. LEARNING PIANO AND VIOLIN, WHICH IS WHY I ALSO MAKING SURE YOU CHILDREN LEARNING. AND LAOLAO EVEN TEACHING PROSTITUTE HOW TO SING THE NATIONAL ANTHEM. DO I TELL YOU THIS STORY?"

"Yes, I love that story, Ma. Someday I'll write about it."

"NO ONE WILL BELIEVING YOU, GOOD CATHOLIC LADY GOING TO BROTHEL TO TEACH THE GIRL MUSIC. I WISH I STILL HAVE ALL THE LOVE LETTER THEY WRITE TO HER, WOULD MAKE A GOOD BOOK."

"Laolao led a storied life," I said.

"AT LEAST SHE ACCOMPLISHING SOMETHING WITH HER TIME," Ma said, baiting me. "DID NOT WASTING HER LIFE."

"That's very true. She even met the Pope," I said before Ma could bring it up.

Ma was quiet for some time before speaking.

"DO YOU THINK I WASTING MY LIFE? I CHOOSE TO SPENDING TIME RAISING YOU PEOPLE. CANNOT BE BOTH SUCCESSFUL AND A MOTHER."

"You were a successful mother, though. We turned out okay, so you didn't waste your time."

"WHEN LAOLAO COMING TO VISIT FIRST TIME TO SEE YOU, I BRING YOU OUT AND ASKING YOU TO SAY YOUR SQUARE ROOT AND CUBE ROOT TO HER. YOU WERE ONLY

THREE! SO SHE COVER HER EAR, SAY, 'NO! NO! NO!' AND SHE RUN AWAY!"

"Wait, why would she cover her ears and run?" I actually hadn't ever heard this part of the story. It often felt with Ma that there was forever yet another more interesting layer waiting for the upper one to be peeled back. Maybe this was why her stories might still feel fresh to her group of elderly friends.

"YEAH, SHE COVERING HER EAR BECAUSE SHE THINK YOU MUST BE TAKEN OVER BY SOMETHING BAD."

"Like, possessed?"

"WHA? NOT OBSESS. JUST A LITTLE STRANGE. SO SHE COVER HER EAR AND RUN. LAOLAO DOES NOT LIKE TO HEAR LITTLE CHILDREN TALKING LIKE THEY ADULT, DOING MATH LIKE SIXTH GRADER WHEN ONLY THREE! SHE THINK IT SCARY TO RAISE TOO SMART CHILDREN."

I didn't want to explain that most sixth graders in America probably had never heard of a cube root. And I also didn't want to break it to Ma that I had only learned all those tricks because it made Ba proud of me, which was pretty much my motivation for everything—and why I had needed four years of expensive psychotherapy in my thirties to unpack it all.

"What did you do after she ran away?"

"I ASKING HER, WHY YOU SO SCARE? SHE SAY, 'IT IS SO BAD TO MAKE CHILDREN BE LIKE THIS!' I THINK SHE IS JUST SO SCARE."

"Huh. I wouldn't have picked 'scared' as a likely response."

"WELL, EVEN THOUGH SHE RAISE CATHOLIC, SHE ALSO STILL VERY SUPERSTISH. BELIEVING ALL KIND CRAZY THING. SHE THINK CHILDREN WHO CAN DO MATH AGE THREE WILL BE BAD LUCK. LIKE DEVIL CHILDREN. IS SHE RIGHT? HAHA!"

I felt an odd chill shudder through me. Ma still knew how to yank at my subconscious fears about bringing ill fortune to the family. I have no idea where that dread comes from, but one likely source involves a mirror.

When I was six, I had asked to hop across the street to play with Joey Slate, the neighborhood's *enfant terrible*. Joey's mother was dressed perpetually in a bathrobe, hair still in curlers, smoke wafting upwards from the cigarette hanging loosely from her mouth. The Slates didn't maintain their yard, and there were rumors of beatings and too much liquor. Ma had absolutely forbidden us from ever going there, a rule she reiterated in response to my request. In the haze of anger only a small child could summon, I screamed, "I hate you! I hate you! I HAAAAAATE YOU!" before slamming the door very hard—enough to knock down the mirror hanging next to it, which struck the floor and broke into four big pieces. Four. A dreaded number in Chinese. I momentarily saw my own reflection in one of them, my eyes wide. I now knew what fear looked like on my own face. Ma took a moment before opening the door and looking down at the pieces on the floor.

"TOO BAD FOR YOU," she said matter-of-factly as she picked them up. "BREAK MIRROR, SEVEN YEAR BAD LUCK."

June 1941
Chongqing, China

Bombers were strafing the city twice a week. With what remained of the Chinese government now scattered or holed up in deep bunkers in the hills around the wartime capital of Chongqing, the Japanese Imperial forces were aggressively laying waste to as much of the city as they could, indiscriminately targeting hospitals, schools, markets, and factories in a prolonged campaign to cause misery and despair and, it was hoped, ultimately capitulation. It was wartime 20th-century China, but it could well have been wartime Ukraine, 21st century.

The aerial bombardment had begun three years ago, and the cost to life and property was steep. But as the Germans had discovered with Russia in the European theater, the conquest of a nation as large and populous as China was no simple feat, and it, too, had become a bitter war of attrition. For each Chinese killed, another one would stand to take his place, as Ba used to tell us. What they lacked in bullets, they made up for in flesh and blood. The "March of the Volunteers" was a popular resistance song that spoke of millions being of "one heart" on their long road to victory, and that wasn't far from the truth. There had been a grim joke that the Chinese could march directly into the sea and drown, one after the other, but once a year had passed, there would be more Chinese than when they'd begun.

With each home or school destroyed, Ba would see an even fiercer resolve in the eyes of his friends and neighbors. He'd never known what hate felt like until he spied the bombers flying overhead, carpeting the city with their incendiaries, the Japanese Zeros strafing civilians with artillery fire. The attacks, especially the slaughtering of women and children in Nanjing, had unified their fractured country in a way nothing before could. It sometimes took an existential threat for people to find their common bonds.

In the first wave of bombings three years ago, the city had been woefully unprepared. There were no shelters, warning sirens, or anti-aircraft batteries in place, so the city lay exposed and vulnerable. Thousands had died in those first attacks, but the hope had been that such brazen atrocities might finally bring America into the war. Instead, the U.S. responded only with a ban on the sale of airplane parts to Japan. The bombings intensified after that, with Japan secure in the knowledge that there would be no repercussions.

One of the bombs had fallen on their small street, destroying a neighbor's home and collapsing roofs all around them. No one was killed or injured from that, but they weren't sure how long their luck would hold. The bombers flew sorties at night to avoid surface-to-air defenses finally set up around the capital, and citywide sirens only provided a few precious minutes to seek safety. The nearest shelter was several kilometers away, so when the warnings blared to wake them, Ba and his family would have to run the entire way to ensure they got there before it filled up.

Their routine was well-rehearsed: At the first sounding of the alarm signaling incoming enemy aircraft, Ba would wake his younger brother, our uncle Ken, and help him put his shoes and clothes on quickly. Nainai and Gugu would check to see that they had bags filled with dried goods and water, in case they were in the shelter for more than a night. Yeye would throw one copy of his scholarly books and notes into a suitcase and fill another with what money and gold they had remaining. Yeye was in poor lung health from smoking, so the sprint to the shelter was not easy for him. Ba would have to carry both suitcases, one in each hand, with Uncle Ken on his shoulders, as they all made for safety. Ba never complained about having to carry the bulk of their possessions, even though Gugu couldn't be bothered to carry more than a bag or two.

"If the bombs hit, the bombs hit," Gugu would say after their tenth run had turned into their hundredth. For all their panicking, only one bomb had ever struck close by, and even then, no one had been hurt. "We are in too poor a section of the city," she concluded. "There is nothing here to bomb except penniless scholars."

"Be thankful for that," quipped Nainai, who Ba said never got along well with his sister once she had grown. "The government has spared us from the Japanese bombs by paying and housing us like paupers. Even if this house falls, all we need is mud floors and some boards again to have a new one. What foresight!"

"They will keep bombing us until all we have left is mud," said Yeye. "And even then, they will not be done."

"It means we can't be defeated," said Gugu, ever the starry-eyed revolutionary. "We can eat bitterness, starve, and use leaves to clean our behinds, but we will still fight. Mao will still fight!"

Yeye sighed. Gugu was headstrong, but in this, she was right. What kind of world awaited when all that was left of China was mud and straw?

That fateful night, there was a sweltering summer heat with no breeze, and there had been only gruel for dinner because food supplies into the city had drawn to a trickle. No one had been able to sleep well, so when the alarms came well past midnight, the family was slower to rise and react.

"Hurry up!" Ba said to Uncle Ken, who kept waving him off and collapsing back onto the bed. Gugu also had only begun to shuffle about, absently throwing items into her bag. Five minutes turned to ten, then fifteen, before they had gotten out of their home. "We won't make it there before they close the gates!" Ba warned.

He was correct. Although they pressed ahead, with Ba urging them all along, people were already turning back by the time they got close. Suddenly, the air itself grew thick as a huge explosion not far from them resounded, and the sky lit up from it. Yeye was on his knees. The bomb had hit a few blocks away, but it was enough to knock him down. There was screaming and panic as people began running south along the road.

"Tingyi!" Nainai cried to her husband. "Tingyi! We must run!"

"Where?" he said in a daze. His glasses were on the ground, only visible from the light of the moon and the fires that blazed in the distance. He bent to pick them up, then absent-mindedly began to wipe them clean.

"Are you listening to me?" Nainai shouted. "What are you doing? We need to go!"

"Baba," said my father, who was still trying to balance his brother on his shoulders. Uncle Ken was terrified and was trying to hide his face in Ba's hair. "Baba, there's another shelter around seven kilometers from here. Let's go there. It's a long tunnel that they have converted."

A second blast shook Yeye out of his stupor. "Okay, let's head there."

The road was filled with desperate people making their way through the dark to the same tunnel. After two kilometers, Yeye was short of breath from his weakened lungs. But Ba kept them moving along.

"There are more planes than usual," Ba shouted as he jogged along. They were flying lower missions, and the bombings were intensifying. The enemy could probably see lines of people even through the darkness, snaking their way along narrow roads between shelters. Finally, they were nearing the tunnel entrance, but there was a crowd gathered outside of the heavy gate, which Ba could see was swinging shut, to the protests of the people left outside.

They were too late. They had come all that way for nothing.

"I'm sorry I couldn't move faster," Yeye said as they moved to the side of the road. The sirens were still sounding, but over them, he could hear the wailing of fearful people as they banged on the gate to be let in.

"We did our best," said Nainai, ever practical. "Next time, we mustn't delay getting ready. Do you hear me, Qian?"

"Why is it my fault?" my aunt snapped back. "It's not as if anyone was in a hurry."

"We are all letting our guard down," Nainai said. "The danger is as real as ever, but we act as if it is not. Complacency is the real threat now. All it takes is one mistake, and we could be very sorry."

"The gates open inward," Ba noticed, frowning and looking over to the crowd still gathered outside the tunnel. "That is a bad design."

"Let's turn back," said Yeye. "Let's head home and hope the Japanese will spare us tonight."

Only a few minutes into their trek back home, a huge explosion ripped through the air, quickly followed by another one even louder than the first. Bits of rock and dirt began to fall all around them. Ba's ears were ringing, and once again, Yeye's glasses were on the dirt road. He grabbed them and looked about for his family, quickly counting to make sure they were all still there.

"Run!" Yeye yelled. "Run!"

The next fifteen minutes were a blur. The world was on fire around them. Smoke filled their lungs and stung their eyes, so they covered their faces with a cloth as they made for home, uncertain if they were fleeing to safety or to their deaths. Even my normally unflappable aunt was crying and shouting their names over the noise, making sure they all stayed together. Twice, Ba fell but managed not to let his brother be hurt. His face, knees, and elbows were scraped raw, but he picked himself back up each time and ran along, the suitcases somehow not coming apart as they banged along the ground. Ba knew their whole lives were in those two cases—a year's worth of unpublished writings and the entirety of their savings. If they made it through this night, he would see about securing the cases better.

By the time they got home, the sirens were still blaring, and they huddled in the dark. Neighbors came by to check on them, and word had already spread in the area. The second shelter they had been trying to reach, the one made from an old tunnel, had taken a direct hit from two Japanese bombs. The people inside had panicked as smoke and fire filled the back area, and they had pressed forward, like a single organism, toward the gates. But Ba had been right: The gates were terribly designed. Because they only opened inwards, the people surging forward had crushed the ones in front against the gates, preventing them from swinging inward to open.

The grim tally was only known days later. Thousands of people had died in that shelter, suffocated by smoke, burned by fire, or trampled by each other in a desperate attempt to escape. Had his own family arrived just five minutes earlier, they would have been among those killed at the entrance, crushed to death near the unyielding iron.

Yeye took out a cigarette and enjoyed a long smoke. Perhaps they had been lucky he couldn't run like his son, or even like Sanye could at his advanced age. Any faster, and they would have been inside that shelter. He made a silent prayer that their luck would hold through the rest of the war.

September 2008
Phone Call

"HOW WAS TRIP?" Ma asked me.

"Actually, it was pretty amazing. I feel like we were there for a month! I didn't know it was possible to meet so many people in a week."

I had made my first visit to New York City with my friend and future business partner, Lorenzo, who had taken an interest in what I was now doing in theater. I had stopped practicing as a full-time attorney, and I had this insatiable and somewhat insane desire to move to New York and become a Broadway composer full-time. My enthusiasm had been contagious enough for Lorenzo to catch, too. He had recently sold his company, and because of the non-compete agreements he'd been required to sign, theater was one of the few safe places where he could freely operate. We had been workshopping a new show I'd written called *Homeland,* which had a Korean immigrant mother figure loosely based on Ma, and I wanted to see if it could find legs in New York. We booked the trip almost on a whim, but soon filled our itinerary with daytime meetings with producers and nighttime shows. Then the universe started to roll some interesting dice.

"YOU MEET LOT OF PEOPLE?"

"We did. But most amazingly, we met that actor George Takei."

"WHO?"

"George Takei. Remember, he was the Asian actor on *Star Trek.*"

"I DO NOT REMEMBERING."

When we were growing up, Ba only permitted us to watch a total of five hours of television a week. Shows which passed muster included

313

Bonanza and *Little House on the Prairie*, which had strong, moral father figures, but excluded *Happy Days*, because Ba felt The Fonz was a bad role model. We had petitioned hard for the right to watch *Star Trek*, and it was the show's clear social message of inclusion, exemplified by the helmsman Hikaru Sulu, which had won him over. George Takei was the only Asian face on television, even if you counted *Kung Fu*, which was supposed to be about a Chinese immigrant martial arts master but somehow starred a white actor, David Carradine, whom they had cast over the obvious choice of Bruce Lee.

As little boys, the three Kuo brothers often role-played members of the Enterprise on one of its missions, with John and Kaiser supplying the storyline. We all liked to play Spock, who was Asian-y in his own way, and of course, Sulu, with his distinctively low, rumbling yet mellifluous voice. It was that voice that I'd heard seated in the row behind me at an Off-Broadway production of *Forbidden Broadway*, causing me to turn around and see my childhood idol in person, sitting next to his husband, Brad.

"Anyway, crazy thing, Ma. He was in the row directly behind me and Lorenzo, and we got to talk to him and exchange opinions about theater and the different shows we had booked tickets to see. I thought, how cool is New York that you turn around and there's George Takei sitting behind you! I've never actually met a famous person before."

"THAT IS NOT TRUE. YOU MET ROSALYNN CARTER."

"Oh, yeah. So, the second famous person. Anyway, Lorenzo and I were still on a high from having met George the night before when we saw him again the next night! We were seeing a show called *In the Heights*, and guess who was in our row?"

"YOU ARE KIDDING."

314

"No, honest to God, George Takei, just a few seats down from us!" I didn't want to get into the fact that he was there with Brad, his husband, because same-sex marriage was still uncertain terrain with Ma.

"HE MUST THINK YOU CHASING HIM."

"Well, the technical term is stalking, and yes, that's exactly what he joked. Anyway, we're waving, and he's waving back, and I'm thinking, wow, the world is really small."

"THAT IS WHAT I ALWAYS THINKING, TOO. SO SMALL WORLD." Ma hadn't yet told me the story about her childhood nemesis Lorraine Fu, who, beyond all probability, was dating my father when Ma first met him in Ohio. She waited until after Ba had passed away in 2014 to tell that story, probably because Ba was no longer there to tell his side.

"Anyway, I look over at George during Act One, and he's wiping tears away while the father in the show is singing a song, something about his daughter and wanting to help her. So at intermission, we go over and say hi again, and I get to ask him why he got so emotional during that song. He starts telling us about how it reminded him of his own father's struggles during World War Two and his inability to rescue his own family when they were all held prisoner in internment camps. It was an amazing story he told us, just in that ten minutes of intermission. Made all the hair on my arm stand up. I kept looking at Lorenzo as if to say, 'Are you thinking what I'm thinking?' because we were always looking for great stories to make into a show. Do you know about the Japanese American internment camps?"

"GEORGE WAS CRY?"

"Yeah, he was really emotional."

"SOMETIME OLD PEOPLE CRY MORE. I NOTICE AMONG MY FRIEND. ALWAYS CRY, CRY, ESPECIALLY THE OLD MEN."

"Well, the point of all this is, I told George that I am a musical theater composer and that the story he told me really ought to be the basis of a show on Broadway. He said he agreed, and then I asked him if I could be so bold as to send him a storyboard and a song sample in a few weeks. He gave me his email, so I'm going to do it! I want to write a musical about this and work with George Takei on it! Isn't that crazy how that panned out?"

"SOUND LIKE YOU HAVING REALLY GOOD LUCK, SEEING HIM TWO TIME IN NEW YORK."

"I know, like what are the chances that you, one, run into George Takei sitting behind you at a theater on your second night in New York, and two, see him again the next night at a different theater, sitting in your same row? I'd say the random chance of that is really low."

"MAYBE YOU HAVING MY LUCK. DID I EVER TELL YOU ALL THE LUCKY THING THAT HAPPEN TO ME WHEN I YOUNG? LIKE TIME THE ROOF COLLAPSING ON ME, AND NURSE HAPPEN TO BE HOLDING ME INSTEAD OF ME LYING IN THE BABY BED, SO NURSE GET HURT ON THE HEAD, BUT I STILL LIVING?"

I hadn't heard that story before, but I was somewhat annoyed that Ma had changed the subject and made it about her.

"Ma, I just told you that I met George Takei and am going to be working on a Broadway musical with him."

"WHO IS GEORGE TAKEI?"

"Ma, were you even listening? Anyway, you can look him up. He's kind of a big deal, especially among Asian Americans. Don't you remember *Star Trek*?"

"SO, YOU HAVE GOOD LUCK TO MEET THIS GEORGE TAKEEE. CONGRATULATION! MAYBE BAD LUCK FINALLY DONE FOR ALL OF US!"

Over the decade, Ma constantly alluded to the supposed bad luck that followed us around, delivering surprise good luck only every seven years or so. My own seven-year luck cycle would play itself out again when our show finally made it to Broadway. I always worried that there might be a karmic cost to having such good fortune as to run into George Takei twice a week and birth the idea of our musical right then and there. It turned out to be true: The price the universe exacted of having met George at Lin-Manuel Miranda's *In the Heights* in 2008 was to open our musical opposite Miranda's next hit, a small show called *Hamilton*, seven years later in 2015. We got swamped by it, along with nearly every other show that season.

But even had I known that was going to happen, I doubt it would have changed my behavior back in 2008. Following my chance meeting with George, I began furiously researching the Japanese American internment and working up a title song to send to George. I saw an email pop up from Ma, re: GEORGE TAKEE.

She had sent along a link to a story about George's recent marriage to his long-time partner, Brad Altman. Ma had been listening after all and decided to do some Internet sleuthing. This was her way of telling me she knew all about George now. Her disapproval rang through her terse email.

I SAW STORY ABOUT GEORGE TAKEE.

SO OLD TO BE GET A MARRY.

August 1945
Wuhan, China

It had felt as if Japan would never surrender, despite all the whispered rumors of an impending Allied victory, spoken more like a prayer than the news. Germany was already beaten and Hitler dead, but Japan still slogged on. Perhaps they would never surrender until every last Chinese, Japanese, and American soldier was dead. Ma understood that kind of stubbornness, even at age eight. She hated to lose, too, and swore she would go down fighting rather than bow her head to anyone, let alone a bloodthirsty Emperor. She had heard her father and his friends say the same, though perhaps they were only boasting and beating their chests as usual. She asked her mother about it.

"If the Japanese come for us, we will remain quiet and do what they say," Laolao said simply. "We will wait and watch and learn where they are vulnerable, what mistakes they make out of their blind confidence. In the end, the Japanese invaders are still men, and they make the mistakes men make."

Ma often wondered if that day would come when she would have to pretend she was just a little meek girl, cowering before marauding soldiers. Could she do it? Pretend she was scared, as her mother had asked. She swore she would rather go to her death fighting than fake that she was afraid of them! When she said so much aloud, Laolao smirked.

"Wait until you have your own children," she said. "Then you will understand what you need to do, how you cannot put your pride over their safety. Don't you think I wouldn't love to crack Japanese heads open? Cut their throats with my father's blade? But if I did, I would also lose my life, and where would that leave you? Those who have no other lives to protect can play at being brave. So if the Japanese take the town and seize our house, we will not fight back, at least until we can pick the moment. You need to do this for your little brothers."

318

"I TELLING HER I WOULD OBEY, BUT I THINKING AT TIME IF THEY COMING, I WILL KILL AT LEAST ONE, TAKING TO GRAVE WITH ME. I KEEPING KNIFE ON MY BELT, YOU KNOW, JUST IN CASE."

But the dreaded invaders never came. Earlier that month, and just as another fall and winter loomed, threatening even greater starvation, the Americans dropped an atomic bomb on a place called Hiroshima. Word spread quickly: an entire Japanese city laid waste in seconds! Everyone was cheering and celebrating, and Ma joined her father, who hugged and hugged her, dancing around with their arms outstretched like lunatics. Only Laolao remained quiet.

"Mama, why aren't you happy?" she asked.

"I am happy, little tiger," she said, referring to Ma's birth year. "I just find it hard to believe this news or our luck."

Laolao finally smiled when news broke that a second magic bomb had fallen on a city called Nagasaki. Most Chinese hoped even more devastation lay in store, that the Americans would exterminate the Japanese like vermin. It was decades later, when George Takei told me the story of how his aunt died cradling his little baby cousin in an irrigation ditch within the blast zone at Hiroshima, that the true human cost of those bombs sank in, how many innocents paid the price for their warmongering leaders.

Back in 1945, though, Ma and every other Chinese prayed for more bombs, and more death, out of revenge for what Japan had done. In a matter of days, though, it was over. The once unstoppable Japanese, who had humbled even the United States at Pearl Harbor, had surrendered without condition. And just like that, the endless war was over.

Ma had never known a day without war. As far back as she could remember, the Japanese or the communists were on the move, just a

319

few days behind them. "WE ALWAYS RUNNING PLACE TO PLACE, JUST ONE STEPPING AHEAD OF JAPANESE. NEVER SETTLE DOWN."

For Waigong and Laolao, the end of the war meant they could return with the family back to their home, a half-day trip down the river by boat. The country would need its leaders back in place, and her parents had both agreed to stand for election to the new national legislature. Waigong had already made the trip and sent word that it was safe now to return, at least while peace and reconstruction talks with Mao and his rebels continued and that the rest of the family should follow him.

The trip by the river was complicated both by strong rains, which made the river swell and in some places overflow its banks, and by the crush of returning refugees. The harbor was crowded with families desperate to get back to their homes, piling onto cargo boats that seemed too small and unstable to handle so many extra passengers. But Laolao was anxious to return, and they were nearly out of money—not that there was much food to be purchased anywhere. So one morning, she put Ma on the back of a cart with her brothers and made for the river, determined to use the last of their cash to purchase boat rides home.

"There are so many people," Ma complained as they approached, a sea of bodies lying between them and the nearest vessels, as everyone jostled with their luggage, sacks, and even live chickens and ducks to secure any kind of passage.

"Just hang on to your brothers' hands, one in each," Laolao said. "And stay right behind me where you can see me."

Laolao was taller than most of the people around her, so it was easy for Ma to keep by her as she pushed her way through the noisy, chaotic crowd. "SHE LOOKING LIKE A GIANT, YOU KNOW, AND

DRESS WESTERN SO PEOPLE MAKE WAY FOR HER LIKE SHE IS MOVIE STAR," Ma said to me.

After twenty minutes, they had made it up to the front, where Laolao began bargaining with someone to buy the few remaining seats on his boat. Ma stood on her tiptoes and tried to count the number of people jammed upon it. The craft dipped low in the water as workers began to pull up the ropes that bound it to the pier.

Laolao had just settled on a price when Ma suddenly felt scared. "LIKE A COLD HAND SQUEEZE MY HEART," she told me. Ma cried out, and she pressed her brother's hand in hers hard. Her brother began to cry. Laolao turned to calm him, and Ma felt compelled to speak.

"Your boat doesn't look safe," she said.

"What's that?" the boat's owner said.

"Your boat. It looks dangerous. Overcrowded already. I have a bad feeling. I don't want to board it."

"Fine then! I don't need you and your bad luck around!" the man cried. "Here, take back your money. You and your brats aren't coming on."

"What did you say?" Laolao said, turning on Ma. "Apologize!"

"I won't!" Ma, stamping her foot. "We can't get on that boat! I have a bad feeling!"

"Keep your child quiet!" the man shouted. "She is scaring the passengers!"

It was true. Some of the people on board were murmuring, and one woman, her face white, was moving to get off the boat. "Give me my money back, too!" she said. "I am not going on this boat!" A shouting match ensued, other superstitious passengers began to demand to be let off, and Laolao pulled Ma and her brothers aside. She shook her hard.

"What are you doing? Why did you say that?" Laolao demanded.

"You told me I was a lucky baby, Mama, don't you remember? I didn't die when the roof collapsed all around me. And I didn't die when I fell off the donkey, even though Baba didn't notice until two hours later. But he still found me sitting by the side of the road when he went back. You said I was lucky!"

"What does this have to do with anything?" shouted Laolao, but her face showed she was also now afraid. Ma had indeed survived twice already when she shouldn't have.

"Perhaps our ancestors were looking out for me, like Baba said," Ma offered.

"Only God can look out for us," Laolao replied sternly.

"Maybe He made me a lucky girl, then," Ma said without hesitation. "He put His hand on my heart just now, and I say that boat is unlucky. We have to go another time. There must be other boats."

"Not until this afternoon," Laolao said. "All the others are filled. This is the last one for hours."

"Then we should wait hours," Ma said emphatically. Behind her, the woman who wanted off the boat had pulled her three children from it and obtained a refund. Others quickly took their places.

"I felt it too," the woman said. "A cold feeling, telling me not to stay on board. I am glad to be off that boat."

"Now we are stuck here in this heat with no food to eat and no boat to ride," said Laolao.

"Here. Have some *zhongzi* as my thanks," the woman said, handing Mary Tanlee a cold-wrapped packet.

"May I eat it?" Ma said, knowing her mother's attitude towards food not from their own kitchen.

"You might as well. Split it with your brothers, though," Laolao sighed.

Later that afternoon, my grandfather waited anxiously at the docks far down the river, where a crowd had gathered. Someone pointed to the churning waters, and people began to cry out in shock. Corpses were floating downstream, mostly women and children, drowned from a terrible ferry accident earlier. Boats were launched to try and find survivors. People were desperately fishing bodies out of the river, trying to identify them. There were dozens. My grandfather spent the better part of the day praying with each person hauled out of the water that his family members were not among them. He had peered into forty dead faces of children and not seen any of his own. Others were not so lucky. The wails of parents and grandparents filled the early evening air.

After the bodies were all laid out by the riverbank, a few who witnessed the tragedy began to recount what had happened. The ill-fated boat had hit turbulent water and started to leak, and the people on board had panicked, causing it to capsize. There was nothing for most passengers to hold onto, so most were simply swept into the river. Only a few made it to the shore alive.

Hours later, Ma's family rounded the bend and saw crowds still gathered on the banks and many figures covered in blankets. Laolao crossed herself and said prayers under her breath while Waigong waved and shouted at them, the tears and relief on his face visible even from a distance. Laolao pulled Ma closer to her and wrapped both arms around her.

"Lucky child," Laolao said, her whole body trembling as she kissed her on the head. "God has touched you. You are my lucky child."

May 2021
New York, New York

It was the third attack reported in New York City alone in a month. Someone had approached an Asian woman outside the subway near 42nd Street and, echoing the propaganda coming out of Tucker Carlson's sneering mouth on Fox News, demanded that she remove her mask. When the woman refused and tried to move past, the assailant struck her in the head with a hammer.

Earlier that week, I had told myself I would stop watching any more videos of attacks or looking at any pictures of the victim's wounds, but I still found myself again unable to look away. An elderly Asian man in East Harlem got attacked from behind and then kicked in the head repeatedly while he lay on the ground, as cars passed by without stopping. It reminded me of the attack two weeks earlier, when a woman walking in my old neighborhood of Hell's Kitchen was struck from behind and then kicked repeatedly in the head and stomach while she was down, and the doormen who saw it all happen simply closed the door and left her on the sidewalk. Ma had heard about that one.

"WHY THEY ATTACKING FILIPINO?"

"They think they're Chinese, I guess."

"FILIPPINE GOING TO HATE CHINA EVEN MORE NOW."

324

Well, maybe China should stop trying to move into Philippine waters with warships, I mused, but then thought better of saying it aloud.

"I don't think the Filipinos blame the Chinese just because people can't tell us apart."

"WHY THE BLACK PEOPLE HATING US NOW?"

The attacks in New York that had been caught on video had often shown large Black men attacking elderly Asians. This pattern stirred up racist sentiment, especially among Asian immigrants. One acquaintance wrote to me privately and asked how I could continue to support Black Lives Matter when that community was attacking us. "Black Lives Matter is not attacking us," I tried to explain. But he wasn't willing to hear it or look past his own gross generalizations. Ma was essentially there now, too, in her head.

"Black people don't hate us, Ma. It's complicated. And a lot of these attacks are from white people, like the guy in Atlanta. He killed all those Korean women. The dude was white. Anyway, we live in a system that pits one minority group against another. It's like a caste system, like in India, but we use races to define ours."

"INDIA SO SAD. SO MANY PEOPLE DIE. CHINA DO A BETTER JOB WITH DISEASE."

At least she had moved past the topic of Black-on-Asian violence and onto the more familiar ground of bashing India. But in truth, the hatred behind the recent violence against Asians in the U.S. had unnerved me. Walking around my neighborhood no longer felt casual. I had a lurking but admittedly irrational fear that I could be the next random target, and that my number could be up. The music might stop, and I would be the one Asian standing there, waiting to get hit in the head from behind or stabbed while waiting for the subway. Or pushed in front of one, like in *House of Cards*. I've always harbored a morbid, worst-case-scenario mindset, which was a bad thing during a

325

pandemic where they were also going around stabbing and beating Asian people.

I hurried past a busker who had positioned himself at 124th, one block from the new Whole Foods. That store had arrived a few years ago, as if to announce that the gentrification of Harlem was complete. Most of the shoppers inside were new to the neighborhood and were willing to pay exorbitant prices for groceries. Most long-time locals took a pass. My friends and I called it "White Foods" after my roommate Tom had a telling slip of the tongue. "Do you need anything? I'm going to White Foods. WHOLE foods!!!" His eyes were saucers as he covered his mouth in horror, and I howled. White Foods, indeed.

The homeless, street entertainers, and earnest progressives with clipboards usually ignored me when I put up my intent-on-getting-somewhere look and sometimes even pretended to text or talk to someone on my phone. This day, however, perhaps it was my extra layer of caution, the fact maybe that I looked instinctively behind me, that exposed me as an easier mark.

"Hey, Chinaman!" the old busker on 124th shouted. "Bruce Lee!" I felt a flash of annoyance, and then it occurred to me that no one had called me "Chinaman" to my face in decades. Something had shifted. It felt disquieting, even menacing. My mind raced to excuse him. He's probably homeless. Maybe crazy. I'll bet he shouts insults at everyone who passes. He probably doesn't know that word is scary and racist.

When I got home, I told my friends about my encounter. On the one hand, it was an example of how anti-Asian sentiment was now so pervasive that it had somehow seeped down to the random guy catcalling strangers on the street. On the other hand, he'd dubbed me Bruce Lee, so maybe he thought I knew martial arts and that he shouldn't mess with me.

326

"I can't believe all the attacks are happening here," said my roommate, Blair.

"And the Bay Area, near my brother," I added. Our big cities were supposed to be deeply blue, liberal places free from overt racist attacks. People got hit with hammers or worse in the South, right? Not New York. Not San Francisco. At least, not until recently.

"Maybe it's just baked into the math. A rise in anti-Asian hate crimes, and you're going to get most of them where the Asians live," I said, again trying to make sense of the nonsensical.

I had decided to stop talking to Ma about any of the growing violence. She already pictured Harlem as a crime-ridden and dangerous place, even though there were now two Starbucks within blocks of my apartment and rumors of a Trader Joe's coming in. The chances I would be randomly attacked on the street while walking alone were still statistically tiny, probably lower than catching Covid-19 from a stranger in line at one of those Starbucks, so it made little sense to worry her unnecessarily.

A lot of my Asian friends had started freaking out, carrying mace on them, staying home, or at least not walking alone anywhere in the City, and looking behind all the time while walking, as I found myself doing more often. After all, Trump had made "Chy-na" the scapegoat for everything, and that made it feel like open season on us.

Six thousand reported incidents, but millions of Asians in this country. That's still low odds, right? I'd have to be pretty unlucky to have an attack happen to me, and I'd never felt like an unlucky person, if you don't count those seven years after breaking Ma's mirror. Plus, we had been conditioned over the course of the pandemic to roll imaginary dice in our heads every time we did anything, even normal things like getting in an elevator or a taxi. Now there was a new calculus. Walking while Asian. Commuting while Asian. *Put it out of your mind. You won't get stabbed by a racist lunatic.* After all, the odds of an Asian dying in a car accident were probably higher.

Especially the way we drive, I thought before scolding myself.

That's when it happened again. I was coming out of my apartment building with one of my neighbors who'd ridden the elevator down with me. I was wearing a Disneyland Shanghai t-shirt with a gigantic, smiling Mickey Mouse splashed across the front of it. We were standing in a corner, getting ready to cross, when a young man standing next to us spoke up.

"There are rats everywhere now," he growled loudly enough for me to hear. It seemed he was talking to me, so I looked at the street, searching for the rats he apparently was referring to. I didn't see any.

"All over this neighborhood, too," he said again, pointedly. I looked up at him and met his gaze. "They don't even speak English either," he hissed.

"Come on, let's hurry," my neighbor said. We moved away from him quickly.

"What was that all about?" I asked, not really wanting to know.

"He was picking on you!" she responded in her strong Eastern-European accent. She seemed as appalled and shocked as I was.

"He was," I agreed. I replayed the moment in my head. He was standing so close to me. There was real hatred in his voice, real menace. I'd never heard anything like it. Could he really have attacked me for no reason other than I looked Asian? Was I just unlucky to have run into him right there on the corner? Or maybe I was just very lucky that all he did was threaten me?

328

That's the weird thing about luck, especially in a volatile place like America, where violence comes at innocent people out of nowhere. Fortune was fickle. Luck isn't always a lady. If you ever find yourself shit out of it, you might be well and truly screwed.

January 2012
Taipei, Taiwan

At age 80, with a full head of carefully parted, brilliantly white hair, his deep-set eyes draped by dozens of overlapping folds suggesting both great fatigue and great wisdom, Ba certainly looked the part of a returning dignitary. Young people, even those prone to feign indifference, offered up their seats and bowed slightly out of respect for him. That suited Ba's sensibilities. There was even that one time when he and Ma boarded a train together, and the attendant had even shouted, "Make way for this grandfather... and his daughter!"—a story Ma joyfully repeated to friends and acquaintances at every opportunity.

Ba was now far older than Yeye had been when he evacuated the Kuo clan (minus my rebellious Gugu) to Taiwan from the mainland in 1949. Ba was even older now than Yeye had been when he had died of heart failure in 1975, cigarettes and a richer, Western diet clipping short his brilliant life by at least a decade.

Now he was returning to Taiwan to take part in a historic moment: the very first chance to vote in a democratic election for a president of the Republic of China. The rules had been extended to allow returning overseas Chinese to vote. Ba and Ma both backed the Kuomingtang party's nominee. It was the first time for either of them to vote as Chinese citizens.

Some would have said it was an extravagance, especially for an 80-year-old grandfather of five, to fly out to Taiwan for the sole purpose of casting a vote in the island's presidential election. But Ma had insisted that they go together and that Ba again receive a routine health check-up while there. Although he questioned aloud whether it was worth the time and expense to travel to Taiwan, Ba readily acquiesced. After all, he had never before been allowed to vote for any sort of Chinese leadership, and even though this was only for the presidency of a small island, it held strong symbolic value. There might never be real elections on the mainland in his lifetime, or even his children's lifetimes, so this was as close to democracy as any might ever see for the Chinese people.

The fledgling democracy taking root in Taiwan was a rather new invention. Neither the Communists in Beijing nor the Nationalists in Taipei had been particularly interested in democracy until Jiang Qinguo, who had been a student of Yeye, finally lifted martial law in 1987. The first real presidential race took place in 1996, resulting in the reelection of the president, but his party fell out of power just four years after corruption scandals rocked it, and a pro-native Taiwanese party, the DPP, came to power. That lasted eight years until the new DPP leader was himself embroiled in corruption scandals and wound up in prison. So goes the cycle of politics.

Ba was all for democratic reform, especially with the potential for checks and balances. More importantly, he appreciated a free press that could expose tainted officials. Chinese government cadres, whether Nationalist, Communist, or even Qing, had been rotten for generations, and the idea that they could be named, shamed, and even jailed gave him hope. What both he and Ma worried about, though, was an increasingly active Taiwanese independence movement, which had found its voice within the DPP. Like most in their generation, for my parents, the island of Taiwan was an inalienable part of China, the way Manhattan Island was unquestionably part of the United States. The fact that it was governed by a different group of Chinese under a different system was a technicality they had lived with and accepted their whole lives. In the 1990s, they were happy to see relations between the mainland and Taiwan warm as money and know-how from Taiwan industrialists resulted in manufacturing relocating to the continent. Yeye would have been astounded at the progress achieved. The two Chinese worlds, Ba believed, would be forever bound by the cement of self-interest.

Instead, deep wounds inflicted long ago began to fester and seep again, as the native Taiwanese started demanding a greater say in government and society. The history of their slaughter and brutal suppression during the White Terror decades ago was no longer shrouded but in the public discourse regularly. Ma didn't like to talk about it, and Ba saw it as a long-term problem. Local businessmen and leaders began speaking in Taiwanese instead of Mandarin, and children born on the island thought of themselves not as Chinese but as Taiwanese. All this meant that there might soon come a day when independence might be declared, perhaps as a part of a national referendum or vote by the legislature.

Such a shift would almost certainly trigger an armed response from the mainland to quash it. Beijing had already invested far too much political capital in the idea of Chinese reunification, and it had strong and legitimate concerns, my parents believed, that similar independence calls in other parts of the country, notably Tibet or Xinjiang, would follow. Because of this, it was assumed Beijing would never allow Taiwanese independence to happen.

Whatever people's views on independence, Ba preferred the status quo as a far better, if admittedly temporary, solution. The current KMT president, as someone born on the mainland like him, straddled the political divide. "No unification, no independence, no use of force," he promised.

Ba liked that approach, and it rather mirrored his own medical status, which Ma insisted he get checked while there. In Ba's mind, things were working fine, so why roll the dice? A botched surgery to correct Laolao's heart problems had left her brain without sufficient oxygen for too long, and she had spent her final years with dementia. Ba would sooner go to his grave with his mental faculties intact. Similarly, for Taiwan to flirt with independence, to stir that pot too much, was to court calamity. And Ba had lived through enough calamity to never want to risk it.

He had been idealistic once, but now he was simply pragmatic. At the founding of the Chinese Republic, Dr. Sun Yat-sen's three original People's Principles were *minzu, minquan,* and *minsheng*, meaning nationalism, democracy, and prosperity. Both Taipei and Beijing had done a good job with prosperity, but Taipei chose democracy while Beijing chose nationalism. It was difficult to have both, Yeye had said. But it was Ba's hope that, someday, the country would reunite and actually fulfill all three. Taiwan's lurch toward independence threatened that hope, and so he had doggedly come to Taiwan to cast his vote in favor of the next KMT candidate to stand for the presidency, who had a more pro-China and thus, more realistic approach to cross-strait relations.

Ba found himself short of breath from carting their luggage through Songshan Airport, the cheap Chinese casters on his imitation Samsonite suitcase predictably deciding to stage a strike at that precise moment. He was an expert at ignoring physical discomfort, and so he paused deliberately as if to take in his surroundings and look for familiar faces. Through this trick, he gained for himself a welcome respite, a moment to stop and rest. Ma stopped, too, and glanced his way, assessing. Ba hated whenever Ma caught him wheezing or weak, her concern and judgment weighing more than their travel bags. "I'm fine," Ba said before she could speak.

Ba had seemed invincible while I was a kid. That lasted until his fateful first trip back to China, during which he barely slept for two weeks from the frenzy of activity. Yeye had thrust in his hands a checklist of colleagues and relations, people whom it would have taken months to track down under normal circumstances. But Ba had been relentless and had managed to locate them all, even his deeply unhappy sister, our Gugu, the one Yeye had left behind in 1949, who had been afraid for years even to write her own father back. After that exhausting experience, Ba returned home and promptly suffered his first heart attack.

He had been just 47, half a lifetime ago. The incident had come as a shock, and it should have served as a wake-up for his own health generally. Instead, it wound up deepening his faith in his own physical fitness and invincibility. The experts had been surprised to find that, even though one of his arteries was nearly completely blocked, his body had managed through some rare form of angiogenesis to sprout new blood vessels around the blockage. "Amazing," his cardiologist had marveled. "And very lucky. I've never seen anything like that. You won't need surgery, at least not yet, but you'll need to make some changes to your lifestyle. Less red meat, more exercise. That sort of thing."

That sort of thing never really happened, despite Ma's many attempts to curtail Jenkai's love of steak. Over time, Ba even forgot that he was technically a "heart patient" in the eyes of the healthcare system and my mother. If anything, he felt even more confident, knowing that his body had found a natural way around a big problem. Perhaps it would continue to do so, and he liked to say.

"JENKAI HAS LUCKY BECAUSE HE ALREADY SAVE ANOTHER MAN LIFE. GETTING TWO CHANCE TO LIVE!" Ma told anyone willing to listen. It had been a military training exercise. Ba would explain, taking over the retelling so that Ma wouldn't exaggerate, back when service was compulsory in Taiwan. Ba was running a miserable obstacle course across a muddy field with a group of cadets when one of them ("SO STUPID!") touched a downed but live electric wire. The man was rendered unconscious, and the wire was sparking on top of him. Without a thought to his own safety ("MORE STUPID!"), Ba grabbed a cloth and hauled it off the man, saving his life. Ma was convinced this act had granted her husband significant karma points and that this was the true reason his heart had found a way to grow itself back to health.

But luck only got you so far. In the late 1990s, when he was in his 60s, Ba found himself once again short of oxygen and under Ma's annoying eyeful of concern, which privately for her had already turned to alarm. On a trip back to Arizona from China, which they had arranged in order to finish the sale of their home in America, Ma insisted on driving him to Tucson Medical Center "just for a check-up." There she sprang her trap. She already had a cardiologist waiting to see him and had prepared an overnight bag in case he needed to stay for further evaluation. The scans and tests to which she forced him to submit revealed he was on the verge of yet a major heart attack and that without immediate surgery, he would probably not live, "NOT EVEN ONE MORE WEEK," Ma predicted ominously. The doctors refused to let him leave the hospital, and Ma made sure they scheduled the surgery soon.

Ba had put off the idea of heart surgery for years, not wanting to pay the high cost of it, nor to imagine his ribcage cracked open by a giant machine, a surgeon, and nurses cutting and sewing his insides. But Ma had duped him well and thoroughly, and now he was stuck in the hospital and had no choice but to agree to the triple bypass procedure. To his astonishment, he learned the surgery was now covered completely by Medicaid, something he'd never had occasion to think about before, and that helped convince him it was worth doing. But it also meant the impersonal doctors, who Ba figured made no extra money from this, sent him home from his operation in just two days, long before he felt he was ready to be released.

With his blood flowing normally again after that surgery, the world came back alive. Ba had forgotten what it was like to wake up with energy and have the vigor to spare. Ma boasted that his white hair had even started to grow black at the base, and she joked that his whole head would be black again within a year. (That didn't happen). To prove his new vitality, Ba regularly bounded up and down the hard marble stairs of our home in Beijing, like a man twenty years his junior. Ma scolded, but she was also happy to see him return to something close to his former self.

The surgery was only supposed to grant my father another seven years of unobstructed blood flow, but by the 2012 elections in Taiwan, it had been twice seven years already, and his luck continued to hold. Lately, however, he hadn't quite felt up to exerting himself. Once again, he felt slightly robbed of his full lungs' worth of breath, even on brief walks. Of this, he made little mention to his family, but I noticed it when we went anywhere together for very long. Ba didn't want to unnerve us unnecessarily. But Ma could sense that he had slowed considerably, and she began to cut back even further on his meat and fat intake, which made him grumpy and irritated at her.

Add to that, Ba's most recent incident, over the prior Christmas, had given us a bad fright. He and Ma had met Mimi and her husband, Aaron, in Taipei for the winter holidays, and they had gone out to do some sightseeing. As a lover of gadgets, Ba was eager to try out his new high-powered yet compact video camera, although Ma kept telling him to stop staring through it and actually enjoy the surroundings. With his favorite camera gear strapped around his neck, Ba now resembled a tourist on the very island where he spent much of his youth.

"You need to watch where you are stepping. You shouldn't always be looking through the camera," Ma had warned him as they ascended the steps to a temple on a steep hill. Mimi had checked in with him several times on the walk as Ba tried to hide his shortness of breath.

335

Even in winter, the air was sometimes warm and oppressive, and Ma fussed about what this might do to his blood pressure.

"I'm perfectly fine. Just a little hot," said Ba.

Ba broke off from them to test out his new camera uninterrupted. He was checking out its zoom capacities and had spun around with it to capture the view from up high when he suddenly lost his balance. The next thing he knew, he was tumbling down stone stairs to the cries of his family. His shoulder hit the bottom of the stairs hard and popped. The world went white as pain shot through him. Within a few seconds, his eyes refocused, and he realized he was lying on the ground, his arm at a strange angle beneath him.

They managed to call for help, and Ba amazingly was able to stand, even after tumbling down seven steps onto his shoulder, which had mildly dislocated but snapped right back in when he stood. He was rubbing it when the others reached him, and they managed to get him down the stairs and out of the park grounds so they could get to a hospital. "I'm fine, really!" Ba protested, embarrassed by all this attention.

"YOU JUST LUCKY DID NOT BREAK HIP," Ma said angrily, but there was fear in her voice, too.

At the hospital, they set his arm and shoulder efficiently, without the dreaded long waiting period for a doctor, and they were all impressed with the level of service he had received, especially compared to his hospital experience in America. That was, in part, why he agreed to Ma's next plan to get them both full check-ups when they came back the following month to vote in the national election.

The election happily went Ba's way, but the check-up didn't. When the doctor entered the examination room, he looked concerned and pulled up a monitor to show them the ultrasound images.

"What is it?" asked Ma, ready for the worst.

"Our review revealed something that we need to address right away."

"Tumor?" asked Ma in Chinese, always ready for the worst. "In his brain? I told my friends he hasn't been normal lately. Very grouchy for no reason. We think it must be a brain issue."

"Tanlee, let him finish," said Ba.

"There is an embolism in his renal artery, just above his kidney."

"An embolism! I knew it was something," said Ma.

"Be quiet," Ba said.

"It is a very large one. More than 10 centimeters. That is very unusual and very dangerous. I am actually shocked it has not burst yet. In a few more days, it might well have."

"What can be done?" asked Ma. "Nothing, I bet! Too late."

"It's not too late. But if it were to burst, there would be a significant chance of morbidity."

"So you are saying he would die?" she asked, her hands clutching that fake brand-named purse she insisted on carrying.

"Tanlee, please!" said Ba. Like me, Ma always imagined the worst. Perhaps it was a defensive mechanism so that everything else sounded like good news by comparison.

"We will need to operate right away. We'll have to place a stent for sure. He can't leave the hospital, it's too dangerous," the doctor said. "But the procedure is pretty safe, even routine. He should be fine afterwards."

"You see? You will be fine. Like I said. Just like before, when I took you to the hospital in Tucson," Ma whispered. "We caught it just in time."

"I guess I should thank Taiwan!" Ba said with humor.

"Why Taiwan?" Ma asked.

"If they hadn't decided to hold their election in January, I may not have been able to come! My wish to vote just saved my life."

"Come on. Just admit it. I was the one who made us come here. So your wife saved your life," Ma, scowling but relieved. "Actually, I saved you twice. You are a lucky man."

Chapter Ten

COLOR

or

"SHE LOOK MORE AND MORE CHINESE"

December 2017
London, U.K.

After Ba passed away, Ma continued to visit Mimi and Aaron, who now lived an hour north of London in the impossibly serene British countryside outside of Oxfordshire, where they grew all manner of vegetables, raised chickens, and had ambitious plans to become beekeepers. I had begun making regular trips to the West End with my producing partner, Lorenzo, to scout for new shows, so our visits usually included some time with Ma, Mimi, and Aaron in the city to take in some theatre.

On one scouting trip, I decided to bring everyone to London's revival of *Dreamgirls*. I picked a show that my Michael, who had come along, would love. But I also thought I might expose Ma to a story outside her usual preference for historical dramas about rich, white people.

I should have thought it through. The volume of the Motown-style music inside the Savoy Theatre was several decibels too loud for Ma's taste, and she utterly failed to appreciate the vocal acrobatics and riffs of the performers, even as Michael and I basked in acoustic heaven. At the apex of the show, the two leading ladies reconciled their seven years of differences over the course of a single song called "Listen." Ma turned to me incredulously.

"SO THEY ARE NOW FRIEND AGAIN?!"

"It's a musical, Ma," I said, thinking that would explain everything.

Michael tried to help in his deep, South Texan accent. "Heck, in a musical, people fall in love and get married in a single song. It's just the way musicals go. I know, it can feel absurd, but isn't it woooonderful?"

Ma furrowed her brow and scowled. She could accept the idea of lifelong grudges, having held a few of her own. But in her experience, they did not wrap up in any way neatly with hugs. Or duets.

After the show, Ma grew quiet as we walked away from the crowds to catch an Uber. I assumed she was just tired, but she had been considering the show.

"COLOR PEOPLE HAVE COME LONG WAY," Ma said after we'd settled into the car. Ma was trying to show us she, too, had evolved. But I was instantly on guard; our Uber driver was Black, probably an immigrant from either Africa or the Caribbean.

I tried to keep my voice lowered while preventing Ma from going too far down this path. "We don't say 'colored people' anymore."

"WHAT I SAY THEN?"

Mimi looked at me and giggled, knowing this conversation would end up on Facebook for entertainment and historical value. "Ma, we say 'people of color' now. It's more polite."

"WHAT IS IT?"

"People of color," I said over the noise of traffic.

"OKAY, OKAY. PEOPLE WITH COLOR."

After I moved to Harlem, which was filled with "people with color," Ma came to visit often. Her casual dishing with my neighbors and random pedestrians on the street always came with a side of mortification. Ma possessed no sense of physical boundaries, yet she had a deep curiosity about certain things. For some reason, Black people's hair was one of them. On her first visit, a stunning, young, African American woman with curves that even "trendy" men would notice, inside pants that were quite possibly airbrushed on, hopped into the elevator on our way down to the lobby. Ma immediately sought to make friends.

"THIS IS NOW THE STYLE EVERYWHERE I SEE."

"What is?" the woman said, smiling. I was grateful that she didn't seem put off. For me and nearly every other New Yorker, it was against the Rules of City Elevators to make small talk with strangers. Ma always got a pass.

"THIS SHORT CURLY HAIR."

Oh God, I thought. Wait, no, don't touch—oh no. Too late. Ma's fingers were on the woman's hair. I didn't know what to do. I debated whether to apologize, to say something, anything at all. Would that make it worse? I had lectured Ma on this before, that touching other people anywhere without consent was a massive social faux pas, but it did not deter her, or perhaps she just forgot. I held my tongue but bit down on it nervously. The woman quickly assessed Ma's age and ethnicity and remained, thankfully, good-natured.

"Oh, yes, it is. Much easier to take care of."

I mouthed "I'm sorry" to her behind Ma. I wondered if she had a mother who might speak to someone like me VERY SLOWLY to make sure I understood.

The curvaceous Black woman's eyes crinkled back at me. She was clearly amused, and I was sure she would be telling her friends and co-workers about this, just as I would be relating this classic moment on social media.

"I USED TO HAVING MY HAIR LONG AND IN BRAID, COMING DOWN TO HERE," Ma said, indicating her hip. "BUT NOW I AM EIGHTY AND PREFER EASY HAIR!"

Ma waited for the woman to remark that she did not look eighty at all, but no compliment was forthcoming.

"Oh, this hair isn't easy," the woman said. Ma seemed disappointed. I suppressed a grin. "Well, have a nice day!" the woman chirped as she left.

"OKAY. YOU, TOO!"

Ma waited until the woman was out of earshot before leaning in to whisper.

"THE BLACK TENDING TO HAVE MUCH BIGGER BUTT. YOU NOTICE?"

I sighed. "Not in this instance, no, Ma," I lied.

Ma considered the woman as she left the building.

"MUCH BIGGER THAN ASIAN. MAYBE IT OUR DIET."

April 1991
Phone Call

"You're being ridiculous." I was on the line with Ma for the third time that week, trying to talk her down. My brother John's wedding to his fiancée, Rachael, was fast approaching. The closer the fateful day got, the more absurd Ma's threats became.

"I ALWAYS SAY, IF YOU DON'T MARRY A CHINESE, THEN OUR FAMILY JUST GOING DISAPPEAR."

"Ma, the Jews have been trying to enforce ethnic purity for just as long, with only modest success. And they're still around," I said. It often worked to bring up the Jews, who were the only non-Chinese people Ma seemed to admire.

"NOT EVERYWHERE, THEY NOT AROUND," she said. "JEWS COMING TO CHINA, SETTLE IN YOUR FATHER TOWN OF KAIFENG. BUILDING TEMPLE, EATING SPECIAL FOOD. BUT THEY DECIDE OKAY TO MARRY CHINESE GIRL, NOW ALL DISAPPEAR."

Ma used to drop hints that our family was descended from this lost tribe of Israel, the famous Jews of Kaifeng, pointing out Ba's ginger-haired cousin and my brother Kaiser's abnormally prominent chin. His family's ancestral home was on a street called "Pulled Tendon Alley," which Ma argued meant kosher food, but in fact, was probably a relic of a Hui Muslim minority settlement in the town, where they also avoided pork and pulled the tendons out of meat before eating it. Nevertheless, it was part of our family lore that we were part Jewish, instead of part Uzbeki and part Kazakhi, as our DNA tests indicated. No amount of proof or skepticism ever dissuaded Ma from George Santos-ing our genealogy through the years.

343

To me, it was odd that Ma should claim foreign descent for her children but reject any notion of intermarriage for them. That was a curious and unresolved contradiction. Not until years later did it dawn on me that her prohibition on intermarriage was just another way to press guilt and her influence down upon her children.

"I TELL YOUR BROTHER, IF HE MARRY A WHITE, HAVE A MIXED BREED CHILDREN, I WILL NOT VISIT THEM AS GRANDMA," Ma said, her hackles fully up.

"Ma, that's a terrible thing to say. You don't really mean it."

"NO, IT DOES! I REFUSING TO VISIT. THEY CAN HAVING WHITE GRANDMA, NOT THIS OLD CHINESE ONE."

"Why take your prejudices out on the kids?" I asked. "What if Rachael's family said they didn't want John because he was Chinese? Wouldn't that be racist?"

"WHO DOESN'T WANT JOHN?"

"No, I'm not saying they don't want John. It's a hypothetical."

"WHA?"

"It's make-believe. It's not true, but what if they said that? What if someone said, 'I won't visit them because John is Chinese.' Wouldn't that be wrong?"

"THEY NOT WORRY ABOUT FAMILY DISAPPEAR."

Ma's incurable worry that there wouldn't be enough Chinese left in the world if we Chinese Americans married other races was always a bit of a head-scratcher, judging from the billion and a half of us already in the world. She once even claimed that Chinese people don't like to have sex, and when I pointed out all those hundreds of millions

344

of babies, she shrugged it off, saying they were all just trying to carry on their family line.

"First of all, John and Rachael haven't had any kids yet, so we don't know if there will be grandchildren for you to ignore. And I don't believe you when you say you won't visit them after they're born. You'll take one look at them and change your mind."

"NO, I NEVER WILL. YOU CAN TELLING HIM THAT."

"Tell him yourself! He won't believe you either. John is never going to marry a Chinese girl, Ma. He's too American, and there are too many white girls around. And besides, all the Chinese girls want to marry white guys."

"NOT ALL. I HAVE MANY FRIEND WHO CHILDREN NOT ENDING UP WITH WHITE." I wasn't sure this was actually true. Most of my friends who were Asian Americans were dating white people. A lot of them were dating Jews, come to think of it.

"I don't understand why you and Ba moved here if you just want us to be Chinese. It's like you came here for the opportunity and freedom, but then you don't want your kids to have their own." I was at the point in the argument when I began to throw guilt back at her. Implying that she was the cause of our unhappiness was a surefire way to escalate things.

"TOO MUCH FREEDOM," Ma said. "LOOKING WHAT IT DO, EVEN TO YOU."

Yeah, she went there. My coming out had been a multi-year process. When I first broke the news, Ma said she would refuse to accept it as truth. I would come home for visits and find myself seated at dinner next to another "daughter of a friend," who was always just as confused as to why she'd been recruited for this experiment. After three of these efforts failed, Ma finally retreated to her personal

345

Maginot line, a defensive trench she filled with twin poison gasses of guilt and recrimination.

"Speaking of what it did to me, I don't want you to freak out at the wedding, so I'm telling you now that I am bringing Bernie."

"WHO BERNIE?"

"Ma. My boyfriend. For, like, five years now. I told you about him. And you met him. Twice." I didn't for a moment believe that Ma had forgotten Bernie's name or the fact that he was with me. I'd even forced Ma and Ba to have dinner with us, where Bernie—a polite, low-key engineer at Hewlett Packard—had tried his best to talk science with Ba, while Ma's eyes roamed the apartment looking for evidence that two men could never live together and maintain a home. Even by her standards, everything was perfectly in order and immaculate, the way Bernie kept things, but this had only darkened her mood.

"I DON'T KNOWING BERNIE."

"Ma, don't try that. He's my boyfriend, you've met him before. I'm bringing him to the wedding."

"WHY? TO EMBARRASS ME?" Ma's favorite tactic was to make everything about our efforts to undermine her in front of her social set.

"No. Because it's a celebration of love, and I want the person I care about to be there, too." In truth, I had debated for a long time about whether to bring Bernie. I didn't want his presence to upstage or ruin the day for John and Rachael. But Rachael was adamant that I bring him, saying that not doing so would be caving to Ma's homophobia. I wanted to defend Ma and say she wasn't really homophobic. She was just angry that life wasn't working out according to plan. For example, I was pretty certain that if I gave her a Chinese grandchild, she wouldn't care at all that I continued sleeping with Bernie. But I agreed with Rachael that Ma was being ridiculous, and bringing up my request early might mean less drama at the wedding.

"IF YOU BRINGING HIM TO WEDDING, I WILL SET MYSELF ON FIRE!"

"Huh?" I said, not certain I had heard her correctly.

"IF YOU BRINGING HIM AND EMBARRASS ME AT WEDDING, I SETTING MYSELF ON FIRE!" Ma had that edge to her voice where she was summoning the most horrific image and future she could imagine and laying it out for you. This was her "nuclear" option, but she misjudged my response.

"Fine then, I'll bring the lighter fluid!" I shouted. "You're being ridiculous, Ma. If Kaiser can bring Daisy, then I can bring Bernie. There's no difference."

"DAISY IS A CHINESE," Ma said pointedly, which was actually not what I was expecting as her retort. Kaiser had been dating a lovely woman named Daisy, and Ma had designs. "KAISER IS ONLY ONE GOING TO PICK A CHINESE WIFE."

I still wasn't sure why Daisy being Chinese had anything to do with Bernie not measuring up, or how Ma had leapt from Kaiser dating her to his marrying her (which never ultimately happened) until I realized what she was really saying: Daisy would not embarrass her. She would not have to explain or apologize or avoid the subject of Daisy at all.

"First of all," I said, "She's not his wife, not yet anyway. So she's not even family. You shouldn't count your chickens."

"I NOT COUNTING CHICKEN," Ma declared. "I JUST HOPING. I JUST WANTING TO HOPE."

"I'm going to bring Bernie, but I promise we won't embarrass you," I said, laying out my own terms. "Your friends will just see me with a friend. They'll probably think he's one of Rachael's relatives anyway."

"IF YOU BRINGING HIM, HE CANNOT BE IN FAMILY PHOTO," Ma said, redrawing her red line in rapidly shifting sands. "HE NOT FAMILY."

"Fine, but then Daisy can't be in the photo. She's not family either."

Ma agreed, probably so she could make a point later to Kaiser that he had better get moving with his own marriage to Daisy, which of course wasn't anywhere close to being a reasonable discussion, given the brevity of their courtship.

"And Ma," I said. "Promise me you won't say anything rude at the wedding about John not marrying a Chinese girl. You come off sounding racist."

I could feel Ma glowering on the other end of the call. "IT NOT RACIST. I JUST WANT PURE GRANDCHILDREN."

January 1995
Oakland, California

> Four years have passed since MA threatened to boycott ever seeing John and Rachael's children. Rachael is now many months pregnant.

JAY: We're supposed to suggest some girl names at Rachael's baby shower.

348

MA: WELL, SINCE SHE BORN YEAR OF PIG, WHY DON'T THEY NAME BABY AFTER PIG?

JAY: The only pig name I know is Wilbur. That's a boy's name, and it's pretty archaic.

MA: NO I MEAN JUST NAME HER "PIGGY."

JAY: What? No, Ma, that's terrible—

MA: WHY? IT GOOD NAME.

JAY: Trust me, it's not. This is how Kaiser wound up with his name. No consultation.

MA: PIGGY IS GOOD NAME! FOR YEAR OF PIG.

JAY: No one names their kid "Piggy," Ma! No one.

MA: YEAH NO, I HEAR A LOT. SO POPULAR.

JAY: …

MA: …

JAY: Ma, that's "Peggy."

MA: YOU SEE? GOOD NAME.

April 2007
Beijing, China

Eighty-eight rickshaws. That was how many three-wheelers formed the grand procession of guests in Beijing, and I couldn't recall seeing

Ba so happy as he enjoyed the spectacle. If thirty years ago you had told Ba that he would be celebrating his daughter's wedding in high style back in mainland China, with friends and relations from all over the world flying into a new and gleaming *capital airport* with its own *Burger King*, and that they would stop the busy traffic of *thousands of cars* dead while onlookers gawked at the sight of eighty-eight rickshaws in a row, he would have laughed outright.

If you had also told him that his daughter would be marrying a white man, and that he would not be merely begrudgingly okay with her choice but genuinely delighted, that he would not have just been polite to but actually have become very good friends with the groom's parents, he would have dismissed you as absurd.

But life has a way of upending expectations.

The vows took place in a Tibetan temple in Beijing, which seemed fitting given Mimi's growing interest and passion for spirituality. Ba himself was not particularly very religious or even superstitious. His was the world of physics, math, and engineering. Life and our place in it were a series of puzzles to be solved, equations and laws to unlock, and if that process brought him closer to something others called God, that was fine by him. Mimi preferred to dwell comfortably in the realm of the ineffable and unknowable, which probably meant she would lead a happier life. And really, that was all Ba ever said he wanted for Mimi, his only daughter, his favorite.

The entirety of the Kuo clan had descended on Beijing. All three of us boys, including John with his wife Rachael and their three children, were present. Kaiser was there with his wife, Fanfan. Their daughter, Guenevere, had a fitting name given Kaiser's long fascination with knights and the Arthurian legend. Kaiser was also showing off his new infant, Johnny, whom he'd named after our older brother. I had promised a sonnet with which to roast Mimi at the reception. It was another rare gathering of us all, and I couldn't stop looking at Ba, so full of joy and at ease.

Mimi had been living in China on and off for many years and even ran a surprisingly successful business called "Yoga Yard," of which the authorities were deeply suspicious. Anything remotely related to the practices of the Falun Gong cult, which dubiously claimed to have some 100-million adherents around the country, drew the Public Security Bureau's attention. The Chinese word for "yoga" was *you gong*, so the "*gong*" suggested an unwelcome affiliation to that banned organization. No matter how many times Mimi had explained patiently that there was no actual connection between yoga and Falun Gong, the suspicion remained and perhaps grew worse after she became defensive. So, Mimi switched tactics and began to sweet-talk the local Public Security Bureau officer, who promptly asked her to join him and a friend for dinner. Mimi has always been an incredibly radiant and beguiling woman, but she has never really accurately judged the effect she has on most men. The officer began calling Mimi regularly, even offering to drive her to the airport in his official vehicle, until he finally got the hint that a romance wasn't in store. As a compromise, he asked Mimi to become something of an informant to teach him about the "habits and ways of foreigners in Beijing" who attended her classes at Yoga Yard. Do that, and she could stay open. It was more of a face-saving compromise, and in the end, she was thankful that he never asked her to provide a report.

Prior to meeting Aaron, Mimi hadn't found much happiness in love. She had dated both Chinese and white men, but it had been the Chinese ones that had brought her the most sorrow. Her first mainlander boyfriend had been Ding Wu, the lead singer of Kaiser's now famous heavy-metal rock band, Tang Dynasty. Apart from the affair being almost a cliché—Sister of Lead Guitarist Dates Rock Singer, as if scripted for breathless, tabloid coverage—it was also prone to drama and tragedy. Ding Wu had a problem with opiates, the drugs that seem to haunt us Kuos in some capacity, generation to

351

generation, and Mimi ultimately had to choose between saving Ding Yu or saving herself. Ever the pragmatist, she chose herself, but not before locking herself in isolation for days after the break-up.

Her second love had been the soap-opera star, Li Yapeng, whose film career took off right around the time they began to date. When Ba asked why Yapeng never mentioned Mimi in any of his interviews, Ma shushed him, reminding everyone that Yapeng's acting contract had a clause that prevented him from speaking publicly about any romantic attachments. With his height, strong features, and regular TV appearances as a leading man, Yapeng had legions of young, female fans who would be crushed to learn he was already spoken for. One of those fans had even stalked Yapeng and discovered his frequent visits to the Kuo residence, and then proceeded to park herself in front of our house, hoping to catch even a glimpse of her idol. The pressures of quick stardom got to Yapeng, whom Ba truly liked and Ma adored, even though neither of them truly understood him or his demons. When that relationship ended, Ma seemed truly disappointed, having gotten quite good at name-dropping a movie star among her social set. Yapeng went on to marry Wang Fei, the Chinese pop-star equivalent of Madonna, who bore him a child with a cleft palate, a misfortune which Ma frequently mentioned.

Mimi's fiancé, Aaron, stood markedly apart from the others. He was a photographer, so he was curious and open, and he always made you feel he was more interested in you than you should be in him. He was naturally polite and deferential toward Ma in a way that none of the Kuo children's other spouses or partners had ever been.

"How are you feeling, Ma?" Aaron asked Ma earlier that morning, once the parents and the happy couple had gathered. None of her daughters-in-law ever bothered to ask after her, let alone willingly share the spotlight on a day that was all theirs. Ma beamed.

"OH, YOU KNOW, MAYBE A LITTLE TIRED. I COULD NOT SLEEPING."

"It's an exciting day. Your only daughter getting married. And to a guy like me! I wouldn't be able to sleep either, knowing that." Aaron winked at his father, Paul, whom Ma called "Papa Paul."

Ma laughed despite herself. She loved Aaron's self-deprecating manner and the way he teased.

"I THINK SHE DO ALL RIGHT," Ma conceded.

"Not too bad?" said Aaron.

"I think Aaron got the better deal," said Paul. "So I slept like a baby!"

Paul's wife, Laurie, whom we called "Mama Laurie," came over and took Ba's hands, drawing him aside. He had grown used to her warmth and her genuineness, but the directness and formality, together with the raw and open emotions she wore, still took him aback. I moved nearby to eavesdrop. Mama Laurie always spoke words like they were scripture, poems from the heart.

"This is such a happy day for us," Mama Laurie said to Ba, her eyes shining. "And it is such an honor to be joining together as a family with yours."

"Well," Ba said, trying but failing to match her rhetorical level. "It is a special day. And we are very happy, too."

Mama Laurie hugged Ba lightly about the shoulders. Ba was never comfortable with big, American hugs, so by going with a lighter touch, I knew Mama Laurie was intuitively respecting his boundaries, even while demonstrating her own affection. It was admirable how well the Deemers navigated the cultural map.

353

Ba had always maintained that the biggest challenges in mixed marriages were cultural. He'd told us for decades that the gap felt simply too wide to cross: How could two sets of in-laws from different countries be comfortable and act naturally around each other? But he had learned, after returning to China to live, that his best and dearest friends always seemed to straddle the two cultures in some way. When he was with Chinese who had never lived outside of China, he felt that some kind of perspective was missing, and he never made very close friends with them. With the Deemers, who were Americans living in Beijing, there was actually more commonality of experience. He had been wrong, but he seemed to understand this and was delighted by it.

Aaron had won Ma over to the marriage without any of the hand-wringing over his race or the threat of more mixed children. And she didn't threaten self-immolation over any of the guest invites. She had finally come around to being a proper and loving grandmother to John's kids and even seemed to revel in how the Chinese locals would swarm around them, remarking on how beautiful these "mixed bloods" were.

Mama Laurie and Ma would become fast friends. Over the years that followed their children's union, they visited each other quite frequently, the Deemers' traditional courtyard-style home in Beijing just minutes away from ours. Ma spent more time with Mama Laurie than with most of her other friends, at first always talking about the children, but then expanding to their lives, their husbands, their hobbies, and their work. They shopped for antiques together and tried local restaurants, the cheaper the better. The families merged into one larger happy one, almost in the way families did in times long past. Years later, when Ma learned that Mama Laurie had quietly checked herself into hospice back in North Carolina and passed away from cancer, she felt as if her own sister had died, and was inconsolable for a very long time.

Mimi smiled up at Aaron, whose lanky figure was a whole head taller than her. I looked over at Ba. He had told me frankly that he hadn't thought he could live long enough to be here for such a day. There had been a time when that was far from certain, after a heart attack, a blocked artery, and open-heart surgery had left a deep question over how much time he had left. Seeing how Mimi relaxed around Aaron, with a trust and familiarity that had taken decades for Ba to form with Ma, I felt pretty good about their chances for happiness.

"How does it feel to see Mimi married after all this time?" I asked him.

"I am feeling happy," Ba said. I think it was the first time I'd ever heard him say that out loud.

December 2019
Oakland, California

"LITTLE BABY LOOKING MORE LIKE CHINESE," Ma said as she regarded Tahira, who was absorbed with *Mulan*, a secret weapon of distraction John had put up on the television for the second time that day. Tahira was just two years old, but her very existence gave Ma a rare title: *tai laolao*. Great-grandmother.

Tahira's mother was my niece, Kaili, the first of three children Ma had threatened never to visit after John married their mother, Rachael. But a lot had changed since that 25-year-old threat was issued.

One of those changes was Tahira herself, who wasn't a "planned" baby. Kaili was now officially a single mother, still pre-med and in school, though she was still seeing the baby's father on and off. He was a young man named Brandon, with whom Kaili had bonded during one harrowing night at a party gone terribly awry in Oakland,

355

where three young revelers had been shot. Kaili, who had EMT training, managed to stop the bleeding and save the life of one of the wounded, while Brandon had kept her company. The trauma of that experience brought the two of them together, which later led to them dating, then to a surprise pregnancy, and finally, the birth of Tahira.

Brandon's striking features came from being half-Chinese and half-Black. It wasn't uncommon these days for kids in Oakland to be of mixed heritage. Whenever John threw any of his famous food fests, his group of friends and their kids would turn his house into a kind of United Colors of Benetton. By the genetic math, Tahira was half Chinese, a quarter European, and a quarter African American.

"I think she looks like Lea Salonga's daughter, Nicole. She looks Filipina." Lea was the star of my show on Broadway. I used to name-drop her shamelessly, especially around Ma's "helpers" from the Philippines.

Ma scowled. "ANYWAY, EVERY DAY, I THINKING SHE LOOK MORE AND MORE CHINESE. BUT I KNOW, SHE NOT TRUE HAN CHINESE. NO SPLIT PINKY TOENAIL."

"Huh?" John asked. This was new.

"EVERY PURE HAN CHINESE BORN WITH SPLIT PINKY TOENAIL," Ma explained, as if everyone in the world except her own children knew this. "I HAVING, LAOLAO HAVING, AND YOU ALL HAVING, TOO."

None of us had never examined our pinky toenail closely enough to notice if it had a split.

"Mine is split," Kaili cried, peering at her toes. "So I'm Han, even though I'm only half!"

We all spent the next few minutes taking our socks off and looking at our toes. Ma insisted mine had a split, though I could see none. We all looked pretty ridiculous, like toddlers trying to chew our own feet, while Ma continued with her opinions on the Han Chinese.

"YOU KNOW MY FRIEND, YOU MEET HIM ONCE, XING CHEN, FROM LIVERMORE? YOU CALL HIM CHEN SHU SHU?"

"Ma, I can't remember all the shushus that I've only met once," I protested. "I can't even remember the ones I've met like five times."

"ANYWAY, HE SO MAD THAT HIS DAUGHTER MARRY A JAPANESE."

"He is? Why?" Kaili asked.

"I TOLD HIM, THEN WHY YOU SEND HER TO JAPAN TO STUDY? IT LIKE KAISER'S GIRL, WHO ONLY LIKE THE KOREAN BOY."

"It's the K-pop influence," John said, shrugging.

"SHE EVEN MAKE HERSELF LOOK KOREAN. ANYWAY I DON'T THINK CHEN SHU SHU EVEN GO TO HER WEDDING, HE SO MAD."

"That's sad," said Kaili.

"VERY SAD!" Ma said, not understanding Kaili meant about missing the wedding. "SHE SHOULD HAVE GIVEN HIM PURE CHINESE CHILDREN. ANYWAY I AM HAPPY AT LEAST ONE OF MY CHILDREN GIVING ME PURE CHINESE CHILDREN."

It was an awkward dig at John in front of his own kids.

"But Fan Fan is Manchu," I said, adopting my best cross-examination voice. I did *not* want Ma to win this bizarre argument. "Kaiser's kids are half Manchu. Is that Chinese?"

"YES. OF COURSE."

"What about Tibetans, they're part of China. Are they Chinese? If I had half-Tibetan kids, would they be Chinese?"

"YOU? HAVING CHILDREN?" Ma said, scowling and scoring a point.

"I mean, if I did."

"CHINA HAVE MANY RACE. NOT ALL ARE CHINESE."

"So what makes Manchus Chinese?"

"I DON'T MEAN CHINESE. I MEAN 'HAN' CHINESE."

Now the truth was clearer. "But Manchus aren't Han. They're Manchu," I pressed.

"MANCHUS LIVING WITH HAN MANY THREE HUNDRED YEAR. SO ALMOST LIKE THE SAME."

"But not Tibetans?" I knew I was in dangerous territory, and was probably losing the argument. Arguing about China's treatment of Tibetans was like bringing up Nazis in a political conversation. They were the ultimate example, the final go-to when the argument wasn't going anywhere.

"WELL, TIBET IS PART OF CHINA. BUT TIBETAN, NOT HAN CHINESE."

And that was that. Ma's racial politics had an objectively inconsistent logic, but in her head, it all made perfect sense, and there was no changing it. Tahira, who was only half "Han" Chinese by math, was laughing and pointing at the television.

"Let's get down to business!" Kaiser sang along with the movie. "To defeat... the Huns!" At least we could all agree that the movie's heroine, Fa Mulan, who had lived during the Northern and Southern dynasties sometime around 1500 years ago, was "Chinese." If she ever lived at all. And even if a Filipina named Lea Salonga sang her part in the movie.

Tahira squealed and tried to babble along with Kaiser. She was named after an Islamic word for peace, which on top of her ethnic heritage, was a big middle finger to the Trump Administration. This baby was Chinese and Black and Caucasian, and she had a Muslim name. She represented the hoped-for future in so many ways.

She also had come into the world as a fierce affirmation of life. John's wife, Rachael, had been battling cancer for many years, and Kaili had decided to transfer to Berkeley from her school on the East Coast to be closer to her mother, so she could spend more of their remaining time together. When Kaili learned she was pregnant, it felt like the universe was trying to balance things out, giving a new life for the one ebbing away. Even though Kaili was still in college and dreamed of becoming a doctor, she had decided absolutely that she would go forward with having Tahira. Rachael was able to hold her granddaughter in her arms for a few months before she passed. It was the gentlest of blessings amidst the crushing despair.

"I think she looks a lot like Jay," said her grandma Tara, who was Brandon's mother. "Look at those big eyes."

"EYES LOOK LIKE JAY'S," said Ma, agreeing. Chinese people were always talking about my eyes, which were unusually big when I was a kid and now just seemed to accentuate my fatigue as an adult.

"WHEN YOU ARE BORN YOUR UNCLE SAY, WHAT AN UGLY BABY!"

"Wow," I said.

"I SAY TO HIM, NOT UGLY. LOOKING AT HIS EYES! SO BIG. YOU EYES AS BIG AS NOW BUT ON A BABY FACE LOOKING SO BIG. KIND OF SCARY."

"Scary."

"OH YEAH. MY FRIEND ALL ASKING ME, DID YOU GIVING HIM SURGERY, CUT THE BABY'S EYES? I SAID, YOU CRAZY? THAT IS HIS NATURAL EYES."

"Chinese people are obsessed with this stuff," I sighed.

"THEY THINK I GIVING YOU EYE SURGERY, CAN YOU BELIEVE? BUT YOU HAVE THE FOLDED IN THE EYE ALREADY."

"Well, thank goodness for that. No need for surgery with these 'scary' eyes."

"NOT REALLY SCARY."

"Not really?"

"JUST NOT VERY CHINESE."

"And look at the way Tahira can give side eye. Just like her great-uncle Jay!" Tara exclaimed.

Tara was always ribbing people, but she seemed to gravitate toward me whenever I visited. We were the two social outsiders in the house—a gay man and a Black woman—and we had made it a point to sit by each other at meals while drinking plenty of bourbon. Tara was the farthest thing from a grandmother you might envision. She was what every urban, homosexual male might daydream of having in a Black woman friend: She had retired from her job in finance, so she had lots of free time and plenty of money. She still enjoyed the party-loving single life while being rather no-nonsense about things. She was as likely to text dick pics to me as to go toy shopping for her granddaughter.

With Brandon and Tara now in our lives, Ma had been pressed into sharing the holidays with not just white people but Black people, and we marveled at the adjustments she had made. The only time I could remember Ma ever being social with a Black person was four decades ago.

Lee Brown was an activist in New York whose socialist leanings matched Ma's at the time. (Ma had at various times been a socialist, an entrepreneur, a Democratic fundraiser, and a dabbler in Republican circles. The latter stopped after her favorite GOP Congressman, Jim Kolbe, came out of the closet—to my utter delight. I asked Ma if she'd known about Kolbe's sexuality, and Ma had frowned and said, "OF COURSE I SUSPECTING, JUST NOT KNOWING IT.")

When Brown had shown up at the house, his unruly afro making his head seem gigantic, I noticed his light palms, in stark contrast to the very dark tones of his hands and arms. It made him look radiant. We boys hung around the living room shyly, trying not to stare at him while listening to them talk about Mao and where the peace movement was headed. Ma suddenly seemed a stranger to us, someone who knew very cool people and who talked about the world as if she should run it.

361

When Kaiser asked her about Lee Brown many years later, and how struck he had been that Ma actually had a Black friend (something her friends at the Chinese Civic Association would have gossiped about for months, had they known), Ma looked confused, as if he had made the whole thing up.

"Ma, I remember it really clearly. Lee Brown! The activist. You said he was in the papers. You had him over to our house. You guys talked politics. He was definitely Black."

"OH. YEAH. WELL, HE WERE MORE BLACK THAN HE LOOK IN PICTURE," she explained, as if she had to.

Brandon and Tara were now a constant presence in Tahira's life, and therefore in Ma's, whom we had moved to nearby Rossmoor earlier that year. We had once wondered how she would handle having extended family who were Black, given her earlier rather steep learning curve on race. But Ma seemed to simply just roll with the changes, and I only caught her touching Brandon's curly locks once. When I told her not to do that, she grew defensive, but it also explained a lot.

"YOU KNOW WHEN I WAS IN OHIO," she said, referring to her college years, "LOT OF PEOPLE COME TOUCH MY HAIR. THEY NEVER SEE ANYTHING LIKE IT!"

"And... you didn't think they had prejudged you in some way?"

"I REMEMBER ONE BUS DRIVER, LETTING ME OFF AT STOP, BUT HE DIDN'T OPEN DOOR. INSTEAD HE TOLD ME I WAS SO BEAUTIFUL, AND MY HAIR SO SHINY. HE WANT TO TOUCH IT."

"Oh, my God." I pictured a creepy bus driver pawing at her head. "I hope you didn't let him do that!"

"NO, I DO!" Ma said.. "HE TOUCH IT, SAY I AM SO LUCKY TO HAVING HAIR LIKE THAT. OFTEN I THE ONLY CHINESE PERSON. MY COLLEGE GIRLFRIEND TAKE ME ONE HUNDRED MILE AWAY TO HER LITTLE OHIO VILLAGE, WHERE THEY NEVER SEEN SOMEONE WITH BLACK HAIR. EVERYBODY COME OVER TO TOUCH IT."

"And you let them?" I asked.

"ONLY THE GIRL. ALL THE BOY WANT TO TOUCH IT, TOO. BUT IT NOT POLITE, SO THEY HANGING BACK."

"Still, don't you think that's weird? I mean it's not a petting zoo."

"YES THEY PATTING IT. SEE, IT WAVY, BECAUSE I KEEP IN BRAID! CURL LAST THREE DAY. SAYING I MUST BE A MOVIE STAR BECAUSE MY HAIR. I STILL DON'T HAVE TO DYE IT, EVEN AT ALMOST EIGHTY YEAR OLD. STILL LOOKING OKAY?"

"Yeah, there's only a little gray now," I said, a bit callously.

"LOOKING BAD?" Ma's eyes were wide and challenging. I backed down.

"It looks fine, Ma," I murmured.

Ma looked away, distantly, her feelings hurt. "ANYWAY, PEOPLE USED LOVE MY HAIR."

I tried to bring the conversation back to Brandon. "But my point was, Black people don't like it when other people try to touch their hair."

"WHAT WRONG WITH THAT?"

"It's just so… Ohio. A little racist."

363

"OHIO NOT RACIST!" Ma said scowling. Then she tipped her head, considering. "EXCEPT TO BLACK."

Attention turned back to Tahira. She was the only child in the house, and it being Christmas, was therefore the recipient of nearly all the gifts. Ma, per usual, hadn't gotten anything for anyone in years.

"I DID NOT GET BABY ANY GIFT," Ma declared. "I AM BAD GRANDMOTHER. OH, SORRY. GREAT GRANDMOTHER!"

"That's fine, Ma," said John, who per usual, felt both exhausted and harried. With Rachael gone and the baby growing up in the house, John was more father than grandfather to Tahira. And while John had a lot more responsibilities as a result, he was grateful to have Tahira to take care of, that his natural inclination to pour his life into providing for others had a bottomless vessel in the form of an infant. "She has plenty of gifts," John laughed. "I'm sure she won't notice."

Tara had pulled out the third gift for her granddaughter, and Tahira was starting to stack them in a pile to assess later. "Look what else granny got you!" Tara said. "It's a dollhouse!" Tahira opened it up to a size bigger than herself. She seemed pleased and began to put little people and furniture around it.

"YOU GOING TO SPOIL," Ma said. "I NEVER GIVE YOU CHILDREN ANYTHING LIKE THAT."

"We had plenty of toys," I countered. "I probably had a hundred stuffed animals."

"I KNOW. SICKENING," Ma said, her scowl deepening while she refused to acknowledge her role in my collection. She would help me line up all of my dolls and animals and go through all their names with me. Patricia the Cat with black smudges from no one knows what. Snappy the baby, whose snap-off head went missing for a year, which made for the macabre sight of a toddler walking around with a

364

headless doll. Kiki Meow Meow, which upon reflection wasn't a cat at all, but a grinning bear that resembled a cat. How it took Ma so long to figure out I was gay, no one could figure.

"MERRY CHRISTMAS!" said a group arriving at the door.

"Look who it is!" John said to Tahira. "It's Xiao Ayi!" That's Chinese for "mother's younger sister," literally "little aunt."

John's younger daughter, Camille, stepped into the foyer along with her boyfriend, Harry. They were met with shouts, shrieks from Tahira, and Christmas greetings. They set down even more gifts for the baby and began taking off their shoes. The bottoms of shoes meant the outside world coming in, and the less of that the better, as we would all learn in the pandemic to come.

Ma's gaze lingered on Camille and Harry, and I could see her trying to process who was who. There were so many new faces, and it must have been dizzying to celebrate the holidays along with the Black and Latino boyfriends of her granddaughters, when a generation ago the only faces at Christmas time were Chinese. While she had made no racially insensitive remarks so far, she did manage to land criticisms in other ways.

"WHY DO CAMILLE PICKING SUCH A SHORTY GUY?" she whispered to me, looking over at Harry. By all accounts, Harry was a stand-up fellow who was getting a master's degree at UC Davis, and who was known for helping out around the house.

"Ma, you shouldn't judge people by their height. It's not very relevant to who they are." I said, a bit defensively.

"I NOT JUDGING, JUST ASKING WHY."

Maybe Ma wasn't really judging Harry, I thought later, just looking for something over which to be less than perfectly satisfied. Her criticism of our family's lives and choices were more about her feeling excluded from experiences and changes we were all going through, and her judgments were a somewhat warped way for her to insert herself.

"WELL, HATE TO SAY," Ma began, meaning she did not hate to say at all, "BUT EVERYONE IN MY FAMILY TALL. YOUR LAOLAO WAS THREE INCHES TALLER THAN ME, CONSIDER A GREAT BEAUTY."

"So not everyone in your family was tall," I said, still defensive.

"WHAT YOU MEAN?"

"I mean, if Laolao was three inches taller than you, then you weren't tall."

"OH, THAT IS BECAUSE I USING MY HEAD TOO MUCH. TOO MUCH THINKING, SAY LAOLAO. THAT WHY I NOT GROWING TALLER," Ma laughed.

"What, so tall people don't use their brains enough?" John asked, not sure he wanted to pull on this thread any harder.

"LOOK AT KAISER!" Ma said. "HE MORE OF A DUMMY WHEN YOUNG, SO HE GROWING TALL FIRST. HAHA."

"Hey, fuck that," said Kaiser, looking up from the movie. He had been listening after all.

"Kaiser has never been a dummy, Ma," John laughed, but he knew she wasn't being serious.

"I KNOW. I AM SO LUCKY TO HAVE SO MANY SMART CHILDREN." Ma said that so often these days that we couldn't tell whether she was being sarcastic or genuine.

"Anyway, under your theory, Harry must be very smart, since he isn't tall," I said, trying to corner her.

Ma looked at Harry, who didn't quite come up as high as Camille.

"MUST BE GENIUS," she muttered.

Chapter Eleven

INSPIRATION

or

"ARE YOU STILL PRACTICE?"

July 2020
Zoom Call

With no easy way to visit Ma in person during the pandemic, Mimi had come up with the idea for a weekly video chat involving all the Kuo siblings and a few appearances by their spouses, kids, and dogs. It was scheduled for every Sunday, at different times to account for three different time zones.

As was our habit, we steered the conversation toward food. Like millions of others stuck at home during the pandemic, Kaiser had taken up sourdough bread-making, something I'd also picked up after Mimi's husband, Aaron, had revealed its joys. Given the technical difficulties and nuances of great bread-making, we struck competitive tones, one-upping one another on favored malts, how regularly to feed starters, and the proper care of Le Creuset Dutch ovens. Ma managed to bring the conversation expertly back to her comfort zone, while claiming some credit in the process.

"I JUST FEELING LUCKY THAT I HAVE FOUR WONDERFUL CHILDREN, ALL SUCCESSFUL."

"Three," I said, tossing out a familiar line of humor. "You have three wonderful children." Mimi giggled, appreciating the nonspecific shade.

"ONE THING I AM VERY PROUD: ALL MY CHILDREN KNOWING HOW TO DO COOKING. DO YOU KNOW WHY?"

Yes, we knew why. In nearly every family video chat where the topic of food came up, or really whenever any of us cooked a meal for Ma and a guest, she bragged about our cooking skills, and specifically how we acquired them. It was as if her brain heard "cooking" and automatically projected backwards, the memory rising up as an imperative.

"Why don't you tell us, Ma," Kaiser offered, finally without exasperation in his voice. Kaiser had been the most reluctant among us to concede that Ma's cognition, particularly her penchant to retell the same stories, needed to be nurtured rather than discouraged. This was a big change and something of a challenge for him. Doing so would be to surrender to the idea that Ma was in decline, though anyone could see that. The cold reality was difficult for all of us, but particularly Kaiser, who didn't like to confront unpleasant realities. I was grateful that he was now humoring Ma like the rest of us. She took zero notice of Kaiser's change of approach.

"WHEN YOU WERE LITTLE, I MAKE EACH OF YOU COOK A DINNER FOR WHOLE FAMILY, AT LEAST ONCE A WEEK. AT FIRST, ALL COMING OUT GOOFY GOOFY! BUT THEN, YOU SAY, 'AH! THIS TASTE PRETTY GOOD!' AND SO IT BECOME A COMPETITION, SEE WHO MAKING THE BEST FOOD."

It was no competition. Without any doubt, John made the best food, by far, as confirmed by his assignment to all the important holiday meals. There would be days of back-to-back feasting: roast lamb chops with chestnuts and wild-rice stuffing, succulent prime rib with a generous *au jus*, baked Cornish game hen with an orange-marmalade glaze, Dover sole with a white-wine butter sauce. Ba's face would glow with contentment, as John brought out his *chefs d'oeuvres*, long years of deprivation in China erased by the

369

abundance, flavors, and calories of America. The rest of us oohed, ahhed, and sighed, as we devoured John's fare, but Ba ate in silence, savoring each bite and quietly enjoying mealtime with his family who had never known hunger, want, or strife.

To John's main course, the rest of us might contribute a meek side dish. Carrots boiled with butter and onions was Ba's go-to, though none of us had the heart to tell him it was mushy and bland. He regularly overcooked the carrots in a white, Corningware dish with a glass top that burned many fingers whose owners had neglected to let it cool first. A decade later, I prepared carrots for Ba as a side dish to a Cajun chicken stew, cutting them on the bias and sautéing them with fresh thyme and shallots, then swirling them in a tangy mustard and maple-syrup glaze. Ba was quiet, and I wasn't sure he liked them until he asked me to make the dinner carrots my way from now on. The white Corningware disappeared into the deep recesses of our kitchen cupboards, never to overcook vegetables or scorch unwary digits again.

With John's meals, we didn't just receive a feast for the senses. He also had an encyclopedic knowledge of food and cooking. John would casually explain the difference between game hen and plain chicken, assuming generously that we even knew what a game hen was. Or how you had to salt Brussels sprouts to leach out the bitterness, or the possibilities of dried porcini powder in risotto (and why it took so much stirring to get right). This was before the internet or whole cable channels devoted to cooking, so John came into his culinary expertise through observation and practice. But he was generous with his knowledge, and he turned all of us into food aficionados. I still catch myself spouting food facts that John imparted to us long ago over one of his lavish meals.

We younger Kuo siblings all took up cooking, though later than John, and each branched off into specializations: Kaiser with fiercely authentic, spicy Sichuan and Indian dishes, Mimi with her organic and impossibly fresh home-grown vegetables, and me with a fierce drive to make vegetarian dishes indistinguishable from the meat-based comfort foods I'd learned to cook earlier. We gained our love of cooking by watching John, and not because we ever thought we could out-cook him. But in Ma's mind, she deserved full credit for a whole family of chefs, further proving her skills as a mother. "I THINK MAKING SURE YOU ALL KNOW HOW TO COOKING WAS SMARTEST THING. LIKE THEY SAYING, SECRET TO A WINNING A MAN IS COOK FOR HIM," she said, butchering the maxim but preserving its essential message. "I LEARN HOW TO COOK FIVE FAMOUS DISH FROM THREE FAMOUS RESTAURANT, ALL SO I CAN SHOW I WOULD MAKE GOOD WIFE."

"You made them for Ba, I remember."

"PROBLEM WAS, IT WAS ONLY FIVE DISH I KNOW HOW TO MAKING! YOU DADDY DISCOVER THAT I TRICK HIM, WHEN HE ASK ME TO MAKE HIM SCRAMBLE EGG, AND I DON'T EVEN KNOWING HOW. UH OH!"

"Well, at least he was already engaged to you by then," I said, laughing.

"YEAH," Ma said, her eyes twinkling. "BY THE TIME HE DISCOVER I AM NOT GOOD COOK, TOO LATE."

November 1976
Apalachin, New York

Around age eight, every weeknight after finishing my normal schoolwork, I would go upstairs to see Nainai to have my Chinese lesson. It had been Ba's idea to appoint Nainai as my unofficial tutor, after seeing my disappointing marks in Chinese school, where we were sent every Saturday morning, in lieu of wasting time watching American cartoons.

It was already dark very early in the day, the upstate New York winter bearing down on us, when I knocked quietly at Nainai's door to announce that I was there and ready to learn. My small hands held a notebook, each page containing rows of dotted-line boxes, the same squares in which schoolchildren had traced Chinese characters for thousands of years.

"Nainai? Are you ready?" I asked, my painfully Americanized Mandarin flattening and homogenizing the tones the way American culture did everything. "Am I bothering you? Is now okay?"

Apart from my eyes, which Nainai remarked were several sizes too big for my face, I apparently looked much like her own youngest child, who had died at age four. She almost never spoke of that child. I suppose she felt that some pain should die with you, not get passed to later generations.

Even after years of Saturday classes, I still knew very little Chinese, especially once the family switched out of habit or perhaps exhaustion to speaking only English, the language of American schools and, more importantly, American television. That move established English as the *important* language, while Chinese felt at the time like the thing that made us *different*, not just in appearance, but in our very foundation, from the white, American children around us in school.

Because I'd grown up speaking Chinese, I had been sent to speech therapy in kindergarten to correct a slight accent. The experience had humiliated me and hardened me against speaking Chinese at home. After a year working on my S and R sounds, Ma assured Nainai that my speech was no longer an issue. The therapists proclaimed I now sounded just like any other child in Tioga Hills Elementary. But my Chinese had become atrocious.

Nainai knew very little English, despite having lived with Yeye in New York City for years while he wrote and lectured at Columbia University. Once she moved in with us, after Yeye's death the year before, Nainai would sometimes answer the phone or the doorbell, if no one else was around. She knew how to say "Hello" and "Sorry, no here," especially if our neighbor, Steve, came around asking after Ma. Steve looked at Ma with a kind of teenage nervousness, even though he was a grown man with daughters of his own, and Nainai would park herself discreetly within earshot whenever he came by for a visit, with Ma maintaining a polite, if somewhat bemused, manner with him.

Once, when I was much older, I asked Ma about it. "Our neighbor in New York, Steve Campbell. He sure came around a lot to see you," I said, testing the waters.

"WHO?"

"Steve Campbell. Remember, they lived down the street. He had that daughter with the eating disorder."

"SAD FOR HIM, YES."

"He was one of your admirers, I could tell."

Ma scowled and shut down the questioning. "SOME MEN SEEMING ALWAYS WANTING SPEND TIME WITH ME."

Though she couldn't understand English, Nainai often had a sense for what was being said around the house, and nothing got past her. Long ago, she had learned German and even studied abroad, and there were some vague similarities to English. But that was a different lifetime, when she said her brain busied itself toying with new ideas and schemes, not searching in vain for a word or a name. To be fair, none of Nainai's friends in America, few as they were now, spoke any English either. There was simply no practical way for a woman of her generation to learn the language other than watch television, but that was too mind-numbing to consider.

This meant, of course, that with Yeye gone, so long as Nainai stayed in America, she was completely reliant on her family for everything. She couldn't work, couldn't drive, couldn't shop for food, couldn't really even stroll far from the house on her own. Though her feet were never bound as a young girl, Nainai's movements as an old woman were constrained all the same. Our little corner house on Crescent Drive in Apalachin, New York, was now her world, a noble dowager inside a suburban castle, ringed by a moat of tar streets she never crossed. Nainai accepted it, as well as her role as grandmother to three boys and a girl, so unlike her own children, and yet so similar.

"The two parts of the word should be in balance," Nainai said, looking over my work, which could only be charitably described as dismal. "They should be positioned and sized in consideration of the other."

"Balance how? What do you mean?" I asked, impatience and frustration bookending my words.

"In many cases, a word comprises two symbols. One that relates to its meaning, and one that relates to its sound. When writing them, they should feel part of a set, in relationship to each other, not standing alone. If you read more Chinese books, you would get a sense of that."

I shook my head in frustration and then drew them again. They still looked awkward, even after I had traced the example characters. In short, my lessons were not going very well. I only half-heartedly attempted the calligraphy, and Nainai correctly suspected that I had no special appreciation for their deeper beauty.

"Don't think of them as just symbols, like buttons on your calculator. They are more than function. They are alive. They are poetry, beauty!"

"Mine are not beautiful," I said sullenly.

Nainai sighed. I was an American child, and the gravitational pull of this foreign land would always prevail. I would never appreciate that those symbols I so reluctantly drew, little better than chicken scratches on my notepad, might tie me to the history, literature, and art of a great and long-suffering people. That was a culture I might never come to know, Nainai seemed to accept, apart from the food I ate and the names I was called at school.

Nainai's own calligraphy was something she held with pride. Her father had taught her to read and write, unusual as it was in her time for a young girl to study, and she had taken that gift and expanded on it. Her work drew praise, even from her father's acquaintances, learned men who saw women's rights as a quaint curiosity. Nainai's father instilled in her a love of the form. He made her understand relation, balance, order, and meaning. It was something she already seemed to have had within her, something he recognized and nourished. Nainai had once revered her own father, before his dark turn and abandonment of their family. Every skilled stroke of her brush on parchment held a bittersweet memory.

Finally, it was time for my favorite part of our nights together: the stories. Nainai would sit across from me in her dimly lit room and simply talk. Some children were artists, some scientists, some scholars. Others, like me, loved stories. Perhaps over time, Nainai figured, she could instill in me a love of tales, and I could one day tell them to my own children and grandchildren.

She had spent the first part of her own life acquiring knowledge and experience, and now she was devoting the last part to imparting it.

Both Ma and I were good listeners and had the time to spare for her recollections. So she ended each lesson with a story and usually a bit of wisdom, which she often pulled out as a bonus.

Nainai told stories of her family, once wealthy, and then later in a long and bitter decline, after her own father turned from hero to wastrel. She recounted her father's brilliant mind and his careful tutelage of her calligraphy, but also the many things he had done to dishonor and destroy his family's fortune, chief among them negligence and a tendency to be cheated. And she warned me about strangers' promises and get-rich-quick schemes. Given my age, though, she left out a few details about her father that she shared with Ma: that he was an opium addict who sold off their fortune, gold brick by gold brick, to pay for his habits, and that he wanted little to do with most of them, except his daughter, whom he treated like a son, because her brothers were scoundrels and bandits.

She also left out, and rightly so, that her own father was an infamous lover of men and would disappear for days at a time into a smoky, pillow-filled and shuttered den with his new *shutong*—a dashing, young male companion whom he preferred to his own wife, or any other women for that matter—demanding not to be disturbed and eating nothing. The way her father regarded and acted around his *shutong* allowed Nainai to observe, far later in life, that two of her favorite grandsons, Calvin and I, were also touched by that spirit.

"NAINAI WAS ONE WHO TELL ME ABOUT YOU FIRST. BECAUSE SHE HAVING A SENSE, BECAUSE OF HER FATHER THAT WAY," Ma said.

"I guess I'm glad he had kids with his wife first."

"SHE WARN ME EARLY. SO WE ALREADY KNOW. YOU THINK YOU ARE TRICKING, BUT WE KNOW."

376

Ma said that Nainai believed the phenomenon of gay people was far more common than people believed, and her insight and experience helped calm Ma down about it. Ma seemed at pains to point out, and for decades would repeat, that the "problem" with me and Calvin appeared to originate from my father's side of the family.

Nainai told stories of life during the war, how food was scarce and a good night's sleep was scarcer because of all the air raids. How meat sometimes dropped from American relief flights over Chongqing, small, tin cans of Spam that you could still find in the stores today. Deprivation, she said, taught appreciation. She told how Ba, when he was my age, would catch snakes and trade them in for rubber bands to power his toy airplanes, and would dream of becoming a pilot to shoot down the Japanese fighters. The toy planes were more precious because Ba had worked hard for those rubber bands, she taught. She described how you could make clean drinking water from dirty river water with enough patience, and that the same patience could be applied to solve any hard problem. Sit, stir, and sift it long enough, and there will be clarity.

She told me how great leaders had sometimes come calling, walking up to their ramshackle home seeking the counsel of our grandfather, the great and learned scholar, a respected and treasured man, truly, and how she would stand there blocking the door to the President of the Republic itself, insisting that she could not possibly allow an honored guest to dirty himself inside. She recounted how she knew, right away, that Ma was more than just a beauty, because of her skilled way of speaking and writing. She had letters from Ma to prove it, written before Ba had even met her. Poor Ba would only realize later that the courtship already had been decided between the two women, long before he could have a say.

I don't know if Nainai knew I didn't understand all of what she said, or even what purpose there was to the telling of it all. But she clearly felt that it might one day do me good to know.

"Do you miss Yeye?" I asked. Nainai had been speaking about him and had trailed off in thought.

"Your grandfather was a brilliant but exasperating man," she laughed.

"I guess I came to appreciate all his qualities. And there were many fine ones."

"So you do miss him."

"Every day," Nainai said, and was quiet for a time. "Now. Did I ever tell you about how he loved to play cards? It was how he first met your other grandfather, in fact, long before we had even met your mother…"

November 1944
Chongqing, China

Yeye often hosted visitors late into the night, but they had been coming by more frequently of late. Ba was already in bed, on the single, thin mattress he shared with his two brothers, but whenever there were guests in their home, he couldn't sleep. Generalissimo Jiang had long stopped dropping by to try and woo Yeye to join the government, but Jiang still sent members of his inner council to seek Yeye's advice. As a boy, Ba tried not to feel too proud about that, but nothing could keep him from holding his father in awe and wanting very badly to impress him. In fact, Ba had hatched a plan to do just that, but he dared not let anyone in on it, especially his sister Qian, my Gugu, who surely would try to stop him.

That night, Ba strained to hear what the men were saying. The guest was some high-level commander, that was clear. They were talking strategy, both political and military, the latter of which Yeye said was simply politics by violent means, according to the German scholars whose country knew best how to make war. There was a conference, which China had been invited to, now that it was a member of something called the "Big Four." To think that China was now in that club thrilled Ba. America, Britain, Russia… and China! It was a validation every patriot felt, after Jiang had gone to Cairo and sat with Roosevelt, Churchill, and Stalin, perhaps not yet as an equal, but at least as a trusted ally and partner.

"Burma didn't go as well as hoped," he heard Yeye say. "And that I chalk up, in part, to personal disagreements and rivalries. There is no love lost between General Stillwell and Jiang."

"General Stillwell should learn some respect," the commander said. "He could start by not calling Jiang 'the peanut.' The generalissimo bristles each time he says that."

"American bullying and name-calling is built into their national character," Yeye observed with a chuckle. "Mark my words, it will only grow worse as they gain more strength and arrogance. We would do best to simply see such incivility for what it is: a sign of insecurity and weakness."

"They are uncouth," the commander agreed, and they had a laugh. Ba wondered whether the commander had been to the American air bases in the province, from which they launched sorties against Japanese cities. He wondered if the commander ever flew a plane—something that lay at the heart of Ba's secret plan.

"True," said Yeye. "But we need the Americans more than ever. To defeat Japan, they will need to invade it. The Japanese will never surrender for less than anything but total military defeat. They already are pulling their troops home to defend their home islands. This will grant us a useful reprieve."

A respite was desperately needed. Five months after the Allies had landed on beaches in Normandy, the war seemed to be going well in

Europe. Everyone said Germany was near to being defeated. Soviet and American forces were both on the move in Europe. But the war in Asia was another matter. Throughout that year, Jiang had lost vast swaths of territory and hundreds of thousands of soldiers during Japan's "Ichigo" campaign, which had sought to connect Korea to Indochina by land. Jiang faced a humiliating string of defeats, and it eroded the public's confidence in his government ever further. The only thing keeping the situation from worsening was the increasing American pressure on the Japanese homeland.

The idea of Japan surrendering was thrilling to Ba, but he felt a pang of regret. For as long as he could remember, he had hid out in Chongqing with his family, subjected to Japanese air raids and starved of food and supplies. Ba had never had a chance to strike back. He was too young, and too politically connected, to be conscripted. But from the hills outside of Chongqing he could see Chinese fighters, supplied by the Allies, in dogfights with Japanese Zeros, which would sometimes come in low and strafe crowds of people with gunfire. Ba wished to fly one of those Chinese fighters, taking down the enemy for the glory of China. Even if he were to lose his life, it would be worth it. More than worth it. His blood might actually count for something.

Ba tried hard to hear more of what Yeye and his guest were saying. When Japan finally lost the war, a new world would emerge, the commander said. They needed to prepare for what would happen after, Yeye agreed.

After the war. Those words felt unreal, almost like a prayer. Ba had been only five when Japan invaded, and he could not remember a time without war. He was now twelve, and the prospect of the conflict ending left him with a sense of vertigo. If he didn't get shot down, if he lived to see actual victory, what might it be like to live in a place like Nanjing, which would once again be the capital of the Republic?

Would they eat chicken instead of just eggs once a week? Would he own a bicycle? Would there be movies?

Our *gugu*, his older sister, scoffed at all Ba's ideas. She had joined the CCP, and as far as she was concerned, the struggle would simply shift from fighting Japan to fighting the KMT. On the day the war against Japan was over, the struggle to establish a workers' paradise in China would begin anew, said Gugu adamantly. The KMT would fall, and rightly so, because they were nothing but lapdogs of the imperialists in London and Washington who had carved up and weakened China before Japan had struck.

Ba didn't share his sister's hatred of the Americans, who had supplied China with food—even canned meat—as well as military aircraft to fight the Japanese. Sure, that general they had sent over was often disrespectful and arrogant. But Stillwell could say what people within the government could not: that Jiang and his cohorts were cowardly, corrupt, and incompetent. Ba's older friends agreed with this assessment, for the most part, though they knew it would be disloyal to say so. In part because of the government's failings, all of Yeye's best students were members of the Communist Party, which led him to assess early on that Mao would eventually emerge victorious.

Ba and his friends had begun to count the days until they would be old enough to enlist and fight for China, but it was always too far away in Ba's mind. If his father was correct, the war might end within a year, and he would have had no chance to prove his worth and honor. Worse, after that he might simply be pulled into fighting for the Nationalists against his fellow countrymen. Maybe even against his own sister.

So the next day, Ba decided to move up his plan. There was a recruitment center that he passed frequently that was looking for young men to train in China's fledgling air force. There was an age limit of sixteen, an age Ba felt he could pass for with the right forged

381

documents. He was tall enough. But there was the problem of his weight.

The lack of protein and other nutrition in their diet had kept Ba rail thin, his arms, legs, and back lacking in muscle and strength. He was a full five kilos short of the minimum weight to even be considered for the program. So he sewed a special inner lining in his pockets and filled them with stones so that he would weigh in just over the minimum. Ba practiced lowering his voice and putting fire behind his eyes to seem older and more experienced.

At the recruitment center, the official looked over Ba's papers and surveyed with skepticism the scrawny boy who had stepped up. There was determination in that face, but the recruiter had seen a lot like him. He motioned toward the scale, and Ba stepped onto it a bit awkwardly, so as not to cause the stones to clack. He was exactly one jin over the minimum. The recruiter was about to waive him forward when an older man stopped him and grabbed Ba's face to examine it. Seeing no sign of whiskers, the man felt Jenkai's bony shoulders and then began to pat him down. When he reached his pants, the stones clacked loudly. Ba felt his face flush red.

"You are a bamboo reed, thinking it's a tree," the man said, and the men around him all laughed.

"I want to fly a fighter! I want to shoot down the Japanese!" Ba cried. The men only laughed more.

"Stick to your toy planes, little man," said one, not unkindly, but Ba felt his passion welling up.

"I'm not a little man! I'm a patriot. The worst day of my life was the day I saw the first Japanese bombers," he said hotly. "It was the worst day because I knew what hate felt like. Since that day, I have wanted nothing more than revenge for what they have done."

382

The men stopped laughing and looked down, even a bit ashamed. "Little man," said the one who had teased him. "We all want revenge. Any Chinese would die if he could see the country freed. But it ends poorly for most. There is just death and more death. Go back home and be a kid. This war has taken enough children from us."

Ba hurled the stones to the ground and ran home. He would find another way, he promised himself. He would go to another recruitment office and drink a gallon of water if he had to. He would find a way to fight.

But as his father had predicted, the war with Japan would be over just nine months later, only without the invasion everyone assumed would drag out for years. All because of two bombs called "Fat Boy" and, if it could be believed, "Little Man." Ba smiled when he heard that name. And as Yeye and Gugu had predicted, the ceasefire with the Communists did not last, and the nation was soon plunged back into war, this time with itself. Eventually, Ba did get conscripted into the service, as was compulsory for all young men at the time. But this was after the Nationalists had fled the mainland to Taiwan, where wartime readiness became the justification for decades of military rule.

Ba never had to shoot any of his fellow countrymen, including Gugu, who had stayed behind in the mainland and fought counter-revolutionaries in Inner Mongolia for the Red Army. As evidence of her devotion, she kept a single photo from that era on top of a bureau in her modest teacher's housing in Beijing. In it, she appeared with a rifle, on her way to battle the enemies of the Party.

Decades later, when I asked about that rifle in the picture, Gugu simply shrugged and said that she had maybe used it "a few times" in her army duties. Whether she had ever killed anyone in the name of the worker's paradise, she never said.

Ma was in third grade when her family resettled in Nanjing, with her father eager to serve in the new Chinese Republic. By this time, Waigong was already a well-connected politician, and because of those connections, as well as a bit of insider knowledge, they had a fine house in a fine neighborhood, by any standard.

On the walk to and from school, Ma regularly passed the Afghan Ambassador's residence, the only truly distinct house in their area. Nanjing, like the rest of China, was still rebuilding from the war, but the capital and the wobbly government were hamstrung by civil strife. There were few established, diplomatic relations with any other nations, which were all waiting to see whether the Nationalists or the Communists would emerge in charge of the country.

"AS A RESULT, I NEVER SEE ANYONE BUT CHINESE FACE AROUND NANJING. EXCEPT THE AFGHANISTAN HOUSE."

The Ambassador's house was the most foreign-feeling place Ma knew, and she felt pulled to it each day, walking by it as slowly as she dared without drawing attention.

The house was palatial and magical. The scent of exotic spices— cumin, coriander, and saffron—drifted in the air alongside mouth-watering, barbecued lamb. Ma sometimes heard strange, haunting music, voices that riffed along a mystical scale from somewhere within the home's many chambers. The residence boasted multiple stories, with large, open, arched windows and ornate columns, and even a spacious balcony where she would sometimes get to see the two shimmering figures who were the wife and daughter of his Excellency, the Ambassador. They had matching long, dark, and lustrous hair, pinned with clips laden with what must be precious gemstones. Ma wished she could get a better look at their hair, even

384

touch it with her hands. It seemed so much more luxurious than the straight, jet-black hair of her girlfriends or the graying coifs of her aunties.

Even more startling was their attire—or lack of it. Mother and daughter, confined to the house with no way to go about the city on their own, instead lay out on their open balcony with their skin exposed to the sun. Nanjing was very hot in the summer, and Laolao explained with a crisp judgment that foreigners sometimes took off their clothes to *sai taiyang*—bathe in the sunlight—so that their skin grew brown. This was the opposite of what was expected from women in Nanjing's upper circles, where pale skin was prized, while dark skin implied too much time in the fields. But the deep color suited the Afghans, Ma thought, their skin shining like burnished copper, highlighting gigantic eyes and distinct, long, pointed features, earlobes adorned with hoops of gold and lapis lazuli. Though they never left the house, they wore heavy make-up, most notably, indigo eyeshadow to match their gems and chili-pepper-red lipstick. Ma was never permitted any make-up, let alone piercings, which her mother insisted was a sure sign of bondage and sexual license. As they floated above her on the terrace, Ma imagined them as living statues, two rock-hewn goddesses come to life, secreted away in a palace and bathing their bodies with sunlight.

The statues, it turned out, could also talk. The mother and daughter pair spotted Ma staring up at them one day, and to her horror, they waved and beckoned her closer. She looked about nervously. They were shouting encouragement in their mellifluous tongue, smiling and gesturing enthusiastically.

The daughter disappeared for a moment, then returned with brightly wrapped candies in her hands. She began to throw them down to Ma. With each toss, the daughter would laugh and clap whenever Ma caught one. The candies were multi-colored and various, orange and lemon and hawberry, tangy and sticky in the heat. For days

385

afterwards, Ma hoarded them protectively, doling them out only as rewards and favors to her many cousins—well, at least the ones who pleased her.

The candy drop became a regular interaction and very much their secret. Ma would come by at least twice a week, if the sun was out, to see if she could catch another glimpse and gain another handful of treasure. Few could really see what mother and daughter were doing on that balcony (and would have frowned upon it had they known), and no one ever suspected where she got her fine candies either. She wondered what it must be like to belong to such a strange culture, where a mother would pass the time with her daughter as if they were good friends, instead of family. What an odd but thrilling arrangement!

"I COULD NOT IMAGINING LAOLAO, AND I TAKE SUN BATH TOGETHER," Ma said with a laugh. "THAT WILL BE THE DAY."

Their bikinis hinted at a world far more modern and even daring, ever just beyond reach, and hidden behind draped archways. Ma had seen a poster for the movie *Arabian Nights* and she often wondered if the mother and daughter had starred in the film.

"You never went inside?" I asked Ma.

"I NEVER WENT IN. JUST IMAGINING."

But years later, with her memory fading, Ma told it differently, insisting that she had, in fact, gone inside the magical house. My brother and I pressed her for some details, but she couldn't summon any. I wonder how powerful the longing had been that her brain now filled in the gaps.

In 1949, Waigong announced they were leaving, just ahead of the advancing Communist forces, and evacuating to Taiwan. Laolao let her anger uncoil, accusing Waigong of being little more than a war refugee, so often were they on the run. But to Ma, Taiwan sounded exotic and tropical, and the evacuation was like any other they had endured—but this time it came with her first plane ride. The family left first in a hurry, and the servants followed, packing up their belongings onto ships headed south and east. It happened so quickly Ma missed any chance to meet her strange Afghan benefactors in person, to inspect their bikini suits up close, or to touch their beautiful hair.

After her family fled, she wondered whether the two women knew where she had gone so suddenly, and she wished she could thank them for the candies and their kindness, and warn them about the Communists who would never permit sunbathing—it was a bourgeois practice after all. They surely would expel the Ambassador back to Kabul for having made friends with the KMT. In fact, all the foreigners in Nanjing would probably be sent packing, and this made Ma sad. Even at her age, she understood that the Chinese did better when they had someone other than just Chinese around.

Many decades later, a resurgent consumer class of women in China would sport bikinis while sunbathing, though in moderation and often with thick sunblock on. They would also develop a thirst for rare gems and stones, especially the cold, blue treasures of Afghanistan. China's burgeoning gem industry, through Ma's friend, Meiling, at the Gemology Department, placed a special request with Ma, who was now far older than Laolao had been during the war, to see if she might safely obtain some from that embattled country.

Times had changed in Afghanistan. A woman like Ma could no longer travel alone to the border, let alone engage in commerce once past it. New religious laws prevented her from going, though she wanted badly to see the homeland of her mysterious neighbors. She wondered if the mother and daughter had escaped that country or been forced by harsh laws to hide their bodies and faces. Ma reluctantly sent Ba to retrieve the bounty instead.

"How was it? What did you see?" Ma asked him eagerly upon his return.

"Very poor," Ba said. "And dusty. Dangerous to travel. Not much to see, really."

Ma was disappointed. In her imaginings, despite its fall into violent and hard times, Afghanistan was not a land of war, terror, and death. It was where beauty lay on a balcony, skin the color of polished copper, always ready to throw down the finest of candies.

August 2020
FaceTime Call

"ARE YOU STILL PRACTICE?"

"I was good for a while. But I'm not spending enough time on it these days."

"YOU SHOULD PRACTICE."

In truth, I hadn't been playing piano much at all. It was becoming dispiriting, going over the same music for a recital that now might never happen. The lockdown in New York City was called just days before my first public performance in over 30 years. Right up to that point, I had become an insane, obsessed person, squeezing in hours each day in pursuit of a "next level" execution. I had booked the Steinway Hall on Sixth Avenue, enough for fifty people. There was a program, in tasteful font, with phrases like "Op. 69 in A major." It would have been the first time many of my friends and colleagues actually heard me play classically: Bach, Schubert, Chopin, and

Beethoven. The final piece was a piano-cello sonata, a technically demanding work I had chosen to present with my friend, Lance, an accomplished cellist who lived around the corner from me. He had been just as nervous about the upcoming date, and just as disappointed when we had to call the whole thing off.

"YOU SHOULD KEEPING IT UP."

"For whom?" I laughed. "My poor roommates are sick of hearing the same music on repeat." I hadn't worked on any new music during quarantine. The idea of taking remote Zoom lessons from my teacher, an energetic musicologist in her seventies from the Upper West Side named Joan, felt too bitter a compromise.

Joan had been recommended by my ex, Andrew, a piano tuner and music teacher himself, whose name and face Ma also could never seem to remember, probably because he looked a bit like every other white American I'd dated. Andrew was from a small farming town in Wisconsin and, unlike nearly everyone else in my life, was quiet and mild-mannered. But he had a knack for knowing what I really needed, having once insisted I get myself a cat when he was getting ready to break up with me, and later a Corgi puppy after I hadn't dated anyone else in years. When I had mentioned in passing that I wished I could play piano like I once did, Andrew immediately spoke to Joan about it and suggested a lesson. In short order, Joan reignited my love for music, not by focusing on the raw technique, which she was exceptional at explaining, but on the history, nuance, and joy of it all. Joan found a way to sometimes spend an entire lesson examining just two measures of music, demonstrating how the entirety of the art form could be found within them. I found the truth of that transportative and astonishing, and I missed our twice-monthly sessions immensely.

"I JUST GLAD I GETTING A CHANCE TO HEAR YOU PLAY BEFORE WHOLE COUNTRY SHUTTING DOWN. YOU GOING TO INVITE PEOPLE TO HEAR YOU AFTER ALL THIS OVER?"

"That's the plan," I said, not wanting to talk about it.

Fortunately, Ma had come out to visit a week before the recital, and I had suggested that she come to my lesson with me and at least hear Lance and me play together. With Ma in the room, I felt a need to prove myself in a way I hadn't in decades. As my fingers began to fly over scales and passages I had finally begun to master, I wondered whether Ma could tell the difference, whether she would appreciate the work I had put in, how far I had drilled down to the bare essentials before building my technique back up from scratch. At the end of it, Ma was clapping and smiling, her eyes shining at Joan.

"WOW, SO BEAUTIFUL!"

"It really is wonderful, Jay!" said Joan encouragingly. "It has come a long, long way. And Lance, such artistry! You two have been busy!"

"We practice once a week together," I said, trying not to sound pleased.

"It's my favorite time of the week!" said Lance, who, like me, was also a "trendy" man with Chinese parents. His folks had been visiting during one of our rehearsals, and his father had remarked he'd never heard Lance play that well before. "He never says stuff like that. I don't know what got into him," Lance said later, with practiced Chinese modesty.

"DO YOU KNOW MY MOTHER WAS MUSICIAN?" Ma asked. I knew she couldn't pass up a chance to give her version of the "Origin Story"—how two of her children had come to be professional musicians, at least for a time, in the very different worlds of heavy metal and Broadway.

"Jay mentioned that, yes!" Lance said.

"SHE WAS FIRST GIRL TO STUDY MUSIC IN COLLEGE IN NANJING WHEN THEY OPENING IT UP TO GIRL. SHE PLAY VIOLIN AND PIANO! SHE LOVING IT SO MUCH SHE TEACHING MUSIC TO OTHER YOUNG GIRL, EVEN POOR ONE WHO SING FOR MEN IN CLUB. SINGER GIRL ONLY, NOT PROSTITUTE," Ma said hastily as I coughed nervously. "WHEN SHE LATER START A SCHOOL FOR CHILDREN, SHE HAVING A CHOIR AND GETTING DONATED LOT OF GRAND PIANO. EVEN BEAUTIFUL STEINWAY, LIKE YOURS!"

"So your whole family are musicians!" Joan exclaimed, already charmed to sparkling pieces by Ma.

"I THINK IT MUST SKIPPING A GENERATION," Ma said *sotto voce*, as if disclosing a secret she had never thought to tell. "SHE WANTING ME TO LEARN HOW TO PLAY, BUT DURING WAR IS NOT EASY. SO I TAKING MY CHILDREN TO LESSON. DO YOU KNOW HOW I FIRST KNEW JAY WAS MUSICIAN?"

Here it comes, I thought. But Joan and Lance were enthralled.

"WHOLE FAMILY GO TO HEAR PIANO RECITAL AND ONE GIRL PLAYING 'FUR ELISE.' DEE-DA DEE-DA DEE-DA DEE-DA-DOOH! I LOOKING AT JAY AND HE SO CONCENTRATE," Ma said, furrowing her brow comically to imitate me as a small child. "I ASK HIM IF HE LIKE, AND HE SHUSH ME! SHHH! HE CONTINUE CONCENTRATE. THEN NEXT MORNING, I HEAR SOMEONE PLAY DOWNSTAIR. DEE-DA DEE-DA DEE-DA DEE-DA-DOOH! WHO IS PLAYING, KAISER? I ASK. I GOING DOWNSTAIR AND IT WAS JAY, SIT PLAYING! CAN YOU BELIEVE?"

I had no actual memory of this event, but Ma insisted I could play the whole piece, start to finish, just from hearing it once. Given the technique needed for much of it, this was impossible, but that didn't deter her from telling the story. Ma was excited by my budding talent and the shred of a possibility, shared by most Chinese mothers of her generation, of having musical geniuses for sons. She insisted on lessons for me, even at age four. She carted me along with my reluctant brothers to see the local Chinese piano teacher, Mrs. Hsu, who taught all of the Chinese kids within a thirty-mile radius. Her house smelled of mothballs and traditional herbal remedies, and it was excruciating to wait around for an hour after my lesson, playing with the few toys she left out just for such idle times, as I listened to my brothers plunk out their assignments.

The recitals made up for it. Within a year, and with a strong desire to outshine my siblings in something, I was playing above my age bracket, showing off with pieces like "The Entertainer," which I performed at any open piano I could find, to my brothers' deep chagrin. I was small for my age, so the sight of a tiny, Chinese boy playing Scott Joplin ragtime was exceptional and sometimes even earned me half-dollar tips from strangers. At the church where the Chinese families gathered for Mrs. Hsu's student recitals, I played a great deal of Mozart, whom Ma loved to say was "ALSO TALENT" as a child. None of the parents or students, or even Mrs. Hsu herself, was an actual musician, or they would have told me to stop immediately and start my training over. I had learned to play almost exclusively by ear, and thanks to Mrs. Hsu, could only barely read music, even after four years. As for my technique, I had formed poor habits in the name of expediency. I could play the notes, even quickly, but they were inartful and lacking nuance. I was like a figure skater who could only do the big jumps. I didn't know what music really was other than a way to impress other people.

Ma must have realized this by the time we moved to Tucson, or perhaps someone like Rebecca Zheng had made a comment, because Ma began to ask around. In time she found a far stricter and imposing matron of a Polish instructor who reminded me of Julia Child. She insisted on returning us to fundamentals and on instilling in us a truer love of music. Lessons with her were all scales and technical books like Hanon and Czerny, which was the fastest way to bore a ten-year-old who just wanted to keep entertaining audiences. Whether we were beyond hope and fired by our teacher, or whether Ma simply preferred someone willing to come to our home to give lessons, we finally found ourselves the pupils of one of her protégés, a younger woman named Anna Horton, who became my teacher for the next seven years.

My brothers gladly gave up their lessons, especially after a recital where John managed to get to the very end of his Bach two-part invention but couldn't complete the final two measures, electing in a panic to start over from the very beginning. Ma forced a smile and willed herself not to look at the pitying faces of the other audience members. After that, she decided that it was time to allow her two oldest boys to pursue other skills. One pianist in the family would suffice. John, who had suffered through years of violin and the piano lessons, gave up music altogether. Kaiser bought an electric guitar, and the Chinese rock scene was forever changed.

Anna Horton did something for which I would always be grateful: She revealed to me the theory of music. No one had ever bothered explaining how music actually worked, how key signatures were interrelated mathematically, how every major had its minor companion, a yin and a yang right there in the open, if anyone took the time to reveal it. It was like unlocking a secret world, and my brain made sense of it for the first time. I began to play, not because someone else might hear me and be impressed, but because it burrowed and settled into some part of me I didn't know had been waiting.

Ma noted the change in me, seating herself on the couch to listen while I practiced. I grew accustomed to having her there, figuring at first she was ensuring she was getting her money's worth for my lessons, but later understanding that I was to Ma as the music was to me.

Something about my playing filled a void for her, a deep regret that she never had a companion like music to grow up and grow old with. Ba never spoke to Ma the way music spoke to me.

In high school, I began to compete in the national Mason and Hamlin auditions. My chief rival was another of Anna Horton's students, a mousy girl with Coke-bottle glasses named Kristina Um, who had far better technique and discipline. Her sister also played but was not nearly as good, and we often glanced at each other in sympathy while Kristina ran virtuosic circles around both of us. When she beat me in the auditions, and soundly, my only solace was in the announcement: "The winner is Kristina... um... Um!" Ma seemed fine with me losing to a Korean American girl. "KOREAN BEEN THROUGH A LOT, YOU KNOW. NICE THEY CAN HAVE SOME SUCCESS NOW, TOO."

After college, I stopped taking lessons and spent any spare time at the piano, composing Broadway-musical-style numbers. I had always intended to keep up my lessons, but somehow between lawyering in my thirties and composing actual musicals in my forties, I never got back around to it. Years became decades, and muscle memory for scales and arpeggios had faded in my fingers. My left hand seemed only to know how to play chords in service of a show tune. The biggest challenge to starting lessons again was convincing myself that I could do it at age fifty.

"YOU DON'T LOOKING OR ACTING LIKE FIFTY," Ma had said when I explained my dilemma.

"Yeah, but my fingers disagree. They are in full rebellion." Lately, my left hand especially had begun to ache at night and even freeze up, waking me up with a sharp pain that left me breathless. Beginning in her sixties, Nainai had experienced crippling rheumatoid arthritis in her hands, which had become gnarled and painful. Years of household labor had ruined once soft, graceful hands, and in her old age, they became daily reminders that life could be hard. I wondered if all my piano ambitions would get wiped out by an unforgiving set of inherited genes. The cramping and pain had gotten worse during the pandemic lockdown, and I used it as another excuse to not play.

As if she could sense my own decline, Ma had recently started sending me links to her favorite piano performances on YouTube or Youku, its Chinese knock-off. They were usually young Chinese artists like Lang Lang, who, to her pride and delight, were finally being recognized internationally as best in class. It was her way of nudging me.

"YOU SHOULD HEAR THE BEAUTIFUL MUSIC!" she would write, attaching a link. "REMINDING ME OF YOU. ARE YOU STILL PRACTICE?"

Chapter Twelve

LOVE

or

"JUST A LITTLE STRANGE"

September 2016
New York City, New York

> MA and JAY are on the subway. They speak loudly to each other over the rumble of heavy cars, music from a boombox, and the screech of brakes. MA watches as two eager, teenaged, Asian boys attempt to speak to a pretty, Asian girl. It triggers a memory.

MA: IN OUR GENERATION YOU KNOW, NOT SO MANY CHINESE GIRL STUDY IN UNITED STATE, MOSTLY BOY. SO EACH GIRL HAVE MANY CHASERS.

JAY: May the odds be ever in your favor.

MA: SO IT BECOME VERY IMPORTANT WHETHER BOY HAS A CAR AND CAN DRIVE. YOUR DADDY HAVE JALOPY. BUT HE TEACH HIS FRIEND BEVAN HOW TO DRIVE, SO HE CAN CHASING GIRL, TOO.

JAY: Did he succeed?

MA: OH YEAH, BEVAN ALWAYS HAVE SO MANY GIRL AS RESULT. BUT HE DID NOT LIKE THEM, ALWAYS COMPLAIN.

JAY: Womp womp.

MA: YES VERY WOMPY.

Jay laughs.

MA: MANY GIRL THOUGH LOOKING FOR SOMEONE SMART. I CHOOSE DADDY BECAUSE YOUR GRANDFATHER RECOMMEND.

JAY: That's romantic…

MA: WELL, HE FAMOUS SCHOLAR. SO I WANT SIX CHILDREN.

JAY: Why so many?

MA: WELL, BECAUSE IT CHEAPER PER CHILDREN IF YOU TEACH HALF DOZEN AT ONE TIME.

JAY: And that's… economical?

MA: BUT I ONLY HAVE FOUR, PLUS TWO THAT ARE GONE BEFORE BORN.

They sit in silence for a moment, while MA thinks about what might have been.

JAY: So what ever happened to Bevan?

MA: OH, SUCH SAD STORY. LATER HE MARRY UNHAPPY. SAY YOUR DADDY LUCKY THAT HE DID NOT LOOK AT HIS WIFE AND ALWAYS WISH FOR DIVORCE.

JAY: Oh, my God. That's awful!

MA: WELL MAYBE GIRL WHO ONLY LIKE HIM FOR CAR NOT SO GOOD MATCH.

April 1957
Columbus, Ohio

Ba was always doing friends and family favors, now that he had his own car and an actual driver's license. He had purchased a beat-up Chevy Bel Air from a nice white man in Columbus near Ohio State, where Ba was getting his degree. The idea that he could own his own car in America was almost too much to believe, and he had been so excited by the prospect that he had neglected to actually learn how to drive. Rather, he had only seen how cars operated from a distance, watching American soldiers as they drove around Chongqing during the war, honking and whooping as Americans were known to do. (While some of the local Chinese resented their presumptuous behavior, Jenkai had been impressed with the GIs, particularly when he watched them play baseball. It wasn't how they had played the game, it was how they'd eaten the local peanuts. They would crack the shells by hand and carefully put the used shells into their pockets rather than litter the ground. The Chinese were not so respectful; it was why the ground was always strewn with shells and husks.)

Ba hadn't wanted the car seller to know that he was a novice. But when the man asked to meet up by the side of a highway, then suggested Ba actually take the car for a spin, Ba couldn't refuse. It took some initial horrible sounds from the engine and some fits and starts, but Ba eventually got the car in gear and eased it forward, and within minutes, they were flying down the highway, the seller totally unaware that his life was in terrible danger.

Ba paid cash for the Bel Air. His friends excitedly took turns in the driver's seat. With a car, Ba had real liberty. He could even drive all the way out to New York City to see his parents, as well as the pretty but uptight gal he had started seeing, who insisted on going by her American name, Lorraine. Her family, the Fus, had known his own family through overlapping social circles during their time in Nanjing. That the world was in fact so small led Ba to keep his relationship with Lorraine secret from his parents.

Ba had agreed to drive a friend of Yeye's, whom he called simply "Old Chen," to a nearby all-girls Catholic school known widely as Dominican College. Old Chen had promised the girl's father (who, in another small-world moment, apparently was *also* friends with Yeye) that he would find a proper young Chinese student to look after her, so he had roped Ba into the role. Ba reluctantly agreed, even though it was far out of his way. They pulled up to the passenger pick-up area and got out.

"The car's still running," said Old Chen.

"We won't be long, right?" replied Ba pointedly. That was back in the days where you could leave the car engine running and not worry that someone might drive off with it.

They swung by the reception desk and spoke with the young woman there. It was just past breakfast, so she made a general announcement. "Mary Liu, you have two visitors, Mary Liu!"

That's when Ba first saw her. Ma came bounding down the stairs to greet them, a vision of carefree living and vivacity. Mary Liu was unlike any Chinese girl Ba had ever laid eyes upon, her hair wavy and freshly curled like an American movie star's. She had chosen a deep-red lipstick, sported high heels on a pair of tiny feet, and looked like a spring goddess in a yellow summer dress. Ba was thunderstruck.

"Oh, you're not who I was expecting!" Ma said.

She wasn't who Ba was expecting either. "Just a moment," he said. "If you'll excuse me a minute."

"Where are you going?" asked Old Chen, alarmed.

"I... forgot that I left the car running." He had already decided they would be staying much longer.

When Ba returned, the beautiful girl seemed to size him up.

"Oh, I know who you are. You're the Kuo boy. I know your father," Ma said, somewhat teasingly. "Are you surprised? I had dinner with him earlier this month, because he and my father were bridge partners. He learned I was living in Ohio. You're not as I imagined. I wonder if you're anything as smart as he is," she laughed.

"My father is a historian," Ba managed to stammer.

"Oh, I know!" Ma laughed. "Funny thing, I memorized whole parts of his high-school textbook. He made history come to life! I wanted to thank him. I recited parts of it verbatim over dinner, and you should have seen his face! To think, he never even wanted to write that book, but did it because he needed the money. He almost didn't write it! Your father is really an accomplished man. Did he not even mention we'd had dinner?"

In fact, Yeye had been so impressed and moved by this extraordinary young woman's memorization of his work that he immediately phoned his wife to tell her. His friend Liu Jingjian's daughter was right there in Ohio, living not far from Jenkai! She was charming, beautiful and intelligent, a perfect match for their son. Nainai advised caution and to not let Ba know anything while they worked behind the scenes. Nainai set about corresponding by letter with Ma. In fact, she'd already written two warm notes asking politely about her family. Later, Ma gave "Professor Kuo" a scarf and sweater to send to Nainai back in Taiwan, cementing their favorable opinion of her.

"I FALLING IN LOVE WITH YOUR FATHER'S PARENT LONG BEFORE I EVEN KNOWING HIM," Ma explained to me.

By that time, Ma was already far ahead of Ba in her plans, and he was basically a goner. He just didn't know it yet.

"You are not as tall as you looked in your picture," Ma said, further flustering Ba. Her own brothers were all over six feet in height, and Ma wondered whether this trait would carry over should she make a family with the Kuo boy. *Well*, she thought, *at least he is smart*. The smart ones never grow very tall, as Laolao would often say, right to the faces of her brothers. Ma would learn the same backhanded trick.

"You should come have breakfast with us," Ba managed to say.

"Oh, I've already eaten," Ma demurred.

For the rest of that first encounter, she made polite conversation, poked fun at the strictness of her Catholic upbringing and the nuns at her college, and finally agreed to take a short ride in the Bel Air, rolling the windows down and enjoying the feeling of the crisp, spring rushing by, the smell of fresh rain on the pavement, her hair flowing picture perfect, or at least that's how Ba remembered it. When they were done, she coyly left her umbrella in the car, giving Ba a proper reason to call again to return it to her.

On cue, Ba began to telephone her, sometimes three times a day, which she felt was wholly unnecessary. She did agree, after a few more calls, to go to dinner with him, and Ba splurged on a fancy restaurant recommended by his breathless, Chinese classmates. Like his parents, they were eager to see the two become an item. Ma ordered a whole roasted bird, and over the course of the meal, meticulously ate every bit of it down to the bones, as she laughed and chatted about their childhoods and families. Ba had never met a girl like her.

"You… have quite an appetite," he said, trying to make light of her devouring the entire chicken.

"Well," Ma mused. "You gave more than a few hints that this is a fancy restaurant, even if this tablecloth is a bit ratty, and since you clearly are a poor student who cannot afford the price of this bird, it would be rude of me not to eat every bit of it, don't you think?" Ba had nothing to say to that, so just watched her eat and listened to her stories, which seemed to flow nonstop, even through their dessert of *xinren doufu*—almond gelatin "tofu" laden with fruit cocktail—which she remarked was too sweet for her taste.

That summer, Ba had intended to go to live in New York to spend time with Yeye, who was a distinguished visiting scholar on Chinese history and sought by many American universities. But he canceled his plans and decided to stay in Ohio, so he could spend more time with Ma. Yeye approved of this plan immediately, and he changed his schedule as well, so he could be close to his son in Ohio. Each day, Ba would pick up Ma from her summer school class and return her to the dormitory, his father sitting quietly in the back seat, as the courtship unfolded.

Nainai followed all this carefully and asked many questions of Ba, even as she continued her clandestine letter-writing campaign. But there was a big complication. In her excitement, Nainai had mentioned casually to Laolao, whom she knew socially, that her son, Jenkai, had met Laolao's daughter, Mary Tanlee. That alone was enough to send Laolao into a deep suspicion. After she learned of the budding romance, she sought to squash it outright.

"You are not to see that boy anymore!" Laolao demanded in her own set of letters.

When this admonition went unheeded, Laolao let fly her most deadly weapon, gleaned from the very accurate rumor mill that comprised the overseas Chinese student population.

"This Kuo boy is not a gentleman. He is playing you for a fool. Do you know the girl he is *already seeing*?"

As it turned out, Ma already knew that Ba was also dating Lorraine Fu.

The haughty and influential Fu family had lived near the Liu household for most of Ma's early childhood in Nanjing, and had fled with the rest of the KMT cadre class to Taiwan. Madam Fu had a daughter a year older than Ma, and out of a declared sense of charity and healthy dose of cruelty, Madam Fu often brought over used clothing for Ma to wear, explaining that her own daughter had outgrown them but that such good clothes shouldn't go to waste. Laolao accepted these "gifts" with a smile, and then dutifully bade Ma wear them to show appreciation for Madam Fu's generosity.

Even as a small girl, Ma understood that this was actually a way for Madam Fu to lord it over their family and maintain the existing social hierarchy. Song Manxi's daughter, Mary, would always wear secondhand clothes, because while Manxi may have been beautiful and graceful, she was not and would never be as feared or respected as Madam Fu. Young Lorraine took after her mother completely, delighting in tormenting Ma, reminding her publicly that she was wearing her old clothes whenever she saw her out with them on. "That dress used to be bright and colorful, when I wore it. I suppose it's been washed too many times and bleached by the sun. You should stay out of the sun, Tanlee!" Lorraine said, her friends laughing at the jab.

When Ma ran home to her mother in tears, Laolao instead scolded her and told her to stop being so prideful, even though Laolao also secretly resented Madam Fu for trapping her and her daughter, with clothes handed down to them, as if they were Madam Fu's poor servants.

To Ma, the knowledge that her new boyfriend was already seeing someone else had come as a shock. But that was the way men were, as she'd seen in her own father, who had more than one wife and probably many other girls on the side. The knowledge that the other girl was Lorraine Fu, however, had been almost too much. A classmate of Lorraine had casually mentioned that Lorraine was dating a boy who attended Ohio State named Jenkai, and Ma had to keep her surprise from registering visibly.

Why was God so angry at her? Why would He allow such an unlikely and unhappy circumstance? True, Jenkai was already seeing Lorraine when Ma had made her own intentions known, so technically, Ma was the real interloper. But Jenkai was not engaged to Lorraine, Ma figured. And Ma knew enough about men to know Lorraine was just the occasional weekend tryst, almost obligatory by now, carried forward by little but momentum. In Ohio, however, Ma had the home advantage, and despite her mother's threats, she was going to fight for Jenkai Kuo.

"I know that you have a secret," Ma said to Ba as another weekend excursion to New York approached. "I know that you don't go to New York just to see your parents."

As he would find himself for much of the rest of his life, Ba was entirely caught off guard by her words. How could she have heard about Lorraine? He sensed some kind of trap, but also felt he might not mind being caught.

"Is that so?" he said nonchalantly. "And what is it you think I also do?"

"I think you also have a girlfriend out in New York."

"That's not true!" Ba protested. Lorraine was not officially his girlfriend, so it wasn't a lie.

"Oh, rubbish. I know all about her. Nothing is secret in the circles we run in, don't you agree? I heard it from two different sources, a classmate and a friend of my father who is also in the legislature. There are only so many Chinese girls out here, you know. So you men treat us like prized jewels, always with eyes on us."

Ba had nothing to say to that, so Ma continued.

"I didn't mind, you know, when we first started spending time with each other and I found out about her. I wasn't sure at all that you were someone I wanted to see more often anyway. But now, we have become a bit more serious, don't you think? I wouldn't want your parents to be disappointed; they are such wonderful people."

Ba remained silent in the face of all this, as was his practice when he didn't have full information.

"So I think, whatever else it is you are doing in New York must stop, if we are to continue to see one another. Don't you think that is only right? Oh! Since you won't be going to New York this weekend, I have a surprise for you."

Ba was relieved, in a way. Ma finally had indicated she was serious, and maybe even a bit jealous. And truthfully, he was tired of driving hundreds of miles to New York to see Lorraine all the time, even with his new car. So he telephoned Lorraine before that weekend, and he told her that he wouldn't be coming out, that he wouldn't come to see her any more at all actually, because he had met someone else, and he was in love, and the right thing to do when you're in love is to call things off with anyone else. Lorraine understood that she was the "anyone else" in this story. (Years later, when Ma watched *The Sound of Music*, she instantly saw herself in the role of Maria, with Lorraine befittingly assigned the role of the Baroness, who had to concede the prized Captain Von Trapp to her. In the Kuo house, it became a tradition to watch that movie every year, and the Broadway cast album with Mary Martin as Maria was played on repeat.)

With Lorraine Fu dispatched, it was time to circle the wagons. Ma's "surprise" was a home-cooked Chinese meal for all their recently graduated friends. She had learned to expertly prepare exactly five dishes from their longtime family chef, because her father had insisted that if she wanted to impress a chap one day, she should show him her talents in the kitchen. That seemed silly, that men would be so easily impressed by something any woman could learn so quickly, but she had obeyed and learned how to make those dishes, practicing them many times in various restaurant kitchens around town. The dishes included a delicacy of wok-fried sea cucumbers. She hadn't any fresh ones for the surprise meal (this was Columbus, Ohio, after all), but when she had been in San Francisco on her way inland, she'd found some dried ones in a shop and presciently bought them, thinking one day she would indeed have cause to make the five dishes.

Ba was so impressed with the meal, he called up his parents to boast about Ma. Nainai nodded with appreciation as she heard him gush, knowing that those five dishes were probably the only ones Ma, as a girl of privilege, knew how to make. She herself had started with just five dishes of her own, but as a mother she had learned to cook many more, enough to feed a family of five children. Four, she corrected. She made a note to teach Ma her own recipes one day.

Ma didn't hear how Lorraine had taken the news. When she and Ba announced their engagement, however, she was mortified to learn that the Fus had all received invitations to the engagement party. Apparently, Nainai did not know that Ba and Lorraine had been an item, or worse, that Lorraine and Ma had shared him for a time. Nainai had extended the invitation as a courtesy to any fellow Taiwan evacuees they knew who were now in America, so insular was the initial diaspora. Ma was doubly surprised when Lorraine actually accepted the invite and came to the party, looking the part of the aggrieved paramour-who-should-have-been-the-wife, and hoping, no doubt, to curse the whole relationship with her considerable negative energies.

When it was time for Lorraine to wish the new couple well, she did so with a razor edge and a smile that, many said, was far less than genuine. But she saved her most potent bile for her private chat with Ma.

"Well done, Tanlee," said Lorraine, when she found her alone. She looked down at Ma, just as she had when they were children, her face a picture of self-satisfaction. "Now that he has chosen you over me, I certainly hope that you and Jenkai will have a wonderful, happy life together. Though I must say, I am surprised that things have worked out this way. I didn't think a serious man like Jenkai would pick a girl like you."

"Why, Lorraine," Ma said, her voice as sweet as almond tofu. "You are so kind and generous, as always. But you really shouldn't be surprised about Jenkai. After all, for all of my life, I've always gotten your hand-me-downs."

December 1993
Tucson, Arizona

I was standing just outside the window, looking in. I could see Ma and Ba laughing at a joke Kaiser was telling. John was shaking his head, and his girlfriend was holding his hand, her eyes twinkling. Only Mimi seemed not to be listening, as if instead she were looking around, maybe for me?

407

I banged on the window to get their attention, but my fists made no sound. Was I a ghost, unable to connect to the material world? I shouted, but it came out as a whisper. "I'm outside! I'm here! Let me in!" A flicker of recognition in Mimi's eyes lifted my hopes, but then she reached in with her chopsticks for some vegetables, platters slowly spinning on the oversized lazy Susan Ba had specially built for that giant table, and I could tell she was no longer thinking about me.

I went to the front door but my hand passed through it. I tried to ring the bell, but it did not depress. I was on the outside now, forever, my family lost to me.

I awoke with a start. I checked my hands and rubbed them together. I wiggled my toes, one foot at a time. Not a ghost. A terrible dream, but I was still here, in the spare bed in my sister's room, near the far end of our house in Tucson. Like Ebenezer Scrooge, I awoke to a Christmas morning, the warnings of the Ghost of Christmas Yet To Come still reverberating. I knew what I had to do.

I shuffled in pajamas down the hallway, the same long corridor I had known for most of my life, with its terra-cotta-colored, rough-hewn Spanish tiles my parents had installed to replace the carpet that had been ruined ten years earlier, during a hundred-year desert flood. Our home in Tucson was a sprawling adobe-brick structure, appropriate for the unrelenting desert sun and our proximity to Mexico, the sheer size of it a giant middle finger to the cramped, dirt-floor hovel of Ba's own childhood. Once, he had shown us the house's deed and pointed out the racial exclusionary clause: "Not to be sold to a buyer of Mongoloid race"—meaning us. The courts later ruled that kind of clause unenforceable, but the fact that it was still in our deed and we were now in the house rather pleased Ba.

I'd walked backward down this same hallway when I was eight years old, still small enough to stand on Ba's feet while facing him, holding both his hands, his Christmas present to me a simple letter telling me

I was old enough to know there was no Santa, but could appreciate the gift he was giving me. The offer was a day for just the two of us, anywhere I wanted to go, just like when I'd ride in his lap on his motorcycle through the fields and pastures of upstate New York, Ba enjoying the thrill far more than I did, my "brave face" the best I could muster.

A dozen other thoughts flashed across my mind as I made that Christmas morning walk. I was nearly 25 years old, but I had still never been honest with my parents. The pressure had been building lately, mostly because I hadn't dated a girl in almost seven years. Ma had begun to ask my brothers about that. "Why don't you ask him yourself?" Kaiser said, annoyed to be put on the spot.

Ma later confessed she had spoken frequently to Nainai about the possibility that I was gay, and Nainai had told her that her own father had taken a *shutong*—a male "book companion"—after he was forty. And it was also pretty much known that my cousin, Calvin, was "this way," so they surmised that all the gayness must come from the Kuo side of the family. Years later, Ma would insist on this when talking about my trans nephew, Hartley:

"KUO FAMILY SO STRANGE, NO STRANGE IN LIU FAMILY," Ma remarked, apropos of nothing.

"What's strange, Nainai?" said my niece, Kaili. To her, Ma was her *nainai*. Her grandmother, on her father's side.

"KUOS ALWAYS HAVE TRADITION OF KUO GAY. NO GAY IN LIU."

Kaili laughed but wouldn't let it go unanswered. "Nainai, maybe it's not nice to call Hartley 'strange.'"

"I NO SAY STRANGE. I SAY KUO GAY IS TRADITION. I SEE LOTS OF DIFFERENT WEIRD SEX."

Kaili wasn't sure where to begin.

"ALWAYS AT LEAST ONE IN EVERY GENERATION. WITH ER SHU SHU," Ma said, casting shade on my father's second younger brother, "THERE WERE TWO!"

My brother, John, reports that "Kuo Gay" is now his family's motto, and we're still trying to figure out who the second "Kuo gay" was in my uncle's family, besides Calvin.

Long before Ma had developed this theory, she needed to prepare the way for the possibility of me being gay. She was most concerned about Ba. She took him to see the new Taiwanese film, *The Wedding Banquet* which, for the first time, brought homosexuality and traditional Chinese filial piety into stark relief. I had heard that Ma had dragged him to see it, but that Ba had been uncomfortable for most of the movie, so Ma didn't press the point.

I'd come out to each of my siblings many years ago, at various points in time. With Kaiser, it had been in the middle of an argument when I was only thirteen, when I shouted that I liked boys "like Michael Jackson likes boys!"—which is probably not the way I'd choose to say it today.

With my sister Mimi, it was in a discotheque in Shanghai, when she suddenly sprang the question: "Jay. Are you bi?" When I'd shaken my head slowly and said, "No...," she actually seemed disappointed, which was not at all what I'd been expecting. Then she leaned over conspiratorially and asked, "Are you gay?" I slowly nodded my head and said, "Yessss..." She looked satisfied, then followed up with, "Oh, good. What do you think of that guy over there?" I always thought it funny that Mimi had asked me such a huge question simply to obtain a second opinion on a guy.

I'd told John over lunch years ago, with his then-girlfriend Lisa. They had heard that I was seeing "someone much older" because Bernie

410

was twelve years my senior. When the first dim-sum basket arrived at our table, I asked John what he thought about a big age difference. "Oh, it doesn't matter to me how old she is," John said, reaching in for some *xiajiao*. "Would it matter if it weren't a she?" I asked casually. Lisa cocked her head in surprise. "So, she's… a he?" I nodded. John's eyes flickered, and then blurted out, "You know, Tchaikovsky was gay…" And then went back to enjoying his meal.

With Ma and Ba, it would not be so simple. They still held old-country views about marriage and sex, meaning you shouldn't do the former with non-Chinese, and you should only do the latter when married to one. The reasons for this were complicated and had a lot to do with their notion of what a happy grandparentage would look and feel like for them. I was about to shatter that notion, and hard.

I knocked on their door, and after a moment, I heard Ma say, "COME IN." I peeked past the door, and they were both already awake, looking at me expectantly.

"MERRY CHRISTMAS!!" Ma said brightly. I burst into tears.

"Why don't you sit with us, and tell us what is wrong," Ba said. I could sense he was worried. I was about to deliver bad news. Perhaps it was cancer. Or maybe I was about to be arrested for a crime. Whatever it was, he was listening.

I don't remember the exact way I said it, because it all spewed out in a long and unrehearsed monologue. My father listened quietly, and then asked what I'm sure he was most worried about, "Are you telling us now because you are sick?"

AIDS had been around for more than a decade, but it was still considered by Chinese-immigrant parents to be a Western affliction. Ba thought of gay people and HIV as interchangeable. I hadn't even considered the question, so I was taken aback. "What? No, I'm not— no, I don't have AIDS. I don't have HIV. I get tested regularly. And

411

anyway, I'm in a relationship, the same one I've been in for five years. I don't have sex with other men. You've met Bernie. I said he was my roommate, but it's much more than that."

"I WONDER WHY YOUR SHOE IN HIS ROOM," Ma said, looking at Ba. She had been very nosy when they visited and had gone into what we had made look like just Bernie's room, but where some of my shoes were conspicuously still on his rack.

"Yeah, I didn't do a very good job of hiding it," I said, feeling relieved that we were now at the part where Ma said she'd "always known." I wasn't disappointed.

"IN A WAY, I ALWAYS KNOW YOU LIKE TO BE TRENDY. THIS IS JUST TRENDY, AND YOU LIKING ART AND MUSIC. BUT I AM SO GLAD YOU TELL US FINALLY."

Ba still looked troubled, but stayed quiet as Ma went on.

"NOW THAT YOU TELL US, FINALLY WE CAN TRY SOLVE. I MAKE MY GOAL TO INTRODUCE YOU ONE THOUSAND GIRL, AND YOU WILL FIND ONE THAT YOU CAN MARRY."

"Ma, this isn't about finding the right girl. I know a lot of nice girls. I just don't like girls, not that way."

"You don't have to like to have sex with her to marry her," Ba said, matter-of-factly and without irony. "Most marriage is not about sex. It is about family."

I had anticipated this line of thinking. I summoned my courage to drive the final nail. "I might want a family one day, but with someone I actually love, and with kids of my own. But I can't love a woman like that, any more than you could love a man that way, Ba. I'm gay. That means I won't ever be with a woman."

412

Ba's face looked ashen as he tried to process what I was telling him. Homosexuality was something that happened to other families, to white families. Not to his. What had gone wrong?

"I WILL INTRODUCE ONE THOUSAND GIRL, AND IF YOU REJECT ALL OF THEM, THEN I WILL ACCEPT THIS, BUT NOT BEFORE!" Ma said, her voice now cracking with emotion as she started to cry. She hid herself under the covers, as the hubbub brought my brothers into the room. They had been waiting in the kitchen and had figured out what was going on, probably wondering why I had chosen to ruin Christmas in this particular way. Kaiser climbed on the bed and was trying to talk Ma down from her Chinese-mother ledge. Ba had a defeated look on his face, and I felt terrible.

"Ma, you'll see. It will be fine. It's no big deal, really!" said Kaiser.

"Yeah, Ma," said John. "Actually, homosexuality occurs in almost every species of mammal. And some birds, too," he said. She wasn't placated by the science, but Ba seemed to be listening.

Kaiser poked his head under the covers and tried to cheer Ma up. "Don't be upset, Ma. Anyway, you've kind of known for a long time, right? That's why you asked me."

"You've known already?" Ba asked. "For how long?"

Ma's sobs rose in volume, but through tears under the covers, she winked at Kaiser, then continued to cry even more convincingly. Kaiser was dumbfounded. Ma was *faking* it.

"Mary, don't be sad," Ba said. "De good news is dat Jay is not sick. And he says he will not be having sex with men, so we don't have to worry." Ma's sobs grew in volume.

"I said other men, besides Bernie," I murmured, but this didn't seem to register.

413

After I talked more at length, and with the support of my brothers, Ba seemed to find his intellectual footing. "I thought gays were all bad people," Ba said. "But if my son is gay, I must be wrong, so I need to reexamine my opinions."

I knew that Ba was doing a rare thing. He wanted to understand what this bombshell meant, for the family, for my future, for our relationship. He wondered whether I would get sick, and whether I would be lonely. We had wandered far outside familiar terrain. No one had a map.

The rest of my confession was spent with everyone, including Ba, trying to cheer Ma up. Looking back, I suspect that Ma had pretended to be much more distraught than she really was, precisely so that Ba would have to say positive things to bring her out of her funk. Maybe through saying those things, Ba would convince himself. It was a masterful lesson in manipulation, and it worked flawlessly.

Later that day, I sat with my brother and his girlfriend, Rachael, who hadn't realized her first visit was going to be filled with Kuo family drama. I apologized.

"Well, I guess you couldn't have known this, but we were going to drop some news today as well. You kind of stole our thunder. Rachael and I are engaged."

My mouth fell open, and then I hugged Rachael and started crying again.

"We'll wait another month now to tell them," Rachael said, helpfully. We laughed, and I apologized again, and I wondered how many more bombs Ma could handle from her children.

When Mimi woke up a few hours later, she heard what had happened that morning, and went to look for Ba. She found him in his office, alone, looking distant and tired. She asked him if he was okay.

"You know Mimi, Jay told us something dis morning. He told us dat he is gay."

"Well," she said, with a tightening in her stomach. "How do you feel about that?" She, too, had worried about how Ba would take the news, but was also relieved that this moment had finally come and the sky hadn't fallen. But what Ba said next surprised her, and it stayed with her for many years.

"It isn't de life I would have chosen for him," Ba said. "And I can't say I understand why he is dis way. But he must have known how we might take de news, and he must have had a lot of fear. He must have been afraid we would reject him. To overcome dat fear, it is an act of love."

Mimi nodded through tears and took his hand.

"And how can I turn away my son," Ba said, his eyes shining at her, "when he comes to me with such an act of love?"

March 1958
Columbus, Ohio

Ma was tired of all the questions her American-college classmates had been asking. "Do you have a guy back in China?" "What are the boys like there?" "Do the men even talk to their wives?" "Who pays for the wedding?" The questions were so relentless that Ma eventually wrote to a friend of hers in Taiwan, a tall basketball player who had been a one-time admirer, and asked if he could mail her a photo of himself. She then framed it and placed it with prominence on her nightstand, just so the incessant questioning would end. If anyone asked, that was her guy.

Ma showed me a picture she still had of him.

415

"He was a babe, Ma."

"WELL… HE IS TALL. AND HE PLAYING SPORT, AND IS ABOVE AVERAGE LOOK. GOOD ENOUGH FOR PICTURE."

To Ma, life in America had been a disappointment, so far. None of the other young ladies at Dominican College in the odd state of Ohio seemed like they were there to study. Her dorm mates spent more time gossiping, primping, and talking about men than they did in the library or in class. This wasn't what Ma had expected from Americans. Weren't they from the richest, most capable, most powerful country in the world? And to think, it was only the men pulling at the oars.

Ma had been an exemplary student in her high school, and was already known as a skilled orator. In fact, her speech in honor of International Youth Day, which had been attended by no less than President Jiang himself, had garnered so much attention and praise that it had caused problems. It seemed the KMT was looking for precisely a fresh face and voice just like hers to represent it internationally. They were especially interested given Ma's skill in English, her natural beauty, and the way she had of pulling people in and making them feel a part of something. She had my grandmother's looks and pluck, but she also had my grandfather's political sensibilities and charisma. That made her a prized recruit. Besides, having one of Liu Jingjian's children under their control might help keep the outspoken senator in line.

When Ma was approached later that day and asked to join the KMT, she ran home to tell her parents the good news. But Laolao and Waigong were terrified. Waigong knew it was a ploy, a way to hold his daughter hostage and exact political loyalty. The very next day, with barely time to say goodbye, Ma found herself on a ship heading to the west coast of the United States, her mother in the meantime pulling some strings in the Church to gain her quick admission to a Catholic girls' college in some state in the center of the country called

Ohio. That would have to do for now. At least their older daughter was now out of the KMT's grasp.

But no one had actually thought through what Ma would do once she actually arrived in Ohio. "Don't see any men," were her mother's only instructions. "Especially not any Americans. They will regard you as a trophy and treat you like a mistress. Just keep quiet and study hard, and finish your education."

Laolao had been a student of music, the first young lady to enroll in the program at the new national university in Nanjing. She was an accomplished singer, pianist, and violinist, and she spent her time giving free music lessons to troubled young women in the red-light district, where she combined her faith and her music into a powerful kind of evangelizing. Later, she opened up Taiwan's first girls' music school, where over the years, she acquired more than forty grand pianos, including many prized Steinways, from wealthy donors. It didn't matter what the young women studied, so long as they applied themselves and trained their minds to ponder more than housework and husbands. With her own daughter showing so much promise, Laolao would never stand for anything less than her receiving a full degree, and not just in music. That it would be conferred by an American college was even more satisfying. Ma could become a scientist, or a professor, or a doctor. Laolao was determined that Ma would have the kind of opportunities she never had.

So, when Ma started seeing "the Kuo boy" instead of sticking to the plan, Laolao was livid. She had heard about the romance from Nainai, whom Laolao considered a well-educated if too earnest a woman, and who clearly had designs on Ma as a future daughter-in-law. Apparently, the boy's father also played cards with Waigong, which made Laolao all the more suspicious. She had never known any of her husband's friends to be upright, Christian men.

When Ma tried to defend herself by citing Yeye's credentials—that he was a professor and an author of textbooks, that he was friends with the higher-ups in the government—this only worsened Laolao's mood. She penned a lengthy letter, in her best English, imploring the Dean of Students to intervene and put a halt to the budding courtship, to let her daughter focus on her studies, and to not allow temptation to lead her to disaster. But he had written back saying that, to his knowledge, "Jack" (as he called my father, Jenkai) was one of the most polite and thoughtful boys he had ever met, and that Mary was in no danger of losing her reputation for being with him.

"He holds the door open for her whenever he picks her up or drops her off," the Dean explained, trying unsuccessfully to calm Laolao. "His father is always there, too, as a chaperone. I doubt they've ever had a moment of privacy! Jack does not even so much as hug her goodnight. You can rest assured that the young man is honest and well-behaved."

So, Laolao did what any good mother would do: She investigated. She questioned everyone she knew who had college-age children in the United States if they had heard of this Jenkai character. The world of overseas Chinese was small, and she would get to the truth. It didn't take long before she discovered the scandal: Jenkai was already seeing the Fu girl. Laolao was surprised yet delighted at this news; if anyone would cause Ma to go apoplectic, it was Lorraine Fu.

But instead of backing off, Ma saw the Lorraine situation as a challenge. She was more determined than ever to win Jenkai from her! Laolao's plans unraveled further when she learned that Ma had engaged in a long back-and-forth correspondence with Nainai.

"She studied in Germany," Ma said. "And so, she is worldly in ways no one in our family is." It was a dig on Laolao, whose only true encounters with the West had been through her early roles in movies. Despite all their learning, the Kuo family was not Christian. In fact, from what she could gather, they didn't even believe in any god or heaven at all. That was perhaps the worst thought: that her own daughter might stray from Christ's path.

"If you keep seeing this Jenkai, then you can say goodbye to any support from us," Laolao wrote. "You will be on your own." As Laolao wrote the fateful words, she knew she had to stand firm. Her daughter needed to understand there were consequences to disobedience. She was too young to be making big decisions, and getting in with the wrong man was something that could cost her happiness and a bright future. Laolao had learned this herself through many bitter years. She signed the letter tersely and sealed it, ready to see if the ultimatum would work.

Like her bombshell about Lorraine, the threat backfired completely. Ma wrote back that she would be happy to take a job to pay for her own schooling and didn't need any money from her mother, going forward. After sending off her response, Ma felt light and free, and for the first time ever, she invited Ba up into the house to show him her room, where she kissed him, the other girls in the house peeking around corners and giggling conspiratorially.

Laolao didn't make good on her threat. She continued to send a small allowance to her daughter, while imploring her to stop dating and to focus on her studies. Laolao hoped that, with Ba's time in Ohio ending soon, the affair would terminate on its own. Distance had a way of drawing new priorities in young lives. But Ma had another unwelcome surprise. That summer, she wrote once more to tell Laolao she was going out to California on a trip with Jenkai, to see his new school.

Laolao was horrified. It was one thing to engage in a college dalliance, and quite another to cross the country with a man who was not your husband. Laolao forbade it, threatening more financial consequences, but Ma had made up her mind.

419

The final straw was this: Ma had decided to stay in California and take a job at Stanford, where her "boyfriend" would be getting his Ph.D. Laolao wasn't impressed that Jenkai was soon going to be Dr. Kuo, but that her daughter would take a job in a lab there just to be near him was beyond contemptible. And it had all happened by weird accident. When Ba introduced Ma to his advisor, the professor confessed he was distracted because one of his students, who had been running experiments for him daily, had suddenly accepted a position at another university, and he was now seriously shorthanded.

"I TELL HIM I WAS LOOKING FOR JOB," Ma said to me. "YOUR DADDY LOOK AT ME, WAAAH! WHAT ARE YOU DOING?"

"What did Ba's advisor say?"

"HE ASK, 'ARE YOU GOOD AT MATH?' I SAY, I KNOW HOW TO USE SLIDE RULER. HOW MUCH YOU PAY? HE ANSWER, 'A DOLLAR TWENTY AN HOUR.' SO I SAY, 'PERFECT! WHY DON'T YOU JOIN US FOR LUNCH?'"

"So you got the job?"

"I DID NOT KNOW TILL LATER. TWO GIRL STUDENT COME FIND ME. THEY ASK, 'ARE YOU THE NEW GIRL, MARY?' THEY SAY THEIR PROFESSOR SO HAPPY THAT I WILL BE WORKING WITH THEM!"

And so, Ma stayed with Ba and decided not to go back to finish her degree among those silly girls at Dominican College. The problem was how to break this news to her mother.

It did not go well. This time, Laolao cut her off completely and threatened she would never speak to her again, especially after all the trouble she'd gone through to ensure Ma received a college degree. She simply could not be more disappointed and angry, she railed. If she married this rascal, Ma should not expect Laolao at the wedding, nor would she visit her grandchildren. (Decades later, Ma would repeat this empty threat herself when my brother John said he was marrying Rachael, who, of course, was not Chinese.)

A few years later, when Ba and Ma attended a rally at the Berkeley campus, Ma spied an old friend in the crowd. He was still tall, sporty, and above-average looking. She waved and called his name.

"That's him!" Ba shouted.

"Who?" Ma asked.

"That's the man! That is the man in the photo!"

"I don't know what you are going on about," Ma laughed. "What photo?"

"The photo you had in your room, on your nightstand. It was there that first night you kissed me. I saw it, but I didn't have the courage to ask you who it was. Was he your boyfriend? I so wanted to know why his picture was always there!"

It took Ma a moment to remember the photo that she'd put there to stop the idle gossip about her love life. She had forgotten about it completely, and had even left it up through their months of courtship. She began to laugh and laugh. All this time, Ba had been jealous for no reason. Apparently, Chinese mothers weren't the only ones to hold on stubbornly and suffer in silence for years.

Indeed, Laolao made good on her threat and didn't visit her daughter again for many years. Her first visit was only announced after Ma had already given birth to her first son, my brother John, and she and Ba were living in a suburban neighborhood in upstate New York.

Laolao watched from the window, as Ba pushed a noisy lawnmower across their very pristine American lawn, John strapped to his back and asleep despite the racket, Ba mopping the sweat off his own brow.

"You mean to say your husband does work like this, *all the time*?" Laolao asked incredulously. Ma nodded and smiled as she observed her normally unflappable mother reevaluate her daughter's life choices. To Laolao, men were lazy scoundrels who all would run off and abandon their families if they could. Laolao suddenly fished in her purse and brought out a red pouch, which she slid across the table to Ma.

"For the baby," she said, not meeting her gaze.

May 1996
San Francisco Bay Area, California

> MA and JAY are watching television together. The KUO FAMILY has come together for KAISER's wedding in the San Francisco Bay Area.

MA: YOU BRING MATT TO KAISER WEDDING?

JAY: Mike.

MA: YOU BRING?

JAY: I invited him.

MA: JUST DON'T MAKING SCENE.

JAY: I don't plan to.

MA: NOT ALL CHINESE SO OPEN MIND.

JAY: You don't give your friends enough credit.

MA: JUST NO DANCING WITH MARK.

JAY: Mike. He's not much into dancing anyway.

> One week later, at Kaiser's wedding party.

AUNTIE 1: You should dance with your friend!

AUNTIE 2: He is very handsome!

> MIKE turns beet red.

JAY: Ma doesn't want us to dance.

AUNTIE 1: Well, then I dance with you, and she dance with Mike!

AUNTIE 2: We all dance together!

> The AUNTIES pull JAY and MIKE to the dance floor. MA, watching her friends troll her, lets this go on for only a few minutes before she pulls JAY aside. She looks over at her rival, Rebecca Zhang, and her family.

MA: DO YOU SEE OVER THERE, JOSEPH AND REBECCA ZHANG SON? HE IS A GAY.

JAY: Yeah, that's pretty obvious.

MA: HE WEARING WHITE SPARKLE PANT.

JAY: They pretty much scream gay, yup.

MA: EVERYONE CAN SEE. POOR REBECCA, MUST BE SO SHOCK.

JAY: I figure they've probably known for a while. Look. He's twirling on the floor. And no one cares.

> MA watches the subject of her critiques, who is indeed twirling. She assesses the reaction of the wedding guests.

MA: THEY JUST DO NOT SAY. OUT OF POLITE.

JAY: You seem to care more than anyone.

MA: NO! I DO NOT CARE. MANY FAMILY HAVE THIS PROBLEM YOU KNOW. I JUST FEEL SO SAD FOR REBECCA.

JAY: Maybe she feels bad for you, too.

MA: …

JAY: …

MA: AT LEAST MY SON NOT TWIRLY.

December 2010
Bodega Bay, California

It was rare for Ba and me to have quality time anymore, just the two of us. The family had grown so much larger in recent years, with John, Kaiser, and Mimi all married now, and with five grandchildren to look

424

after and dutifully mold into good Chinese-ish kids with good Chinese-ish values. When the family gathered for the holidays, we needed a big house with enough bedrooms to squeeze us all in, and places where Ba and I could escape to work, or more importantly, be away from the commotion. Ba called such gatherings *renao*, which translates into "hot and noisy" but really meant festive and crowded in a good way.

Earlier that day, John's wife, Rachael, had gathered us all together in the kitchen. She had converted a round table into a pastry station and placed a gigantic sheet of dough in the center. It was a strudel, one to be stretched out to an absurd size and thinness and filled with fruits and nuts. The tradition had passed from Rachael's grandmother to her. Rachael had always been an ambitious baker, having even made her own wedding cake, and now having enlisted an entire extended Chinese and Chinese-ish family to pull the strudel to the edges of the table without breaking it. To do this, you had to pull oh-so-gently, then move together as a team clockwise one step, pulling again. With the dough being pulled equally in all directions, it grew from a flat circle into a table-sized sheet. It was my first time pulling at the strudel, but it would become a tradition.

I had asked my friend, Sally, a boisterous, outspoken woman I'd met on vacation in Cabo San Lucas, now a producer on my new show, to join us for Christmas. The collective Kuos had rented a big house out in Bodega Bay, California, and I'd invited Sally because I didn't want her to be alone for the holidays. Well, that was partly why. I also knew that Sally would love my parents, particularly Ma's directness and Ba's engineer mind. Plus, Ma herself would be on far better behavior with an outside guest present. But most of all, it was nice to have a friend around because my siblings now all had spouses and children, and I didn't care to be the odd Kuo out.

Sally and I shared a common problem: men. Both of us had been trying unsuccessfully to date for some time. While my strategy saw me going to all the gay bars in New York, night after desperate night, and she had signed up for all the dating websites, the results were the same. Both of us were considered too old for the "market," she a widow approaching sixty, and me a Gaysian man then just north of forty. The men in the bars and on the dating sites wanted younger versions of us. Although the rest of life had fallen into place—career, friends, finances—Sally opened up to me about the pain of being alone, and having lost her husband of twenty years to cancer.

Her husband Paul had been her best friend and business partner, and together they'd built a successful enterprise exporting Maruchan brand noodles to Mexico. Sally had made her money five cents at a time, as she liked to say, and was informally known around San Diego as the "Noodle Queen." But after Paul passed, she closed the business and retreated into a multi-year sadness.

I was her first openly gay friend, and she liked that I saw relationships differently than her straight girlfriends. Over the years, I introduced her to many more gay men, whom she believed Paul had sent to her with a message to start enjoying life again. Her life began to reopen with promise, new friends, and a new career as a Broadway producer. But, like me, she didn't have anyone to share her life fully with, so we'd done the next best thing and continued to expand our circles of friends, which now included each other.

Ma, however, was convinced that I was not really single and was secretly sleeping with my roommate, Blair, who seemed to be in every picture with me. When my parents celebrated their 50th anniversary in Beijing, I brought both Blair and Sally, insisting that, as I didn't have a partner to invite, I could invite my friends. At the ceremony, Ma pulled me aside.

"I THINK IT A LITTLE EARLY, YOU KNOW, TO BRING SPECIAL FRIEND TO FAMILY FUNCTION." She smiled tightly, as if she were discussing the fruit arrangements from the banquet.

426

"What do you mean, 'special friend'?" I asked. "Oh, Blair? He's just my roommate."

"NOT SPECIAL FRIEND?" Ma asked, with a penetrating skepticism.

"No. He's just a regular friend. He's a friend like Sally's a friend."

A lantern went off in Ma's brain. "OH! FRIEND LIKE SALLY FRIEND. OKAY. THAT OKAY THEN."

Ma had difficulty pronouncing Blair's name. The B-L combination often defeated her, so she resorted to other creative approaches. "BRAD" was often one, but my favorite came later that week at their anniversary celebration:

"WHERE CLAIR?" Ma demanded.

"Who?" I asked.

"CLAIR!" she repeated.

I smiled. "You mean Blair," I corrected.

"YEAH, CLAIR!" she said again while I howled on the inside. From now on, Blair was Clair, just like my other roommate Tom Garruto had become "Tom Burrito" after another one of Ma's famous word swaps.

"Clair" and I had gone shopping for cheap items with Ma while in Beijing, as one does, and she'd handed me a stack of Chinese yuan to buy some new luggage. I was busy haggling with a vendor, and since Blair also wanted new luggage, I got us a good deal for two matching suitcases. Ma watched all of this with great interest. I'd completely forgotten about it until a month later, when she cornered me.

"DID BRAID EVER PAY YOU BACK?"

"What's that?"

"BRAID. HE EVER PAY YOU BACK?"

"Oh, Blair. Pay me back?"

"I SEE YOU GETTING MATCHY LUGGAGE YOU PAYING FOR. DID HE EVER PAY YOU BACK?"

"Uh… oh, yeah. I'm sure he did. I should have given you back the money."

"MMM. BECAUSE IF NO SPECIAL FRIEND, NO FREE SUITCASE!"

I later decided "NO FREE SUITCASE" pretty much summed up Ma's moral code.

My lack of a special friend in my life, it seems, had also been occupying Ba's thoughts. He found me on that Christmas morning in Bodega Bay, and asked if I'd like to go for a walk with him. It was rare that Ba and I went anywhere alone, so I figured it was to talk about family finances, the business, or my siblings again. More and more, Ba had begun to call me up or take me to lunch and seek my business opinion about his contracts, partnerships, and shareholders in his company. He also had started to talk to me first about his ideas for what his children ought to be doing with the next phases of their lives. Whether this was because I was single and presumably had more time to think about these things, or because we had worked together for so long solving thorny business problems in China, or even because Ba was most familiar with the way my brain worked ever since the days we played chess over lunch together, I was still very touched and flattered whenever he sought my opinion. I suppose there are things you never outgrow, and for me, it was Ba's approval.

428

But this time in Bodega Bay, Ba didn't want to talk about business, or politics, or even which of my siblings he was currently worried about. We walked in silence for much of that morning, remarking on the un-winterlike weather and the beauty of the trail. Then he spoke to me as he never had.

"Jay, I want to talk to you about your future."

"Okay," I said, unsure where this was going. "You mean my decision to move to New York? I don't regret it so far at all."

"No, Jay Jay," he said slowly, and using his singsong voice and my diminutive nickname, which was his way of indicating both affection and concern. "I mean your personal life. Do you see how happy your brothers and Mimi are? Don't you want to be so happy?"

After I'd come out to my parents sixteen years ago, I had probably all of two conversations with Ba about my love life. One was when he unexpectedly asked me after dinner one night whether I intended to continue my relationship with Zhang Yan, my boyfriend who was living with us then, in Beijing. "Zhang Yan is a very nice boy," Ba said, "And very loyal. But you two come from very different educational backgrounds and families. You will never be able to speak to each other as equals. I think he understands dis better dan you do."

I'd resented that Ba was trying to put doubts in my head about Zhang Yan, and even more that those doubts proved to be well-founded. As my Chinese language abilities improved and I stopped communicating with a fourth-grade vocabulary, it became apparent to me that Zhang Yan had never been exposed to anything resembling a formal education. When we went to see *Jurassic Park* when it came to theaters in China, Zhang Yan leaned over and whispered, "I thought you said dinosaurs were extinct." I laughed, responding, "Those are just computers," my Chinese not yet good enough to translate "computer animated." Zhang Yan looked skeptical.

Later, when we saw the movie *Babe*, Zhang Yan was incredulous. *"That pig is talking!"* he muttered. I explained that it was computers again, but this only made him look more carefully. "No, no, look! The pig's mouth is moving exactly when he's saying those words." Zhang Yan also would not believe me when I said that raccoons, which he'd only seen in cartoons, were actually real animals in America. "What's next?" he demanded. "Are you going to tell me that 'tornadoes' like in *Twister* are also real? Come on!" To be fair, the Chinese word for tornado—"Dragon Spin Wind"—could easily be taken for good Hollywood marketing.

Zhang Yan did eventually leave me because, as Ba had predicted, our worlds were too far apart, and he felt too much pressure "to come up to my level." He had tried and failed at English lessons, and he wasn't much for book learning. My more educated friends in China spoke down to him, he said, but he understood why. It was a heartbreaking gap, but one I could do nothing to fill. Ba had seen this years before it had happened, but I didn't want to admit that he was right. Unlike chess, in my love life I hadn't been thinking seven steps ahead.

But as Ba and I walked the trail in Bodega Bay, there was no boyfriend—or even special friend—in my life, and there hadn't been for five years. So, I was certain that Ba was going to use this fact to press me into reconsidering being with a woman. I responded carefully.

"I am very happy, actually," I said. "Being in New York is like starting my whole life over. And I'm meeting so many people." Just not people who seem to want more than a one-night experience, I thought.

"You may be happy now, and I see dat," Ba said. "But here we are, walking a trail together. We look at de beautiful nature, and we enjoy it together. Life is like dis. You walk a trail together. Your mother and I have walked it for fifty years."

"You are really lucky. That's a rare thing."

"Not in my time. My parents also walk through life together for most of their lives. People are meant to have someone to walk alongside. Dis way when you are old, you will not be alone."

I thought of Nainai, who'd lived for twenty years after her husband died, but I didn't want to challenge Ba with that example.

"I'm not worried about being alone," I said a bit too emphatically. "I have lots of friends. And who knows, maybe I'll meet a nice guy, and it will happen. We could even have our own family."

Here was the moment, I thought. This is when he tells me that I should find and marry a woman.

Ba was silent for a while as we walked and pondered. "Maybe dat will happen. I hope dat you do find dis guy, someone you can walk through life with. Someone you can make a family with."

Had I misheard? Had Ba really just spoken hope to the universe that I meet and be with a man?

"Anyway, dis is what I came to talk to you about. Life is too short, too beautiful to not share it with someone else."

We walked most of the rest of the way home in silence, until Ba pointed out some ducks and remarked that their abundant fat and the rich blood in their webbed feet kept them from freezing in the cold. Strangely, my next romantic interest, Andrew, who grew up on a farm around ducks, would also say this to me one day beside a near-frozen lake, making me instantly fall for him.

"Let us get fat like de ducks!" Ba said, making me laugh. "So we will be warm every Christmas!"

That night after dinner, we ate the strudel we had worked on earlier, and it was flaky, fruity, and nutty. The Kuo family would gather and make strudel together each Christmas for another seven years before we lost Rachael to an unforgiving cancer, which she fought off valiantly for many seasons before succumbing. At her memorial service, I read a poem about pulling strudel and how Rachael was still there with us, in the dough, the apple, the nuts, and the spices. These were happy words, but I couldn't get through the last of them without breaking down, even though I'd promised her daughter, Kaili, to not make everyone sad.

Like Nainai and my friend, Sally, after Rachael died, my brother, John, faced the prospect of having no one to walk through the rest of his life beside him. I often wondered which was worse, the quiet loneliness and resignation of being forever alone or the long and unrelenting grief that comes from losing your life-walking companion.

It didn't work out between Andrew and me, or with me and any other man, though for the first time in my life, a romance transitioned gingerly into a warm, and now dear, friendship. Part of me wanted to believe that I remained single because I chose freely and happily to be independent and not because, deep down, I was mortally afraid to face the pain of loving and losing someone. But to this day, I remain uncertain of my true reasons.

March 2014
Taipei, Taiwan

The nurses had finally brought in a cot, and Mimi was relieved. It was the third night now that Ma had slept upright in a chair beside Ba. "My husband for more than fifty years," she would say, challenging the staff to be by anyone's side for as long as that. The nurses would nod with respect, as they strategized over how to keep her cot in the room without violating hospital rules.

Ba had been in and out of Taipei General many times now. The first came after the Christmas holiday that the whole extended family had spent together. "Someplace warm" had been the collective suggestion, and Mimi and John both had recommended Taipei, which seemed exotic yet familiar and, most importantly, tropical. They found a reasonably priced hotel where each family could have their own set of rooms, and then spend days walking about the city, sampling local cuisine and snapping ridiculous photos with Hello Kitty everywhere.

Hen nan de, we had all agreed at the time. *Very difficult to pull off.* Each successive Christmas carried the unspoken risk that it might be the last we spent with Ba. His health was failing; I could see it in his walk and hear it in his more labored breath. It had been more than sixteen years since he had gotten triple-bypass surgery, something that was only supposed to buy the family another seven with him. So in that sense, we were all lucky he had lived to be eighty-two, and that his mind was still sharp and clear. It also meant he was very stubborn and willful, and this obstinance, unfortunately, drove him to push himself too far. Ba insisted on walking back to the hotel after dinner, even through a sudden winter downpour, and within a couple of days, he was down with a cold that progressed rapidly into pneumonia.

Ma understood that Ba hated hospitals, hated the feeling of being helpless, of having IV needles in his arms and hands. Ba hated them ever since he'd been sick as a child, and they'd had to strap his arms

433

to a bed to keep him from scratching himself to infection. From his hospital room in Taipei, Ba had still tried to work, poring over data on spreadsheets and making calls to the company manager in Beijing to discuss their ongoing projects. We wanted to tell him to rest, but the work seemed to energize him, at least for the hours he was at it. But as his physical condition worsened, and the x-rays showed his lungs losing the fight to bacteria, Ma sent an email to us.

"YOU DADDY GETTING A LITTLE TOO TIRED TO WORK NOW. SO HE IS VERY FRUSTRATE AND MAYBE A LITTLE SAD. BUT I AM WITH HIM, DON'T WORRY. YOU SHOULDN'T FEEL NEED TO COME."

Within a day, I was on my way, as were my brothers, crossing half the world again to be with our father. We were glad to have our Aunt Theresa there, because she knew her way around Taipei and its medical system. Ma had even put aside her differences with her sister while caring for Ba.

Ma often remarked that Mimi was the most dutiful of her children, because she called her parents almost every day via Skype. She was Ba's favorite, it was well agreed, and he always brightened when he was able to chat with her. With Ba in the hospital, they ended each call with a great deal of emotion, Mimi promising she would soon be there in person. She always said, "I love you," to end the call, and Ba repeated the words after a pause. The nurses would often eavesdrop and be amazed at this heartfelt exchange. Aunt Theresa, noting their shock, said hurriedly, "Oh, this family is from America," to which the nurses exclaimed, "Oh!" Well, *that* explains *everything*.

Ba had at first protested that Ma shouldn't stay the whole night sitting up in a chair. It was too uncomfortable, and she shouldn't have to fuss so much. Mimi also tried in vain to get Ma to go home, or at least to let Mimi take her place, but Ma said simply to all who could hear, "I am staying in case something happens. He is sick, so he will need people to watch him. I will watch him."

This had become almost a ritual. Ma was absolutely determined to devote herself to her new role as caretaker spouse. There were times when she had confessed to us that she resented Ba, locked as he was in the old ways of thinking about women and family. But we knew Ma loved him, too, for being the father Ma had wanted for her children, and for providing for them all, even through very tough times. Her generation had not managed to reclaim its lost but rightful place, scattered as they were among China, Taiwan, and the United States. But, as Ma liked to say, their children were doing marvelously, and she felt deeply that she had chosen her husband well, when all was said and done.

So now it was Ma's duty to suffer alongside the father of her children, to show him that her love had always been unconditional, even when his own love had at times felt qualified. Her devotion would be fierce as a tiger to the end, and no one would be able to gainsay that she had done all that she could.

"Time to check his diaper," Ma said to the nurse in her crispest Mandarin, which still bore some southern Chinese characteristics but was far more official-sounding than the lilting rhythm of the more pampered Taiwanese. "And his medicine is late."

"Of course, ma'am. Sorry about that," the nurse said, somewhat terrified of Ma, who seemed to know all of the chief doctors and administrators on a first-name basis.

"Don't call it a diaper," Ba said blearily. "It's bad enough that I have to wear it."

"What should I call it then?" Ma asked, testing the softness of the mangoes that her sister had brought. "Adult diaper? Would you like me to peel you a mango? Maybe just half. It's allowed, yes?" she asked the nurse.

"It has a lot of sugar," the nurse replied. "We want to get his weight down by 10 kilos. Less strain on his heart."

"You are starving me to death," Ba growled in English.

"Only because we love you, Ba," said Mimi, cheerily.

"Maybe if you had not eaten so much meat all the time, you wouldn't have extra weight to lose," Ma said. "Half a mango, then."

The nurse opened her mouth to protest, but a look from Ma stopped her. "I'll get his medicine," she said instead.

"You don't have to be here every night with me. I am asleep anyway," Ba said, beginning this same conversation for the third time.

"HERE, I PEEL IT FOR YOU," Ma said, switching to English and putting cubes of mango into a tray cup.

"I'll get you a spoon," offered Mimi.

"You are good to me," Ba said to Ma, as she fussed. "I was not always the best to you."

"We should ask for a new nurse," Ma said, ignoring his attempt at whatever make-your-peace moment he imagined he was about to have. "This one is too unreliable. I'll ask them to give us an older one, more qualified."

"I like her," Ba protested. "She is fine. She is sweet."

"She is young and inexperienced. And too pretty," Ma said. "We need your blood pressure down, not up."

436

"And I want more wine," Ba said. For some reason, Ba kept asking for wine. Just a bit, he insisted. Ba had never been a drinker, so Mimi found it odd, but the doctors said this type of mild delirium was common. She tried to dissuade him, telling him they'd get in trouble if they gave him anything alcoholic, but Ba insisted the doctors wouldn't mind, and had been pestering her about it daily.

Ma had a solution. She bought some grape juice and added it to his daily vegetable juice and simply told him it was a fine wine smuggled in. "It's a French Bordeaux that Mimi bought at Le Jardin restaurant," she explained. Ba, not knowing any French, nor having much experience drinking wine in his life, sipped it carefully and pronounced it excellent.

Days later, after the Kuo brothers also had arrived, Ba's condition worsened. He was having more difficulty breathing, and the doctor came to Ma and the family with some hard choices.

"We need his lungs to clear, and he needs far more oxygen than he can manage on his own," the doctor stated. "We recommend intubation and a ventilator. He will be unconscious or sedated for some time, while we hope his lungs improve. We will try a new antibiotic because whatever strain of bacteria he has appears resistant."

Twenty-four hours later, Ba was in the ICU with tubes down his throat, and Ma was finally convinced she could leave the hospital for nights at a time. She only returned when Ba regained consciousness, though the amount of tranquilizers he was on meant he understood little of his situation. Ma and Mimi talked for long hours, and Ma had begun to steel herself for more bad news. Her conversations had taken on a fatalistic tone.

"ANYWAY I STAY IN BEIJING EVEN IF HE DEAD," she said to us. "SOMEONE NEED TO KEEPING WATCHING THE COMPANY AND LOOKING AFTER BEIJING HOUSE."

"Don't talk that way, Ma," said Mimi. "Ba is going to get better, and you'll need to look after him."

"But I was thinking," I said carefully. "It might be better if we can move him later this year closer to us. Like, to California."

"CALIFORNIA?" Ma said, confused. "WHY? TAIPEI HAS BEST DOCTOR, AND I KNOW THEM ALL HERE, TRUST THEM. YOUR BA GETTING BEST HOSPITAL CARE HERE!"

"I know you like it here, but I've been out to Taipei three times since January, and it's getting pretty hard to manage," I said. "It's just too far to be able to keep coming out."

Ma looked skeptical, so Mimi tried a different tack. "And when you think about it, it's too expensive, all those plane tickets and hotels. We could rent an apartment for half a year for less than what we spent on travel."

"YOU SHOULDN'T WASTING MONEY, COMING OUT EACH TIME," Ma protested. "I CAN TAKE CARE OF HIM FINE." But she had already begun to consider the plan.

"John has already looked into it, and there's a great apartment not far from his house in Berkeley," Mimi continued, having already strategized with me over how to ease Ma into the idea. "Ba could be near John and his family."

"And if needed, I could be there in a matter of hours," I added. "Kaiser, too."

There was a kind of symmetry to it. Ma and Ba had lived in Berkeley back in the 1960s. They saw JFK speak at the Hearst Greek Theater. They had gotten married in a small church in Berkeley. John had married his wife, Rachael, at the Berkeley Rose Garden. Of the Kuo siblings, three of us had attended UC Berkeley for at least part of our schooling. It felt like going home.

"I LET YOU PEOPLE DECIDE," she said, having already determined it was not a bad plan. "IF YOU FATHER GETTING BETTER HERE, HE CAN GO LIVE NEAR JOHN."

It was a big "if." After his lungs had cleared up, they decided to remove the intubation, a step that always risked spreading the infection. Mimi and I were on our shift at the hospital when Ba came to. The doctors had warned that the first few minutes would be critical as his body adjusted to his own breathing and the trauma of the removal of the breathing tube. Ba looked very thin and vulnerable. Ma had told Mimi that this was not how she wanted to remember him. In her stories, which she had begun to repeat more frequently, Ba was the eager, young man who watched her devour a whole chicken on their first real date. He was the good father who came home for lunch every day to spend time with his son, teaching him chess. He was the dignified, white-haired advisor to important government decision-makers.

Ba's stats started to go haywire within a few minutes after the tube came out. His temperature and pulse soared, and his oxygen levels dropped. He began to tremble and shake. Mimi stood by the side of his bed, with me on the other, each of us holding one of Ba's hands. As Ba began to convulse more violently, Mimi's eyes sought out mine, as they had for all our lives, our gazes locking firmly to say wordlessly, "I'm here." Together, we might endure what we could not alone. Ma withdrew to the chair, unable to watch as Ba's shaking intensified. She had told Mimi that if this was his time to go, she would be ready. She had prepared for months, and perhaps one could

439

say years, for the loss of her husband. But still, in that room, Ma could not watch.

It would not be that day. Ba's trembling calmed, then he got past the worst of it, and fell into a deep sleep, his pulse and temperature coming down steadily. Over the coming weeks, with his children in and out of Taipei, but Ma always patiently by his side, Ba improved well enough to amble down the hall with the aid of a walker. He vented his pain and frustration at Ma, but as she told Mimi, it was better at her than at strangers.

July 2014
Berkeley, California

In late spring, Ba flew back to California, with extra oxygen tanks in the seat beside him. Ma complained about the cost, but it was soon forgotten after they moved into their modest new apartment in Berkeley. There, in the final months of his life, Ba spent time with his grandchildren, enjoyed good food, and took deep breaths of the fresh California air, so much cleaner than Beijing's. Mimi called them nearly every day to check in.

The past few months had taken most of the strength out of Ba, so when his heart and lungs began to fail again that summer, he didn't have much fight left. He fell from his bed one night, and Ma and John rushed him to the hospital, calling the rest of us in a panic. The infection had returned. Another intubation left Ba weak and delirious, so much so that his cognition and memory began to give way.

Mimi flew in from London, and she tried to keep him engaged whenever he was lucid. She got him to speak of his life in broad terms, about his childhood and early years in America. She asked him what it was he admired most about Ma in the hope that she might have something to give to her after so much discouragement and difficulty. Ba thought for a moment and said, "Her devotion." Mimi smiled. Ma would appreciate that, perhaps more than any other words.

In those final days, Ba's faculties took a sharp turn for the worse. Mimi and I went in together to see him, uncertain of what to expect. There was a nurse who was working with him to reduce his sense of confusion, which often resulted from long periods in the ICU and the extended use of painkillers. She didn't seem to be having much success.

"Hi, Ba," I said brightly.

Ba squinted at the two new people in the room.

"Mr. Kuo, do you know who this is?" the nurse asked.

"Jay!" he said, after a moment. Mimi and I smiled.

"Hi, Ba!" said Mimi, tentatively.

"Mr. Kuo, do you know who this is?"

Ba paused a moment. "My... daughter?"

Mimi and I breathed a sigh of relief. The nurse leaned over. "What's your name, dear?"

"It's Mimi," she answered softly.

"Do you know your daughter's name, Mr. Kuo?"

Ba looked pained. "Rachael?" he said uncertainly.

John's wife, Rachael, had been in often to see Ba along with her whole family, so his confusion was understandable. Still, Mimi smiled, both sad and amused. She could see Ba reaching for something in his brain or maybe his heart.

"Okay. Mr. Kuo. Who is 'Mimi'?" the nurse asked slowly.

Ba stared at Mimi, then smiled and relaxed, certainty and peace washing over him. He closed his eyes.

"My… favorite!" he said.

February 2022
Rossmoor, California

"SO BABY IS YOURS?"

"It's mine," I explained for the fourth time. These days, I cut Ma considerable slack. The mechanics of IVF and surrogate parenting weren't exactly intuitive.

"AND IS CHINESE?"

"My baby will be one-hundred percent Chinese," I promised. "All of my kids will be fully Chinese, don't worry, Ma."

I actually knew very little about the egg donor, who went by the initials XMA in the database, other than that she was from the northeastern part of China and had a master's degree in education—two facts I knew would please Ma immensely. There was definitely a part of me that jumped at the chance to produce a healthy set of Chinese embryos. After all, I thought, if my children look more or less like me, people won't always be looking around for the mother, wondering where she is in all of this.

442

I had waited until Christmas to tell Ma about my big plans, which had been slowly hatching over the course of the pandemic years. Those long months stuck at home had proven to me that I enjoyed being at home and playing the domestic life, cooking all manner of pastries and breads for my roommates, and playing with my new corgi puppy, Hudson (named for the Valley where I got her). The virus had made my world so much smaller, but also more meaningful. And I wanted to double down on that.

In the absence of a life partner, the thought of children had always seemed an impossibility. But as it became clearer that no husband was in the cards, especially with no effective way to pandemic-date strangers, the idea of having kids of my own had grown from a frequent daydream to a real plan. In short order, XMA and I, with the help of modern medicine and some amount of luck, had created eleven healthy embryos together, now frozen in the vaults of the San Diego Fertility Center, awaiting the next steps.

I had meant to tell Ma in person when I came out to see her for the holidays, but the new Covid variant scuttled our plans, and we had to do Christmas by Zoom. I had rehearsed a whole speech for the family, but Ma kept getting distracted by the *Brady Bunch* Zoom-squares of noisy people on her screen, so I had to hush everyone else up and just blurt it out.

"I have big news to share," I said, drawing out the drama for added effect. "I'm… going to be a dad." The rest of what came out of my mouth I can barely remember, except that by the end, Ma was smiling ear to ear, and she wiped a tear from her eye, especially after I told her the baby was fully Chinese.

"THIS IS BEST CHRISTMAS GIFT YOU CAN BE GIVING ME," she said. At which point, I was crying, too.

Once I'd decided to become an "intended parent" (which, I learned, is apparently my newly earned title), I was on a mission to bring my firstborn into the world while Ma was still healthy enough to enjoy her.

"I'm thinking two, maybe three kids. Probably three," I told Ma. "I want things to be *renao*, just like when we were growing up." *Renao*. Warm and noisy, literally.

"WITH THREE, YOU WILL HAVE *RENAO* FOR SURE. ANYWAY, YOU SHOULD HAVING MANY KID. SO SOMEONE TAKE CARE OF YOU WHEN YOU OLDIE LIKE ME."

"The thought has crossed my mind," I said. "But it's not why I'm doing this."

"WELL, GROWING OLD, NO FUN," Ma said, as her new live-in helper lifted her out of the whalechair to seat her on the couch. Over the past year and a half, Ma's physical condition had deteriorated so rapidly that she needed assistance with nearly everything, from using the bathroom to getting to the dinner table, a reality that wore at her pride and often made her want to give up on living.

"MAYBE THIS IS LAST YEAR I GO ON," she said to me more than a few times. I was hoping the news of the arrival of my baby would help her stay upbeat and motivated. I was eager to get the embryo transfer started, so I could stop dreading the calendar, imagining Ma leaving us just weeks before she could hold her new grandchild.

"WHEN YOU GIRLFRIEND GOING TO HAVING BABY?" she asked.

"She's *not* my girlfriend. She's a surrogate."

"WHATEVER CALL HER."

"Wait, have you been telling people she's my girlfriend?"

"DO YOU KNOW HER?"

"Yeah, Ma. I know her. Well, we met each other over Zoom. Anyway, she's done this before, having kids for other gay guys. And we're in contract now, and trying to figure out a date for the transfer. After that, it's forty weeks till the birth."

Ma looked off and up to the right. She seemed to be doing the math, as if calculating whether she could hang on for that long.

"WAAAA. WHAT A WORLD," Ma said.

"What a world," I repeated, taking her hand. It felt so light to hold, her once-vibrant skin now thin as paper. "Just think, I can have a Chinese baby using a white woman's womb!"

"YEAH, WOW. IT IS… JUST A LITTLE STRANGE."

"Good strange or bad strange?" I asked.

She considered my question thoughtfully. "GOOD STRANGE," she declared.

Ma laid back and closed her eyes, the corners of her mouth turned upward in the barest of smiles.

Made in the USA
Middletown, DE
25 November 2023

43394344R00256